W9-AZV-367

CONTEMPORARY ANALYTIC GEOMETRY

THOMAS L. WADE
HOWARD E. TAYLOR
Department of Mathematics
Florida State University

CONTEMPORARY ANALYTIC GEOMETRY

McGRAW-HILL
BOOK COMPANY
New York
St. Louis
San Francisco
London
Sydney
Toronto
Mexico
Panama

CONTEMPORARY ANALYTIC GEOMETRY

Copyright © 1969 by McGraw-Hill, Inc. All rights reserved. Printed in the United States of America. No part of this publication may be reproduced, stored in a retrieval system, or transmitted, in any form or by any means, electronic, mechanical, photocopying, recording, or otherwise, without the prior written permission of the publisher.

Library of Congress Catalog Card Number 69-13619

67643

1 2 3 4 5 6 7 8 9 0   H D M M   7 6 5 4 3 2 1 0 6 9

| PREFACE

The writing of this book was prompted by the conviction that present-day teachers and students of mathematics need and want a contemporary treatment of analytic geometry.

Much has been said and written* regarding efforts by local, state, and national organizations to provide students coming to college with a "new kind of high school background" in mathematics.† In recent years numerous books have appeared which contribute significantly to upgrading and modernizing the content of courses in plane geometry, algebra, and trigonometry for students in high school and the first year of college. Every college mathematics teacher is aware that the typical beginning calculus course of today is quite different from such a course of fifteen or twenty years ago, as evidenced by the many excellent calculus texts that have appeared in the past several years.

But little attention has been given to including analytic geometry in this updating and modernizing of mathematics. Some steps in this direction have been taken in several of the combined analytic geometry and calculus books.

* See J. H. Hlavaty, Mathematics in Transition, *The Math. Teacher,* vol. 54, pp. 27–30, January, 1961.
† See Paul C. Rosenbloom, Implications for the Colleges of the New School Programs, *The Am. Math. Monthly,* vol. 64, pp. 255–259, April, 1962.

But usually such a combined text provides only a meager treatment of analytic geometry, and more often than not that scanty treatment reflects little or no consideration of the fact that the student is supposed to come to analytic geometry with a "new kind of background" acquired in previous mathematics courses.

We believe that a course in analytic geometry should make use of the basic facts regarding sets and elementary logic and should be based upon the properties of the real number system. We assume that the student has an elementary acquaintance with the real number system. Some, perhaps most, students will be acquainted with the vocabulary and symbolism of sets and with the meaning and use of the elementary logical connectives. These matters are treated in Sections 1.1 to 1.3, and require only one lesson (or they may be assigned for review and reference, depending on circumstances).

We consistently use the concept of a relation as a set of ordered pairs, and we study graphs of a variety of relations that are specified by sentences in two and three variables. This includes the study of graphs of inequalities and other types of sentences, such as compound sentences consisting of conjunctions or disjunctions of equalities and/or of inequalities; an application of these topics is presented in a brief consideration of linear programming in Section 7.3.

We believe that vectors are important and that vector concepts and vector symbolism should be introduced with care (see Sections 7.1, 7.2, and 8.8). We regard vector concepts such as inner products, the angle between two vectors, and the vector equation of a circle, of a sphere, of a line, and of a plane as constituting a medium through which we generalize the concepts of 2-space and 3-space to n-space (see Section 8.9) and not as primary tools for solving run-of-the-mill problems in 2-space and 3-space.

An early treatment of direction cosines and direction numbers (Section 3.6) provides a basis for the study of the parametric representation of a line in 2-space (Section 3.7), which readily generalizes for a line in 3-space (Section 8.5) and for a line in n-space (Section 8.9).

The material on polar coordinates (Chapter 6) is more complete than that usually given, with rather extended treatments in polar coordinates of symmetry, of the parabola, ellipse, and hyperbola, and of points of intersection of curves.

The presentation of the material on solid analytic geometry (Chapter 8) is similar to the presentation of the material on plane analytic geometry in Chapters 1 to 4. Clearly, the use of the set concept and set symbolism facilitates the distinction between the graphs of $\{(x, y) \mid x = k\}$ and $\{x, y, z \mid x = k\}$, and the distinction between the graphs of $\{(x, y) \mid E(x, y) = 0\}$ and $\{(x, y, z) \mid E(x, y) = 0\}$.

The material is arranged to facilitate its use in courses of various lengths and with different emphases. The suggested lesson assignments following this Preface indicate some uses and suggest others. The book is suitable for use during a semester of the senior year in high school, with a schedule somewhat more relaxed that that shown in the third column of the suggested lesson assignments.

In summary, this book is dedicated to the mathematics student who needs and wants a contemporary treatment of analytic geometry, and it is written to be read and understood by the student.

We acknowledge with appreciation the permission given us by John Wiley & Sons, Inc., to incorporate material from our book "Subsets of the Plane" published by Wiley in 1962. The material from "Subsets of the Plane" appears mainly in Chapters 3 and 4 of the present book.

We express our thanks to Professor Theodore Vincent for his very helpful comments and suggestions.

Thomas L. Wade
Howard E. Taylor

SUGGESTED LESSON ASSIGNMENTS

As indicated in the Preface, the material in this book is planned so that it can be used for courses of various lengths. It appears that colleges which offer a course in analytic geometry allot from 2 quarter hours to 3 semester hours to it, or possibly as much as 5 quarter hours in case solid analytic geometry is included. It is difficult to include solid analytic geometry in a course of less than 4 quarter hours. Experience has shown the feasibility of the suggested lesson assignments for the three types of courses indicated below. It appears to be the custom to allot a semester for a course in analytic geometry for the senior year of high school. On a 5-day-a-week basis this would provide for considerably more than the 44 lessons shown in column III below, and therefore would permit a more relaxed schedule.

The few instances of interdependence of sections should be apparent; to illustrate, one would not study Section 4.8 unless Sections 2.8 and 3.7 had been studied (they all pertain to parametric equations), and one would not study Sections 8.8 and 8.9 unless Sections 7.1 and 7.2 had been covered (they all pertain to vectors).

I. 22 LESSONS (2 QUARTER HOURS)		II. 33 LESSONS (3 QUARTER OR 2 SEMESTER HOURS)		III. 44 LESSONS (4 QUARTER OR 3 SEMESTER HOURS)	
ASSIGNMENT NUMBER	SECTIONS	ASSIGNMENT NUMBER	SECTIONS	ASSIGNMENT NUMBER	SECTIONS
1	1.1–1.4	1	1.1–1.4	1	1.1–1.3
2	1.5–1.8	2	1.5–1.8	2	1.4–1.6
3	2.1–2.4	3	2.1–2.4	3	1.7–1.8
4	2.7; 2.9	4	2.5–2.7	4	2.1–2.4
5	3.1–3.2	5	2.8–2.11	5	2.5–2.7
6	3.3–3.4	6	3.1	6	2.8–2.11
7	4.1–4.2	7	3.2	7	3.1
8	4.4	8	3.3–3.4	8	3.2
9	Review	9	Review	9	3.3–3.4
10	Test 1	10	Test 1	10	Review
11	4.5	11	3.5–3.6	11	Test 1
12	4.6–4.7	12	4.1–4.2	12	3.5–3.6
13	5.1–5.2	13	4.3–4.4	13	3.7–3.9
14	6.1–6.3	14, 15	4.5	14	4.1–4.2
15	6.4–6.5			15	4.3–4.4
16	6.6–6.8	16	4.6	16	4.5
17	7.1	17	4.7	17	4.6
18	7.2	18	4.8	18	4.7
19	7.4	19	Review	19	4.8
20	Review	20	Test 2	20	Review
21	Test 2	21	5.1–5.2	21	Test 2
22	Review for final exam	22	5.3–5.4	22	5.1
		23	6.1–6.3	23	5.2
		24	6.4–6.5	24	5.3
		25	6.6	25	5.4
		26	6.7–6.8	26	6.1–6.2
		27	7.1	27	6.3
		28	7.2	28	6.4–6.5
		29	7.3	29	6.6
		30	7.4	30	6.7–6.8
		31	Review	31	Review
		32	Test 3	32	Test 3
		33	Review for final exam	33	7.1
				34	7.2
				35	7.3
				36	7.4
				37	8.1–8.3
				38	8.4–8.5
				39	8.6–8.7
				40	8.8–8.9
				41	Review
				42	Test 4
				43, 44	Review for final exam

| CONTENTS

CONTEMPORARY ANALYTIC GEOMETRY

1 | BASIC CONCEPTS

For the study of analytic geometry as presented in this book the student should be familiar with the vocabulary and symbolism of sets and set operations, with the meaning and use of the elementary logical connectives (if . . . , then; if and only if; and; or; not), and with the properties of the real number system. In this chapter we review briefly the essential facts concerning sets and elementary logic.

1.1 SETS AND SET OPERATIONS

Set

Any attempt to define the word "set" becomes involved in great difficulties and introduces concepts that are clearly not so intuitive as that of "set." So it is common to take *set* as one of the fundamental undefined terms of mathematics. Words that are used synonymously with "set" are "collection," "aggregate," and "class."

Members of a set

We consider that a set has been *specified* or *determined* when we are able to tell whether any given object is or is not in the set. The individual objects that constitute a set are called *members* or elements of the set. If A is a specified set, then any given object is either a member of A or not a member of A. To indicate that the set B has the members 2, 4, 6, 8, 10 we write

$$B = \{2, 4, 6, 8, 10\}$$

The use of braces, $\{\ldots\}$, will always indicate a set whose members either are tabulated or are clearly indicated between the braces. If the number of members *Finite set* in a set can be expressed by a nonnegative integer, we call the set a *finite set; Infinite set* otherwise the set is called an *infinite set*. If a set is finite, as the set B above, we may specify the set by displaying the members within braces. However, if the number of members in a finite set is large, it is inconvenient to display all the members within braces; in such a case we may specify the set by displaying a sufficient number of members to indicate how the remaining members may be determined and by indicating in some way how many members there are. To illustrate, if C is the set of all positive integers less than 100 that are divisible by 3, we may write

$$C = \{3, 6, 9, 12, \ldots, 99\}$$

We may specify an infinite set by displaying a sufficient number of members to indicate a procedure for determining the other members, followed by three dots, $\ldots$, which we read "and so forth." To illustrate, if D is the set of all positive even integers, then

$$D = \{2, 4, 6, 8, 10, \ldots\}$$

To indicate that an object a is a member of a set A, we write

$$a \in A$$

and read these symbols as "a is a member of A" or, alternatively, as "a belongs to A." To indicate that an object b is not a member of a set A, we write

$$b \notin A$$

and read these symbols as "b is not a member of A" or, alternatively, as "b does not belong to A." To illustrate, for the sets B, C, and D specified above,

$$4 \in B \qquad 9 \in C \qquad 100 \in D \qquad 5 \notin B \qquad 10 \notin C$$

When the objects a and b are members of a set A, we write

$$a, b \in A$$

Similarly, we write

$$a, b, c \in A$$

to indicate that each of a, b, and c is a member of A. Thus, for the set C specified above, $3, 6, 9 \in C$. Also $a_1, a_2, a_3, \ldots, a_n \in A$ means that each of $a_1, a_2, a_3, \ldots, a_n$ is a member of A.

Usually the order in which the members of a set are displayed is not significant, and in general it is understood that the members of a set are distinct. When we are concerned with a collection in which the members are not distinct or in which the order of the members is significant, or both, we shall call such a collection by some name other than set (for example, "ordered pair," or "sequence," or "progression").

Equal sets

If sets A and B have precisely the same members, the sets are said to be **equal sets,** and we write $A = B$. (We follow the convention that when a mathematical term is defined by a verbal statement, that term is printed in **boldface type.** When a mathematical term is defined solely by the use of mathematical symbols and the equality sign, $=$, we write "We **define**" followed by the appropriate equality, with the defined term on the left of the equality sign.) If A and B are not equal, we write $A \neq B$. Thus $\{1, 2\} = \{2, 1\}$, but $\{1, 2\} \neq \{1, 2, 3\}$.

Subset

If every member of set A is a member of B, we say that A is a **subset** of B, and we indicate this by writing $A \subseteq B$. If A is *not* a subset of B, we write $A \not\subseteq B$. To illustrate:

$$\{a, b, c\} \subseteq \{a, b, c, d\} \qquad \{4, 5, 6\} \not\subseteq \{4, 5, 7\}$$

Every set is a subset of itself; $A \subseteq A$. Also, observe that

$$\text{if } A \subseteq B \text{ and } B \subseteq A, \text{ then } A = B.$$

Proper subset

If A is a subset of B and there is at least one member of B that is *not* a member of A, then we say that A is a **proper subset** of B, and we indicate this by writing $A \subset B$. If A is *not* a proper subset of B, we write $A \not\subset B$. To illustrate:

$$\{6, 8\} \subset \{2, 6, 8, 10\}; \{a, b, c\} \not\subset \{a, b, c\}; \text{ but } \{a, b, c\} \subseteq \{a, b, c\}.$$

We note that if $A \subset B$, then surely $A \subseteq B$.

Let us consider the set of all rational numbers whose square is 2. This set is well determined, since if we consider any number we can tell whether or not the number is in the set. This particular set, of course, has no members and is an illustration of the empty set. The set with no members is called the **empty set,** or the **null set,** and is denoted by $\emptyset$. Since there is no way of distinguishing between two sets with no members, we agree that there is only one empty set; thus we speak of *the* empty set rather than *an* empty set. The statement $A = \emptyset$ indicates that A has no members; the statement $B \neq \emptyset$ indicates that B has at least one member. We follow the convention of considering the empty set as a subset of every set and as a proper subset of every set except itself.

Empty set or null set

The subsets of $\{a, b, c\}$ are

$$\{a, b, c\}, \qquad \{a, b\}, \qquad \{a, c\}, \qquad \{b, c\}, \qquad \{a\}, \qquad \{b\}, \qquad \{c\}, \qquad \emptyset$$

All these except $\{a, b, c\}$ are proper subsets of $\{a, b, c\}$. The number of subsets of $\{a, b, c\}$ is $2^3 = 8$, and a set with n members has 2^n subsets.

Union of sets   The **union** of sets A and B, denoted by $A \cup B$, is the set of objects that are
Intersection of   members of *at least one* of the sets A and B. The **intersection** of sets A and B,
sets   denoted by $A \cap B$, is the set of objects that are members of *both* A and B. For
$A = \{2, 4, 6, 8\}$ and $B = \{1, 2, 3, 4\}$, we have

$$A \cup B = \{1, 2, 3, 4, 6, 8\} \qquad A \cap B = \{2, 4\}$$

Also, for $C = \{2, 3, 5\}$ and $D = \{-1, 0, 1\}$, $C \cap D = \emptyset$. Whenever it happens
Disjoint sets   that, for sets A and B, $A \cap B = \emptyset$, we say that A and B are **disjoint sets.** We
observe that, for any set A,

$$A \cup A = A \qquad A \cap A = A \qquad A \cup \emptyset = A \qquad A \cap \emptyset = \emptyset$$

EXERCISES

1. Determine which of the following statements are true and which are false:

(a) $2 \in \{1, 2, 3, 4\}$ (b) $2 \in \{6, 7, 8\}$

(c) $7 \notin \{1, 2, 3\}$ (d) $4 \in \{1, 2, 3, 4\}$

(e) $b \in \{b\}$ (f) $\{e\} \in e$

2. Describe three sets each of which is an illustration of the null set. Should
each of these sets be denoted by $\{0\}$ or by $\emptyset$? Explain.

3. List the subsets of $\{a, b\}$. Which of these are proper subsets of $\{a, b\}$?

4. List the subsets of $\{a, b, c, d\}$. Which of these are proper subsets of
$\{a, b, c, d\}$?

5. If $B = \{1, 2, 3, 4\}$, what are the sets C such that $\{1, 2\} \subset C$ and $C \subset B$?

6. Find each of the following:

(a) $\{1, 2, 3, 4, 5\} \cap \{3, 4, 5, 6, 7\}$

(b) $\{1, 2, 3, 4, 5\} \cap \{1, 2, 3\}$

(c) $\{1, 2, 3\} \cup \{2, 3, 4, 5\}$

(d) $\{1, 2, 3\} \cup \{4, 5, 6\}$

7. Find each of the following:

(a) $\{1, 3, 5, 7, 9\} \cap \{2, 4, 6, 8\}$

(b) $\{1, 3, 5, 7, 9\} \cup \{2, 4, 6, 8\}$

(c) $\{a, b, c\} \cup \{1, 2, 3\}$

(d) $\{a, b, c\} \cap \{a, e, f\}$

8. For the sets $A = \{a, b, c, d\}$ and $B = \{b, d, e\}$, find $A \cap B$; $A \cup B$;
$A \cap A$; $B \cap B$; $A \cup A$; $B \cup B$; $A \cap \emptyset$; $B \cap \emptyset$; $A \cup \emptyset$; $B \cup \emptyset$.

9. If $A = \{1, 2, 3, 4\}$, $B = \{3, 4, 5, 6\}$, and $C = \{4, 5, 6, 7\}$, tabulate each of
the sets $A \cap B$; $A \cap C$; $B \cap C$; $A \cup B$; $A \cup C$; $B \cup C$.

10. For the sets $A = \{a, b, c, d\}$ and $B = \{b, d, e\}$, tabulate the sets C such
that $C \subset A$ and $C \subset B$ and verify that for each such set $C \subseteq (A \cap B)$.

11. For $A = \{a, b, c, d, e\}$ and $B = \{c, d, e, f, g\}$, give $A \cap B$ and $A \cup B$.

1.2 THE LOGICAL CONNECTIVES

Statement Suppose that p and q designate statements. (By *statement* we mean simply a declarative sentence that is either true or false but not both.) Frequently in mathematics we encounter statements that are built up by combining the state-

Compound statement ments p and q in various ways. Such "built up" statements are called *compound statements,* and p and q are called the *component parts* of these compound statements. The four most common compound statements are the following:

p and q	(1)
p or q	(2)
If p is true, then q is true.	(3)
p is true if and only if q is true.	(4)

Statement (3) is usually written more briefly as

$$\text{if } p \text{ then } q$$

and symbolized by writing

$$p \;\Rightarrow\; q \tag{3'}$$

Statement (4) is usually written more briefly as

$$p \text{ if and only if } q$$

and symbolized by writing

$$p \;\Longleftrightarrow\; q \tag{4'}$$

Assuming that we know whether the statements p and q are true or false, in order to use compound statements such as (1), (2), (3'), and (4') we need to agree on what is meant by the "truth" or "falseness" of the compound statements.

Conjunction of statements Statement (1) is called the **conjunction** of the statements p and q. We agree that the conjunction

$$p \text{ and } q$$

is *true* when *both* of its component parts are true, and it is *false* when at least one of its component parts is false.

Disjunction of statements Statement (2) is called the **disjunction** of the statements p and q. We agree that the disjunction

$$p \text{ or } q$$

is *true* when *at least one* of its component parts is true, and it is false when both of its component parts are false.

Implication
Conditional

Statement (3), which is symbolized by (3'), is called an **implication** or a **conditional.** In the implication

$$p \Rightarrow q$$

Hypothesis
Conclusion

p is called the *hypothesis* or *antecedent* and the statement q is called the *conclusion* or *consequent*. We agree that the implication $p \Rightarrow q$ is *true* if it is *impossible* for q to be false when p is true; that is, "if p then q" is true whenever the assumption that p is true *forces* on us the conclusion that q is true. To illustrate,

$$x = 3 \quad \Rightarrow \quad x^2 - 6x + 9 = 0$$

is true, because, whenever $x = 3$ is true, $x^2 - 6x + 9 = 0$ *must* be true. On the other hand,

$$x^2 = 16 \quad \Rightarrow \quad x = 4$$

is false, because it is possible for $x = 4$ to be false when $x^2 = 16$ is true.

Equivalence
Biconditional

Statement (4), which is symbolized by (4'), is called an **equivalence** or a **biconditional.** We agree that the biconditional

$$p \Longleftrightarrow q$$

is *true* if *both* of the statements

$$p \Rightarrow q \qquad \text{and} \qquad q \Rightarrow p$$

are true, that is, if it is *impossible* for one of the component parts of $p \Longleftrightarrow q$ to be true and the other false. For example,

$$5x - 4 = 0 \quad \Longleftrightarrow \quad 5x^2 - 4x = 0$$

is false, because $5x^2 - 4x = 0$ can be true (when x is replaced by 0) when $5x - 4 = 0$ is false.

Converse

If, in an implication, we interchange the hypothesis and the conclusion, we produce a compound statement that is called the **converse** of the original implication; that is,

$$q \Rightarrow p \quad \text{is the converse of} \quad p \Rightarrow q$$

and *vice versa*. An important fact to note about the converse of an implication is that knowing $p \Rightarrow q$ is true gives us *no* information about the truth or falsity of its converse $q \Rightarrow p$. To illustrate:

$x = 3 \Rightarrow x^2 = 9$ is *true*, but $x^2 = 9 \Rightarrow x = 3$ is *false*.
$x = 3 \Rightarrow x + 6 = 9$ is *true*, and $x + 6 = 9 \Rightarrow x = 3$ is *true*.
$4x^2 - 3x = 0 \Rightarrow x = 0$ is *false*, but $x = 0 \Rightarrow 4x^2 - 3x = 0$ is *true*.

Sometimes we wish to consider the denial or negation of a statement p. The
Negation **negation** of p is defined to be a statement that is true when p is false and false

when p is true. For example, the negation of "$x = 2$" is "$x \neq 2$"; the negation of the statement "All rational numbers are integers" is the statement "There is at least one rational number that is not an integer." Further, the negation of "$p \Rightarrow q$" is the statement "p is true and q is false."

The compound statement

$$\text{if } q \text{ is false then } p \text{ is false} \tag{5}$$

Contrapositive   is called the **contrapositive** of the implication

$$\text{if } p \text{ is true then } q \text{ is true.} \tag{6}$$

To say that (5) is true means that it is impossible for p to be true when q is false; that is, the falsity of q *forces* on us the falsity of p. Thus, if (5) is true it is impossible for q to be false and p to be true, but this is just what it means to say that (6) is true. Similarly, to say that (5) is false is the same as saying that (6) is false. So, an implication and its contrapositive are either both true or both false; that is, the statement

$$(p \Rightarrow q) \iff (\text{if } q \text{ is false, then } p \text{ is false})$$

is true.

1.3 OPEN SENTENCES AND SOLUTION SETS

We are accustomed to using letter symbols to represent any number in a given set of numbers. Thus we write $a + b = b + a$ to record the commutative property of addition of real numbers, and understand that a and b may represent any real numbers. The statement $a + b = b + a$ is true whenever a is replaced by any real number and b is replaced by any real number. In the sentence $x + 7 = 12$, x may represent *any* real number, although the sentence is true only when 5 is put in place of x.

Symbols used in the way that a, b, and x are used above are called variables. A

Variable   **variable** is a symbol that represents any member of a given set. The given set is
Universe   called the **universal set** of the variable or the **universe** of the variable. Each
Value of a   member of the universe is called a **value** of the variable. Let x be a variable whose
variable   universe is the set $\{2, 4, 6, 8, 10, 12\}$; then x has values 2, 4, 6, 8, 10, and 12. That is, x may be replaced by any even positive integer less than 14. It is fre-
Placeholder   quently said that a variable is a *placeholder* for any member of its universe.
Constant   If a set has only one member, a symbol for that member is called a **constant.** Let A be the set of even integers greater than 4 and less than 8. Then $A = \{6\}$, and a variable with this set A for a universe has only one value, 6, and is a constant.

Suppose that U is a given set and that x is a variable whose universe is U. Let S_x denote a sentence which contains the variable x and which has the property that when we replace x by any member of U we obtain a statement that can be determined to be either true or false. We may let $U = \{1, 2, 3, 4, 5, 6, 7, 8, 9, 10\}$ and consider the following examples of such sentences containing the variable x whose universe is U:

$$x + 4 = 7 \tag{7}$$
$$x + 2 > 5 \tag{8}$$
$$x \div 3 = 2 \tag{9}$$
$$x^2 > 100 \tag{10}$$

Open sentence

Notice that each of the sentences (7) to (10) is neither true nor false; that is, it is not meaningful to ask whether $x + 4 = 7$ is true or false, or whether $x + 2 > 5$ is true or false, etc. Because of this fact a sentence that contains a variable with a specified universe is called an *open* sentence (that is, the question of its truth or falsity is an "open" question). In each case, however, as the variable in an open sentence is replaced in turn by the members of its universe, the sentence becomes a statement about which it is meaningful to ask whether it is true or false. Observe that each of sentences (7) to (9) becomes a true statement when x is replaced by some members of U and a false statement when x is replaced by other members of U; the sentence (10) becomes a false statement when x is replaced by any member of the universe U.

Condition in a set

An open sentence S_x with $x \in U$ is sometimes called a **condition in** U. If S_x is a condition in U and if b is a member of U with the property that S_x becomes a true statement when x is replaced by b, we say that b *satisfies* the condition S_x. To illustrate, for $U = \{1, 2, 3, 4, 5, 6, 7, 8, 9, 10\}$, the condition $x + 2 > 5$ is satisfied by 4, 5, 6, 7, 8, 9, 10 and is *not* satisfied by 1, 2, 3. We use the symbols

$$\{x \in U \mid S_x\} \tag{11}$$

to denote "the set of all those members of the universe U which satisfy the condition S_x." Thus for the universe and conditions of the preceding paragraph we have

$$\{x \in U \mid x + 4 = 7\} = \{3\}$$
$$\{x \in U \mid x + 2 > 5\} = \{4, 5, 6, 7, 8, 9, 10\}$$
$$\{x \in U \mid x \div 3 = 2\} = \{6\}$$
$$\{x \in U \mid x^2 > 100\} = \emptyset$$

If the universe U of the variable is clearly understood, we abbreviate (11) by

$$\{x \mid S_x\} \tag{12}$$

and read these symbols as "the set of all members of the universe that satisfy the condition S_x." To illustrate, if the universe is the set of positive integers, then

$$\{x \mid x < 9\} = \{1, 2, 3, 4, 5, 6, 7, 8\}$$
$$\{x \mid x^2 - 5x + 6 = 0\} = \{2, 3\}$$

*Solution set or
solution*

The set denoted by $\{x \in U \mid S_x\}$, or by $\{x \mid S_x\}$ in case the universe is clearly understood, is called the **solution set,** or simply the **solution,** of the sentence S_x (in the universe U). To illustrate, if the universe is the set of integers:

The solution of $x^2 = 16$ is $\{-4, 4\}$.
The solution of $x^2 \leqslant 4$ is $\{-2, -1, 0, 1, 2\}$.
The solution of $x^2 = -1$ is $\emptyset$.

*Conjunction of
conditions*

*Disjunction of
conditions*

As we noted in Sec. 1.2, the sentence "p and q" is called the conjunction and the sentence "p or q" is called the disjunction of the statements p, q. So, if P_x and Q_x represent open sentences, or conditions, in the universe U, then the sentence "P_x and Q_x" is called the **conjunction** of these conditions. Further, the sentence "P_x or Q_x" is called the **disjunction** of the conditions P_x, Q_x.

The conjunction "P_x and Q_x" is true when *both* of its component sentences are true. Recalling the meaning of the intersection of sets, we see that

$$\{x \in U \mid P_x \text{ and } Q_x\} = \{x \in U \mid P_x\} \cap \{x \in U \mid Q_x\} \qquad (13)$$

Let the universe be the set I of integers, let P_x be the sentence $-4 < x$, and let Q_x be the sentence $x < 4$. Then

$$\{x \mid -4 < x \text{ and } x < 4\} = \{x \mid -4 < x\} \cap \{x \mid x < 4\}$$
$$= \{-3, -2, -1, 0, 1, 2, \ldots\}$$
$$\cap \{\ldots, -4, -3, -2, -1, 0, 1, 2, 3\}$$
$$= \{-3, -2, -1, 0, 1, 2, 3\}$$

The disjunction "P_x or Q_x" is true when *at least one* of its component sentences is true. Recalling the meaning of the union of sets, we see that

$$\{x \in U \mid P_x \text{ or } Q_x\} = \{x \in U \mid P_x\} \cup \{x \in U \mid Q_x\} \qquad (14)$$

Let the universe be $A = \{1, 2, 3, 4, 5, \ldots, 12\}$, let P_x be the sentence $x < 7$, and let Q_x be the sentence $x > 10$. Then

$$\{x \in A \mid x < 7 \text{ or } x > 10\} = \{x \in A \mid x < 7\} \cup \{x \in A \mid x > 10\}$$
$$= \{1, 2, 3, 4, 5, 6\} \cup \{11, 12\}$$
$$= \{1, 2, 3, 4, 6, 11, 12\}$$

EXERCISES

1. Is it true that $x^2 = 36 \;\Rightarrow\; x = 6$? Explain your answer.
2. Is it true that $x = 4 \;\Rightarrow\; x^2 - 8x + 16 = 0$? Explain your answer.
3. Is it true that $x^2 = 9x \;\Rightarrow\; x = 9$? Explain your answer.
4. Is it true that $a^2 = b^2 \;\Rightarrow\; a = b$? Explain your answer.
5. Is it true that $5x - 7 = 0 \;\Longleftrightarrow\; 5x = 7$? Explain your answer.
6. Is it true that $5x - 7 = 0 \;\Longleftrightarrow\; 5x^2 - 7x = 0$? Explain your answer.

7. Write the negation of the statement "There is no rational number whose square is 2."

8. Write the negation of the statement "There is a real number that is both even and odd."

9. Write the contrapositive of the statement "If $a \cdot b = 0$ then $a = 0$ or $b = 0$."

10. Write the contrapositive of the statement "If a, b, and c are real numbers, then $a(b + c) = ab + ac$."

If the universe U is the set of positive integers less than 24, tabulate each of the sets in Exercises 11–14.

11. (*a*) $\{x \mid x \in U\}$ $\qquad\qquad$ (*b*) $\{x \mid x^2 \in U\}$

12. (*a*) $\{x \mid x^2 < 17\}$ $\qquad\qquad$ (*b*) $\{x \mid x^2 - 7x = 0\}$

13. (*a*) $\{x \mid x^2 - x - 6 = 0\}$ $\qquad$ (*b*) $\{x \mid x^2 + 4x + 4 = 0\}$

14. (*a*) $\{x \mid x \text{ is odd}\}$ $\qquad\qquad$ (*b*) $\{x \mid x^2 = 9\}$

15. What is the solution of the sentence $3x = 18$ in the universe of integers? In the universe of negative integers?

16. What is the solution of the sentence $5x = -20$ in the universe of integers? In the universe of positive integers?

In each of Exercises 17–24 find the solution of the given sentence if the universe is the set I of integers.

17. $x > -3$ and $x < 2$ $\qquad\qquad$ **18.** $x < 4$ and $x > -1$

19. $x > -4$ or $x < 5$ $\qquad\qquad$ **20.** $x^2 + 2x = 0$ or $x + 3 = 0$

21. $5x = 35$ $\qquad\qquad\qquad\qquad$ **22.** $4x = 13$

23. $x^4 - 5x^2 + 4 = 0$ $\qquad\qquad$ **24.** $x - \sqrt{x - 1} = 3$

1.4 ONE-DIMENSIONAL COORDINATE SYSTEMS

One-to-one correspondence

Sets A and B are said to be in **one-to-one correspondence** if the members of the sets can be paired in such a way that each pair consists of one member from each set, that all of the members of both sets are used, and that no member of either set is used more than once. When the sets A and B can be put in one-to-one corre-

Equivalent sets

spondence, A and B are called **equivalent sets.** For example, the sets $\{a, b\}$ and $\{c, d\}$ are equivalent, since the members of these sets can be paired as described above; this can be done in two ways, as indicated by the diagrams in Fig. 1.1.

If sets A and B are equivalent, we write $A \sim B$. Observe that $A = B \Rightarrow A \sim B$. Is it true that $A \sim B \Rightarrow A = B$? Give an explanation of your answer.

FIGURE 1.1

Number line or one-dimensional coordinate system

Origin

Unit of measure

Recall that a property of the set of real numbers is that, given a line L, an "order preserving" one-to-one correspondence can be established between the points of L and the set of real numbers. When such a one-to-one correspondence has been established we call the line L a number line for the real numbers, or a one-dimensional coordinate system. Figure 1.2 illustrates such a line or coordinate system. On this coordinate system the point O which corresponds to the number 0 is called the origin. If the point A corresponds to the number 1, then the segment OA is called the unit of measure. A may be any point distinct from O. We customarily represent a one-dimensional coordinate system by a horizontal line, but we could just as well use a vertical line or a line with some other orientation. Also, it is customary to take the direction to the right on a horizontal number line to be the positive direction (as indicated by the arrow in Fig. 1.2), and the direction to the left to be the negative direction. This is an arbitrary choice; the positive direction can be taken to the left if we wish.

Coordinate of P_1

Graph of x_1

The real number x_1 that corresponds to a point P_1 on a one-dimensional coordinate system is called the **coordinate of** P_1, and P_1 is called the **graph of** x_1. We write $P(x_1)$ to mean "the point P with coordinate x_1." Because there is a one-to-one correspondence between the points on the line and the real numbers, we frequently speak of $P(x_1)$ simply as "the point x_1." Referring to Fig. 1.2, we can write $O(0)$, $B(\sqrt{2})$, and $C(-\sqrt{3})$ to indicate that the point O has coordinate 0, the point B has coordinate $\sqrt{2}$, and the point C has coordinate $-\sqrt{3}$.

If the point M_1 has coordinate 2 and the point M_2 has coordinate 7 (Fig. 1.3), it is clear that M_1 and M_2 are 5 units apart, and we commonly describe this situation by saying that the distance between M_1 and M_2 is 5. If the point Q_1 has coordinate 8 and the point Q_2 has coordinate -3, it is clear that Q_1 and Q_2 are 11 units apart, and we say that the distance between Q_1 and Q_2 is 11. Recalling that the *absolute value* of any real number a is denoted by $|a|$ and defined by

Absolute value

$$|a| = a \qquad \text{if } a \geq 0$$
$$|a| = -a \qquad \text{if } a < 0$$

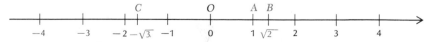

FIGURE 1.2 A number line.

FIGURE 1.3

we note that the distance 5 between M_1 and M_2 is the absolute value of the difference between the coordinates of the points: $5 = |7 - 2| = |2 - 7|$. Also the distance 11 between Q_1 and Q_2 is the absolute value of the difference between the coordinates of the points: $11 = |(-3) - 8| = |8 - (-3)|$. Considerations such as these lead to a general definition of distance between points. Let $P_1(x_1)$ and *Distance* $P_2(x_2)$ be points on a one-dimensional coordinate system (Fig. 1.3). The **distance** *between points* **between** the points $P_1(x_1)$ and $P_2(x_2)$ is denoted by $|P_1P_2|$ and is defined by

$$|P_1P_2| = |x_2 - x_1|$$

It should be clear that the numerical value of this distance will depend upon the scale or units used to establish the coordinate system.

Knowing the distance between two points P_1 and P_2 does not give any information as to whether P_1 lies to the left or to the right of P_2. For the points M_1 and M_2 in Fig. 1.3 we can indicate that M_2 lies to the right of M_1 by saying that the *directed* distance *from* $M_1(2)$ *to* $M_2(7)$ is $5 = 7 - 2$, while the directed distance from $M_2(7)$ to $M_1(2)$ is $-5 = 2 - 7$. Such considerations lead to the following *Directed distance* definition. The **directed distance** *from* the point $P_1(x_1)$ *to* the point $P_2(x_2)$ is denoted by $\overline{P_1P_2}$ and is defined by

$$\overline{P_1P_2} = x_2 - x_1$$

Since the distance between P_1 and P_2 is the absolute value of a real number, it is never negative. However, the directed distance from P_1 to P_2 may be either negative or nonnegative, depending upon whether $x_2 - x_1$ is negative or non-negative.

Length The distance $|P_1P_2|$ is often referred to as the **length of the line segment** P_1P_2 *Undirected* and is sometimes called the **undirected distance** from either of the points to the *distance* other.

Observe that for any point $P_1(x_1)$ and the origin $O(0)$, we have

$$\overline{OP_1} = x_1 - 0 = x_1$$

Therefore, the directed distance from the origin to a point P is equal to the coordinate of P.

The following are some illustrations of the definitions in the preceding paragraphs.

The directed distance from $P_1(5)$ to $P_2(-4)$ is given by $\overline{P_1P_2} = -4 - 5 = -9$.

The distance between $P_1(5)$ and $P_2(-4)$ is given by $|P_1P_2| = |-4-5| = |-9| = 9$.

If the directed distance $\overline{P_1P_2} = -4$, then P_2 is to the left of P_1, and the undirected distance $|P_1P_2| = 4$.

The set S of coordinates of all points P with the property that the distance between O and P is 5 is given by

$$S = \{x \mid |x| = 5\} = \{x \mid x = 5 \text{ or } x = -5\}$$

So $S = \{-5, 5\}$ and the graph of S consists of two points: $P_1(5)$ and $P_2(-5)$.

EXERCISES

In each of Exercises 1–8, points P_1 and P_2 on a one-dimensional coordinate system have the given coordinates x_1 and x_2, respectively. Find $\overline{P_1P_2}$ and $|P_1P_2|$.

1. $x_1 = 9;\ x_2 = 13$ **2.** $x_1 = -3;\ x_2 = 14$

3. $x_1 = 7;\ x_2 = -4$ **4.** $x_1 = -6;\ x_2 = -1$

5. $x_1 = 7k;\ x_2 = 4k\ (k > 0)$ **6.** $x_1 = 7k;\ x_2 = 4k\ (k < 0)$

7. $x_1 = \frac{7}{4};\ x_2 = -\frac{1}{4}$ **8.** $x_1 = 4\sqrt{3};\ x_2 = 3\sqrt{5}$

Graph each of the following sets on a one-dimensional coordinate system.

9. $\{x \mid x^2 = 16\}$ **10.** $\{x \mid x^2 + 5x - 6 = 0\}$

11. $\{x \mid x^3 - 8 = 0\}$ **12.** $\{x \mid x^2 - 2x + 1 = 0\}$

1.5 INTERVALS

Intervals are special subsets of the set of all real numbers. In considering these subsets (and throughout this book) we shall denote the set of real numbers by *Re*. Also, if $a, b, c \in Re$ we write

$$a < b < c \tag{15}$$

to indicate that

$$a < b \qquad \text{and} \qquad b < c$$

(and, consequently, $a < c$). Similar meanings are given to the symbols $a \leq b \leq c$, $a \leq b < c$, $a < b \leq c$. If (15) holds, we say that b is *between* a and c; to illustrate, $1 < \sqrt{2} < 3$, so $\sqrt{2}$ is between 1 and 3. Also $-2 < -\sqrt{3} < -1$, so $-\sqrt{3}$ is between -2 and -1 (see Fig. 1.2).

Throughout this book we agree that *the universe of any variable is Re unless stipulated explicitly to the contrary.*

Closed interval

The set of all real numbers greater than or equal to a and less than or equal to b is denoted by $\{x \mid a \leq x \leq b\}$. This set is called the **closed interval** from a to b and is denoted by $[a; b]$; that is,

$$[a; b] = \{x \mid a \leq x \leq b\}$$

Open interval

The set of all real numbers greater than a and less than b is denoted by $\{x \mid a < x < b\}$. This set is called the **open interval** from a to b and is denoted by $(a; b)$; that is,

$$(a; b) = \{x \mid a < x < b\}$$

Right open interval

The set of all real numbers greater than or equal to a and less than b is denoted by $\{x \mid a \leq x < b\}$. This set is called the **right open interval** from a to b and is denoted by $[a; b)$; that is,

$$[a; b) = \{x \mid a \leq x < b\}$$

Left open interval

The set of all real numbers greater than a and less than or equal to b is denoted by $\{x \mid a < x \leq b\}$. This set is called the **left open interval** from a to b and is denoted by $(a; b]$; that is,

$$(a; b] = \{x \mid a < x \leq b\}$$

The graphs of these four intervals on a one-dimensional coordinate system are shown in Figs. 1.4 to 1.7, respectively. In these figures a heavy dot at a point (as at point a in Fig. 1.6) indicates that the point is included in the interval, and the arc of a circle at a point (as at point b in Fig. 1.6) indicates that the point is not included in the interval.

Each of the intervals $[a; b]$, $(a; b)$, $[a; b)$, and $(a; b]$ is called a finite interval with a as the left end point and b as the right end point. To illustrate, $[0; 5] = \{x \mid 0 \leq x \leq 5\}$ is the closed finite interval with 0 as left end point and 5 as right

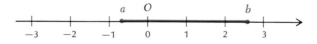

FIGURE 1.4 $[a; b] = \{x \mid a \leq x \leq b\}$.

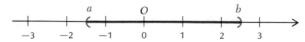

FIGURE 1.5 $(a; b) = \{x \mid a < x < b\}$.

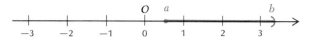

FIGURE 1.6 $[a; b) = \{x \mid a \leq x < b\}$.

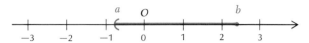

FIGURE 1.7 $(a; b] = \{x \mid a < x \leq b\}$.

end point (Fig. 1.8). Similarly, $(0; 5] = \{x \mid 0 < x \leq 5\}$ is the finite left open interval with 0 as left end point and 5 as right end point (Fig. 1.9).

We have chosen to use the semicolon in the notation for intervals $(a; b)$, $[a; b]$, etc., rather than the comma as is sometimes used. The semicolon notation aids in distinguishing between the interval $(a; b)$ and the ordered pair (a, b) discussed in the next section.

Because of the one-to-one correspondence between points on a line and the real numbers, we frequently speak of the graph of an interval simply as an interval. That is, we use the word "interval" to mean either one of the subsets of real numbers defined in the preceding paragraphs or the graph of that subset on a one-dimensional coordinate system.

Sometimes it is convenient to consider a subset of the set of real numbers whose graph extends indefinitely in one or both directions. In doing so we use one or more of the five intervals

$$\{x \mid a \leq x\}, \quad \{x \mid a < x\}, \quad \{x \mid x \leq b\}, \quad \{x \mid x < b\}, \quad \{x \mid x \in Re\} = Re$$

Alternative notations for these intervals are obtained by using the symbol ∞ as

FIGURE 1.8 $[0; 5] = \{x \mid 0 \leq x \leq 5\}$.

FIGURE 1.9 $(0; 5] = \{x \mid 0 < x \leq 5\}$.

follows:

$$[a; +\infty) = \{x \mid a \leqslant x\} \qquad (a; +\infty) = \{x \mid a < x\}$$
$$(-\infty; b] = \{x \mid x \leqslant b\} \qquad (-\infty; b) = \{x \mid x < b\}$$
$$(-\infty; +\infty) = Re$$

Infinite interval   Each of these sets is called an **infinite interval,** and its graph can be indicated on a one-dimensional coordinate system. To illustrate, the graph of $(4; +\infty)$ is indicated in Fig. 1.10.

The following theorem is especially useful in working with intervals, inequalities, and absolute value.

THEOREM   *For any real numbers a, x, and b, where $b \geqslant 0$:*
1.1
   (i) $|x - a| \leqslant b \iff -b \leqslant x - a \leqslant b$ (16)

   (ii) $|x - a| \geqslant b \iff x - a \leqslant -b$ or $x - a \geqslant b$ (17)

We shall not give a detailed proof of this theorem. Such a proof can be given by using the definition of absolute value and the properties of the real number system. However, the theorem may be seen to be plausible when we recall that $|x - a|$ can be interpreted geometrically as the distance between the points whose coordinates are x and a, respectively. Thus the set $S_1 = \{x \mid |x - a| \leqslant b\}$ can be interpreted graphically as the set of points with the property that the distance between each point $P(x)$ in S_1 and the point $P_1(a)$ is less than or equal to b. Similarly, the set $S_2 = \{x \mid |x - a| \geqslant b\}$ can be interpreted graphically as the set of points with the property that the distance between each point $P(x)$ in S_2 and the point $P_1(a)$ is greater than or equal to b.

Since $a \leqslant b \leqslant c$ means "$a \leqslant b$ and $b \leqslant c$," it follows from the definition of the conjunction of two sentences (see Sec. 1.2) and from statement (16) that, for $b \geqslant 0$,

$$\{x \mid |x - a| \leqslant b\} = \{x \mid x \geqslant a - b\} \cap \{x \mid x \leqslant a + b\}$$ (18)

Also, from the definition of the disjunction of two sentences (see Sec. 1.2) and from statement (17), it follows that, for $b \geqslant 0$,

$$\{x \mid |x - a| \geqslant b\} = \{x \mid x \leqslant a - b\} \cup \{x \mid x \geqslant a + b\}$$ (19)

FIGURE 1.10 $(4; +\infty) = \{x \mid 4 < x\}$.

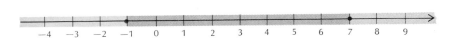

FIGURE 1.11   Graph of $\{x \mid |x - 3| \leqslant 4\}$.

FIGURE 1.12   Graph of $\{x \mid |x - 3| \geqslant 4\}$.

To illustrate,

$$S = \{x \mid |x - 3| \leqslant 4\} = \{x \mid x \geqslant -1\} \cap \{x \mid x \leqslant 7\} = S_1 \cap S_2$$

where $S_1 = \{x \mid x \geqslant -1\}$ and $S_2 = \{x \mid x \leqslant 7\}$.

$$T = \{x \mid |x - 3| \geqslant 4\} = \{x \mid x \leqslant -1\} \cup \{x \mid x \geqslant 7\} = T_1 \cup T_2$$

where $T_1 = \{x \mid x \leqslant -1\}$ and $T_2 = \{x \mid x \geqslant 7\}$. In Fig. 1.11 we have shown the graph of S_1 by color shading and the graph of S_2 by gray shading; the graph of S is the intersection of the graphs of S_1 and S_2, and is shown by darker color shading. In Fig. 1.12 we have shown the graph of T_1 with color and the graph of T_2 with gray; the graph of T is the union of the graphs of T_1 and T_2.

EXERCISES

In each of Exercises 1–10, graph the given set on a one-dimensional coordinate system, and give a geometric description of the set.

1. $\{x \mid 3 < x \leqslant 5\}$

2. $\{x \mid x < 1\}$

3. $\{x \mid x^2 = 16\}$

4. $\{x \mid -2 \leqslant x \leqslant 3\}$

5. $\{x \mid x^2 - 2x - 3 = 0\}$

6. $\{x \mid x(x - 2)(x - 3) = 0\}$

7. $\{x \mid |x - 2| \leqslant 5\}$

8. $\{x \mid |x - 2| \geqslant 5\}$

9. $\{x \mid |x - 4| > 1\}$

10. $\{x \mid |x - 4| < 1\}$

11. Using the symbols $\{x \mid S_x\}$ to denote "the set of real numbers which satisfy the condition S_x," symbolize each of the sets whose geometric description is given:

   (*a*) The set of points which lie to the right of $P(2)$

   (*b*) The set of points which lie between $P_1(-3)$ and $P_2(4)$, including $P_1(-3)$

(c) The set S of points with the property that, for each $P \in S$, the distance between O and P is 5

(d) The set of points which lie to the left of $P_1(-4)$ together with the points which lie to the right of $P_2(6)$, including $P_1(-4)$ and $P_2(6)$

In each of Exercises 12–17, graph the given interval on a one-dimensional coordinate system.

12. $[-2; 5]$ **13.** $(-2; 5)$ **14.** $[-2; 5)$

15. $(-2; 5]$ **16.** $(-\infty; 3)$ **17.** $(-\infty; 3]$

In each of Exercises 18-21, express the given set S as an interval or as the union of intervals, and graph S on a one-dimensional coordinate system.

18. $S = \{x \mid |x - 3| < 4\}$ **19.** $S = \{x \mid |2x - 3| < 5\}$

misprint

20. $S = \{x \mid |x - 1| > 5\}$ **21.** $S = \{x \mid x \geqslant 2\}$

In each of Exercises 22–25, express the intersection $A \cap B$ and the union $A \cup B$ of the given sets A and B as an interval or a union of intervals. For each exercise graph A and B on the same one-dimensional coordinate system (using cross-hatching or different colors for the graphs of A and B). On this coordinate system indicate the graphs of $A \cap B$ and $A \cup B$.

22. $A = \{x \mid -2 < x \leqslant 5\}$; $B = \{x \mid x > 3\}$

23. $A = \{x \mid -2 < x \leqslant 5\}$; $B = \{x \mid 3 \leqslant x \leqslant 11\}$

24. $A = \{x \mid -3 < x \leqslant 2\}$; $B = \{x \mid 2 < x \leqslant 3\}$

25. $A = \{x \mid |x - 3| > 6\}$; $B = \{x \mid 6 < x \leqslant 11\}$

1.6 ORDERED PAIRS, CARTESIAN SETS, AND RELATIONS

Ordered pair

An **ordered pair** of objects consists of two objects, one of which is designated as the first and the other as the second. With a designated as the first object and b

First entry
Second entry

as the second, we denote the ordered pair by (a, b) and call a the **first entry** and b the **second entry** of the ordered pair. The ordered pairs (a, b) and (c, d) are equal if and only if $a = c$ and $b = d$:

$$(a, b) = (c, d) \iff a = c \text{ and } b = d$$

The two entries of an ordered pair may be members of the same set or members of different sets. If $A = \{1, 2, 3\}$ and $B = \{4, 5, 6\}$, then the ordered pairs

$$(1, 4), \quad (2, 5), \quad (2, 6), \quad (3, 6)$$

are of the form (a, b), where $a \in A$ and $b \in B$. The entries of $(1, 2)$ and $(3, 1)$ are members of set A only.

Cartesian set   The set of ordered pairs consisting of *all* the ordered pairs that can be formed by using members of U as entries is called the **cartesian set of** U. The cartesian set of U is denoted by $U \times U$ (read "U cross U"):

$$(x, y) \in U \times U \iff x \in U \text{ and } y \in U$$

To illustrate, if $U = \{1, 2\}$, then

$$U \times U = \{(1, 1), (1, 2), (2, 2), (2, 1)\}$$

Also, if $U = \{2, 4, 6\}$, then

$$U \times U = \{(2, 2), (2, 4), (2, 6), (4, 2), (4, 4), (4, 6), (6, 2), (6, 4), (6, 6)\}$$

Let x and y be variables whose universe is U, and let S_{xy} denote a sentence containing the variables x and y. If the sentence S_{xy} has the property that whenever x is replaced by a member of U and y is replaced by a member of U a statement is obtained that is either true or false, but not both, then S_{xy} is called a *Condition in*   **condition in** $U \times U$. If an ordered pair (a, b) has the property that S_{xy} becomes a $U \times U$ *true* statement when x is replaced by a and y is replaced by b, we say that (a, b) *satisfies* the sentence S_{xy}. The symbols

$$\{(x, y) \mid S_{xy}\}$$

are used to denote "the set of all ordered pairs in $U \times U$ which satisfy S_{xy}."

Relation in a set   If a universe U is given, a **relation in** U is a set of ordered pairs whose entries are members of U. Thus, each ordered pair in a relation is a member of the cartesian set $U \times U$; hence *a relation in U is a subset of $U \times U$*. If $U = \{1, 2, 3\}$, then each of the following is a relation in U:

$$R_1 = \{(x, y) \mid y > x\} = \{(1, 2), (1, 3), (2, 3)\}$$
$$R_2 = \{(x, y) \mid y = x\} = \{(1, 1), (2, 2), (3, 3)\}$$
$$R_3 = \{(x, y) \mid y < x\} = \{(2, 1), (3, 1), (3, 2)\}$$
$$R_4 = \{(x, y) \mid x - y = 1\} = \{(2, 1), (3, 2)\}$$
$$R_5 = \{(x, y) \mid x + y < 4\} = \{(1, 1), (1, 2), (2, 1)\}$$
$$R_6 = \{(x, y) \mid y = 5x\} = \emptyset$$

Domain   The **domain** of a relation R in a set U is the subset of U composed of all the *Range*   *first* entries of the ordered pairs belonging to R. The **range** of a relation R in a set U is the subset of U composed of all the *second* entries of the ordered pairs belonging to R. Table 1.1 gives the domain and the range of each of the relations R_1 to R_6 described in the preceding paragraph.

TABLE 1.1

RELATION	DOMAIN	RANGE
R_1	$\{1, 2\}$	$\{2, 3\}$
R_2	$\{1, 2, 3\}$	$\{1, 2, 3\}$
R_3	$\{2, 3\}$	$\{1, 2\}$
R_4	$\{2, 3\}$	$\{1, 2\}$
R_5	$\{1, 2\}$	$\{1, 2\}$
R_6	$\emptyset$	$\emptyset$

EXERCISES

1. If $U = \{1, 2, 3\}$, list the ordered pairs whose entries are members of U.

2. If $U = \{1, 2\}$, tabulate each of the following relations:

(a) $R_1 = \{(x, y) \mid y = x\}$ (b) $R_2 = \{(x, y) \mid y > x\}$

(c) $R_3 = \{(x, y) \mid y < x\}$

3. Give the domain and the range of each of the relations in Exercise 2.

4. If $U = \{1, 2, 3, 4\}$, list the ordered pairs that are members of the cartesian set $U \times U$.

5. If $U = \{1, 2, 3, 4\}$, tabulate each of the following relations:

(a) $R_1 = \{(x, y) \mid y = x\}$ (b) $R_2 = \{(x, y) \mid y > x\}$

(c) $R_3 = \{(x, y) \mid x + y = 6\}$ (d) $R_4 = \{(x, y) \mid y < x\}$

6. Give the domain and the range of each of the relations in Exercise 5.

7. If $U = \{1, 2, 3, 4, 5\}$, give the cartesian set $U \times U$.

8. If $U = \{1, 2, 3, 4, 5\}$, tabulate each of the following relations:

(a) $R_1 = \{(x, y) \mid y = x\}$ (b) $R_2 = \{(x, y) \mid y < x\}$

(c) $R_3 = \{(x, y) \mid y = x + 3\}$ (d) $R_4 = \{(x, y) \mid y^2 = x\}$

9. Give the domain and the range of each of the relations in Exercise 8.

10. As a generalization of the cartesian set $U \times U$ of a set U we have the *cartesian product* $U \times V$ of sets U and V. $U \times V$ is the set of ordered pairs that can be formed with members of U as first entries and with members of V as second entries:

$$(x, y) \in U \times V \iff x \in U \text{ and } y \in V$$

If $U = \{1, 2\}$ and $V = \{1, 2, 3\}$, give $U \times V$ and $V \times U$. Observe that $U \times V \neq V \times U$, but that $U \times V$ and $V \times U$ have the same number of members.

11. If $U = \{1, 2, 3\}$ and $V = \{1, 2, 3, 4\}$, find $U \times V$.

12. A *relation in* $U \times V$ is a subset of the cartesian product of $U \times V$. For U and V of Exercise 11 tabulate each of the following relations:

(a) $R_1 = \{(x, y) \in U \times V \mid y > x\}$

(b) $R_2 = \{(x, y) \in U \times V \mid y = x\}$

(c) $R_3 = \{(x, y) \in U \times V \mid y - x = 2\}$

13. Give the domain and range of each of the relations in Exercise 12.

1.7 TWO-DIMENSIONAL COORDINATE SYSTEMS

We now describe how the concept of a one-dimensional coordinate system can be used to establish a one-to-one correspondence between the set of points in a plane and the set of all ordered pairs of real numbers, that is, between the points in a plane and the members of the cartesian set $Re \times Re$. On a plane we construct 2 one-dimensional coordinate systems OX and OY perpendicular to each other so that their origins coincide, as shown in Fig. 1.13. The two number lines so constructed form a two-dimensional (rectangular) coordinate system. The line OX is called the *x axis* and the line OY is called the *y axis,* and the point of intersection of these *coordinate axes* is called the *origin.* Figure 1.13 shows the *x* axis horizontal with the positive direction to the right, and the *y* axis vertical with the positive direction upward. This orientation is not necessary, of course, but it is commonly used unless there is a special reason for doing otherwise.

Two-dimensional coordinate system

x axis

y axis

Coordinate axes

Origin

Using a two-dimensional coordinate system, we can establish a one-to-one correspondence between the points in a plane and the ordered pairs of real numbers $Re \times Re$.

Let P be any point in a plane on which a two-dimensional rectangular coordinate system has been constructed, and construct two lines through P, one line

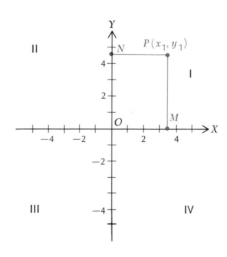

FIGURE 1.13 A two-dimensional coordinate system.

perpendicular to each coordinate axis (Fig. 1.13). Let M be the point at which the line perpendicular to the x axis intersects that axis; let N be the point at which the line perpendicular to the y axis intersects that axis. Let x_1 be the coordinate of M on the x axis and let y_1 be the coordinate of N on the y axis. The numbers x_1 *Coordinates* and y_1 are called the **rectangular plane coordinates,** or simply the **coordinates,** of *Abscissa* the point P. The coordinate x_1 is called the **abscissa** or x **coordinate** of P, and the *Ordinate* coordinate y_1 is called the **ordinate** or y **coordinate** of P. In this way each point P in a plane has associated with it an *ordered* pair of real numbers (x_1, y_1). Note that in the two-dimensional coordinate system the point M has coordinates $(x_1, 0)$ and the point N has coordinates $(0, y_1)$.

Conversely, to an ordered pair (x_1, y_1) of real numbers there can be associated the point in the plane that is the point of intersection of two lines, the first line perpendicular to the x axis at the point $M(x_1)$, and the second line perpendicular to the y axis at the point $N(y_1)$.

Thus, the one-to-one correspondence mentioned in the first paragraph of this section is established. We write $P(x_1, y_1)$ to denote "the point P with coordinates x_1 and y_1," and the point is called simply "the point (x_1, y_1)." The point $P(x_1, y_1)$ *Graph of an* is called the **graph** of the ordered pair (x_1, y_1) of real numbers.
ordered pair To plot or *graph* the point $A(3, 4)$ we may proceed as follows: Start at the origin and measure 3 units to the right (since the abscissa is positive) along the x axis; from the point thus reached, measure 4 units upward (since the ordinate is positive) along a line perpendicular to the x axis. This locates the desired point (see Fig. 1.14).

Similarly, to graph $B(-4, -5)$, start at the origin and measure 4 units to the left (since the abscissa is negative) along the x axis; from the point thus reached,

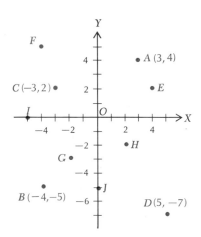

FIGURE 1.14

measure 5 units downward (since the ordinate is negative) along a line perpendicular to the x axis. This locates the desired point (see Fig. 1.14).

Also graphed in Fig. 1.14 are the points $C(-3, 2)$ and $D(5, -7)$.

Quadrants   The coordinate axes divide the plane into four regions, called **quadrants.** These quadrants are numbered I, II, III, IV. Customarily, quadrant I is that region in which each point has both coordinates positive; quadrant II is that region in which each point has a negative abscissa and a positive ordinate; and so on, as shown in Fig. 1.13.

A plane in which a two-dimensional coordinate system has been constructed *Coordinate plane*   is called a coordinate plane.

1.8 GRAPHS OF RELATIONS AND FUNCTIONS IN Re

In Sec. 1.6 we defined a *relation* in U to be a set R of ordered pairs whose entries are members of U; that is, a relation in U is a subset of $U \times U$. One of the most common ways of specifying a relation in U is to make use of a *condition* in $U \times U$. If S_{xy} is a condition in $U \times U$, then

$$R = \{(x, y) \mid S_{xy}\}$$

is the relation that is the set of all ordered pairs in $U \times U$ which satisfy the condition (or sentence) S_{xy}. An ordered pair (a, b) belongs to the relation $R = \{(x, y) \mid S_{xy}\}$ if and only if the sentence S_{ab} is a true statement; when this is true we write $(a, b) \in R$.

Graph of a   The **graph of a relation** R in Re is the set G of all points in the coordinate plane *relation*   with the following property:

$$P(a, b) \in G \iff (a, b) \in R$$

If a sentence S_{xy} with variables x and y is a condition in $U \times U$, then the graph of that sentence is the graph of the relation

$$R = \{(x, y) \mid S_{xy}\}$$

Graph of an   Such a sentence often occurs in the form of an *equation* or in the form of an *equation*   *inequality.* Thus it is natural to define the **graph of an equation** in two variables *Graph of an*   as the graph of the relation specified by the equation, and the **graph of an in-** *inequality*   **equality** in two variables as the graph of the relation specified by the inequality. If $E(x, y)$ is an expression that contains no variables other than x and y, the graph of the equation $E(x, y) = 0$ is the graph of the relation R given by

$$R = \{(x, y) \mid E(x, y) = 0\} \tag{20}$$

The representation of ordered pairs of real numbers by points in a plane, together with the study of sets of such points that are graphs of sentences (especially equations and inequalities) in two variables, constitutes **plane analytic geometry.**

Since a relation R in Re may have an infinite number of ordered pairs as members, we cannot in general tabulate all the members of R. However, if the relation R is specified by an equation $E(x, y) = 0$, we are frequently able to proceed as follows. In the equation $E(x, y) = 0$, replace x by selected real numbers, in turn, and for each of these numbers find a value for y that will satisfy the resulting equation. In this way construct a table of ordered pairs that are members of the relation R. Then graph the points having these ordered pairs as coordinates and obtain the graph of R by connecting them in a smooth curve. The assumption that the graph of $E(x, y) = 0$ is a smooth curve is true for many situations (as in Example 1, which follows), but it is not always true. However, it is heartening to know that much of our subsequent study of plane analytic geometry will consist of an analysis of graphs and relations that enables us to construct graphs of relations with only limited use of point-by-point graphing.

◆   EXAMPLE 1

Graph the relation

$$R_1 = \{(x, y) \mid y = x^2 - 1\}$$

Solution

We find that the ordered pair $(-3, 8) \in R_1$ by replacing x by -3 in the equation $y = x^2 - 1$ and noting that the resulting equation is satisfied when y has the value 8. The other ordered pairs of Table 1.2 are determined similarly.

TABLE 1.2													
	P_1	P_2	P_3	P_4	P_5	P_6	P_7	P_8	P_9	P_{10}	P_{11}	P_{12}	P_{13}
x	-3	$-\frac{5}{2}$	-2	$-\frac{3}{2}$	-1	$-\frac{1}{2}$	0	$\frac{1}{2}$	1	$\frac{3}{2}$	2	$\frac{5}{2}$	3
y	8	$\frac{21}{4}$	3	$\frac{5}{4}$	0	$-\frac{3}{4}$	-1	$-\frac{3}{4}$	0	$\frac{5}{4}$	3	$\frac{21}{4}$	8

We graph the points whose coordinates are the ordered pairs of Table 1.2, and join these points to get the smooth curve of Fig. 1.15. This curve is a finite portion of the graph of the relation R_1 and is the graph of the equation $y = x^2 - 1$, which specifies R_1. The curve in Fig. 1.15 is a *parabola*. Parabolas will be studied in Sec. 4.1.

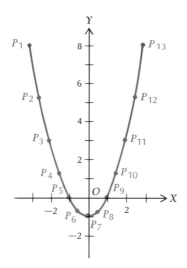

FIGURE 1.15 Graph of $\{(x, y) \mid y = x^2 - 1\}$.

For the relation R_1 considered in Example 1 the domain is Re and the range is $[-1; +\infty)$. Here we have followed the convention that, unless specifically stated to the contrary, the domain of a relation in Re specified by a sentence S_{xy} is the set D of all real numbers with the property that $a \in D$ if and only if there exists a real number b for which S_{ab} is true, that is, for which $(a, b) \in R$:

$$D = \{x \in Re \mid \text{there exists } y \in Re \text{ for which } (x, y) \in R\}$$

For relations in which the domain is specifically stated, consider the following examples:

$$R_2 = \{(x, y) \mid y = x \text{ and } -4 \leqslant x \leqslant 1\}$$
$$R_3 = \{(x, y) \mid y = |x| \text{ and } x \in [-2; 3]\}$$
$$R_4 = \{(x, y) \mid -3 \leqslant x \leqslant 1 \text{ and } 0 \leqslant y \leqslant 2\}$$
$$R_5 = \{(x, y) \mid y = \sqrt{25 - x^2} \text{ and } x \in [-3; 4]\}$$

For R_2, the domain is $[-4; 1]$ and the range is $[-4; 1]$; for R_3, the domain is $[-2; 3]$ and the range is $[0; 3]$; for R_4, the domain is $[-3; 1]$ and the range is $[0; 2]$; for R_5, the domain is $[-3; 4]$ and the range is $[3; 5]$. The graphs of the relations R_2 to R_5 are shown in Figs. 1.16 to 1.19.

It is instructive to consider the relations R_2 to R_5 and their graphs in light of the idea of intersection of sets. Recall that the intersection of sets A and B is denoted by $A \cap B$ and is defined to be the set whose members belong to both A and B. If S_{xy} and T_{xy} are sentences in the variables x and y, then, from the definition of the

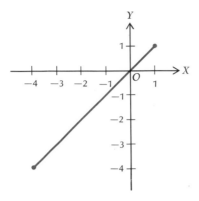

FIGURE 1.16 Graph of
$R_2 = \{(x, y) \mid y = x \text{ and } -4 \leqslant x \leqslant 1\}$.

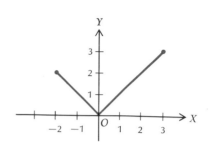

FIGURE 1.17 Graph of
$R_3 = \{(x, y) \mid y = |x| \text{ and } x \in [-2; 3]\}$.

conjunction of sentences (Sec. 1.2) it follows that

$$\{(x, y) \mid S_{xy} \text{ and } T_{xy}\} = \{(x, y) \mid S_{xy}\} \cap \{(x, y) \mid T_{xy}\} \tag{21}$$

With the use of (21) we can write the relations R_2 to R_5 as follows:

$$R_2 = \{(x, y) \mid y = x\} \cap \{(x, y) \mid -4 \leqslant x \leqslant 1\}$$
$$R_3 = \{(x, y) \mid y = |x|\} \cap \{(x, y) \mid x \in [-2; 3]\}$$
$$R_4 = \{(x, y) \mid -3 \leqslant x \leqslant 1\} \cap \{(x, y) \mid 0 \leqslant y \leqslant 2\}$$
$$R_5 = \{(x, y) \mid y = \sqrt{25 - x^2}\} \cap \{(x, y) \mid x \in [-3; 4]\}$$

Thus, the graphs of each of these relations can be considered as the intersection of two sets of points. To illustrate, consider the graph of the relation R_4. Observe that the graph G_1 of $\{(x, y) \mid -3 \leqslant x \leqslant 1\}$ is that vertical strip of the coordinate plane in which all the points have x coordinates between -3 and 1 inclusive; G_1 is

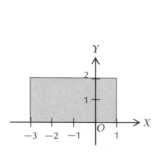

FIGURE 1.18 Graph of
$R_4 = \{(x, y) \mid -3 \leqslant x \leqslant 1 \text{ and } 0 \leqslant y \leqslant 2\}$.

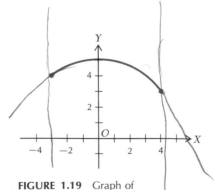

FIGURE 1.19 Graph of
$R_5 = \{(x, y) \mid y = \sqrt{25 - x^2} \text{ and } x \in [-3; 4]\}$.

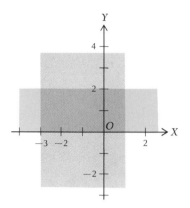

FIGURE 1.20   Graph of $\{(x, y) \mid -3 \leqslant x \leqslant 1\} \cap \{(x, y) \mid 0 \leqslant y \leqslant 2\}$.

shown in Fig. 1.20 as the region shaded in color. Similarly, the graph G_2 of $\{(x, y) \mid 0 \leqslant y \leqslant 2\}$ is that horizontal strip of the coordinate plane in which all the points have y coordinates between 0 and 2 inclusive; G_2 is shown in Fig. 1.20 as the region shaded in gray. Then the graph G of R_4 is the intersection of G_1 and G_2 and is shown in Fig. 1.20 shaded in darker color.

The reader should note the distinction between the graphs of the sets

$$S_1 = \{(x, y) \mid -3 \leqslant x \leqslant 1\} \qquad \text{and} \qquad S_2 = \{x \mid -3 \leqslant x \leqslant 1\}$$

Each of these sets is specified by the same sentence (here an inequality) $-3 \leqslant x \leqslant 1$. However, S_1 is a set of ordered pairs of real numbers, while S_2 is a set of real numbers. Hence the graph of S_1 is a set of points in a two-dimensional coordinate system (G_1 in Fig. 1.20), while the graph of S_2 is a set of points in a one-dimensional coordinate system [the set of points on the x axis between $P_1(-3)$ and $P_2(1)$ inclusive].

Recall that the union of sets A and B is denoted by $A \cup B$ and is defined as the set whose members belong to at least one of the sets A, B. Thus, by using the definition of the disjunction of sentences (Sec. 1.2) it follows that

$$\{(x, y) \mid S_{xy} \text{ or } T_{xy}\} = \{(x, y) \mid S_{xy}\} \cup \{(x, y) \mid T_{xy}\} \tag{22}$$

As an illustration of (22) consider the relation

$$R_6 = \{(x, y) \mid x = 3 \text{ or } y = 4\} = \{(x, y) \mid x = 3\} \cup \{(x, y) \mid y = 4\}$$

The graph of R_6 is the union of the graph of $\{(x, y) \mid x = 3\}$ and the graph of $\{(x, y) \mid y = 4\}$. The graph of $\{(x, y) \mid x = 3\}$ is the line L_1 of Fig. 1.21 consisting of all the points in the plane with x coordinate 3; the graph of $\{(x, y) \mid y = 4\}$ is the line L_2 of Fig. 1.21 consisting of all the points in the plane with y coordinate

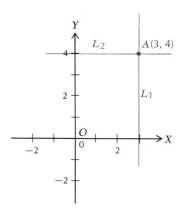

FIGURE 1.21   Graph of $R_6 = \{(x, y) \mid x = 3\} \cup \{(x, y) \mid y = 4\}$.

4. The graph of R_6 consists of the two lines L_1 and L_2 of Fig. 1.21. On the other hand, the graph of $R_7 = \{(x, y) \mid x = 3 \text{ and } y = 4\}$ is the intersection of L_1 and L_2, namely, the single point $A(3, 4)$.

▶ EXAMPLE 2

For each of the following relations construct the graph or show that the relation is the empty set.

$$R_8 = \{(x, y) \mid y^2 = 2x \text{ and } x = 2\}$$
$$R_9 = \{(x, y) \mid y^2 = 2x \text{ or } x = 2\}$$
$$R_{10} = \{(x, y) \mid y^2 = 2x \text{ and } x = \ \ 2\}$$
$$R_{11} = \{(x, y) \mid y^2 = 2x \text{ or } x = -2\}$$
$$R_{12} = \{(x, y) \mid (y^2 - 2x)(x - 2) = 0\}$$

Solution

Using (21), we can write

$$R_8 = \{(x, y) \mid y^2 = 2x\} \cap \{(x, y) \mid x = 2\}$$

Proceeding as we did in Example 1, we can construct the graph G of $\{(x, y) \mid y^2 = 2x\}$; this graph is the parabola shown in Fig. 1.22. The graph L_1 of $\{(x, y) \mid x = 2\}$ is the line that is perpendicular to the x axis at the point $(2, 0)$. G and L_1 intersect in the points $A(2, 2)$ and $B(2, -2)$, and the graph of R_8 consists of these two points.

Using (22), we can write

$$R_9 = \{(x, y) \mid y^2 = 2x\} \cup \{(x, y) \mid x = 2\}$$

So the graph of R_9 consists of the union of the parabola G and the line L_1 in Fig. 1.22.

The relation R_{10} consists of those ordered pairs of real numbers whose entries satisfy both the equations $y^2 = 2x$ *and* $x = -2$. Observation of the first equation shows that, in order for $y^2 = 2x$ to become a true statement, x must be replaced by a *nonnegative* number. Hence there is no ordered pair (a, b) of the real numbers for which $b^2 = 2a$ and $a = -2$ are both true, and R_{10} is the empty set $\emptyset$.

Again using (22), we can write

$$R_{11} = \{(x, y) \mid y^2 = 2x\} \cup \{(x, y) \mid x = -2\}$$

The graph of $\{(x, y) \mid x = -2\}$ is the line L_2 in Fig. 1.22 perpendicular to the x axis at the point $(-2, 0)$. Therefore the graph of R_{11} consists of the union of the parabola G and the line L_2.

In order to obtain the graph of R_{12} we recall that if a and b are real numbers, then

$$a \cdot b = 0 \quad \Longleftrightarrow \quad a = 0 \text{ or } b = 0 \tag{23}$$

From (23) it follows that

$$R_{12} = \{(x, y) \mid y^2 - 2x = 0 \text{ or } x - 2 = 0\}$$

and hence $R_{12} = R_9$. So the graph of R_{12} is the same as the graph of R_9.

Function   A **function** is a relation with the special property that to each member of its domain there is paired one and *only one* member of its range. That is, a function is a nonempty relation with the property that no two of its ordered pairs have the

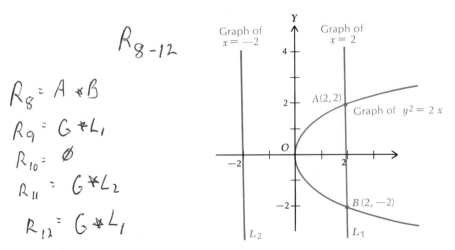

R_{8-12}

$R_8 = A * B$

$R_9 = G * L_1$

$R_{10} = \emptyset$

$R_{11} = G * L_2$

$R_{12} = G * L_1$

FIGURE 1.22   Graph of $\{(x, y) \mid y^2 = 2x\} \cup \{(x, y) \mid x = 2\} \cup \{(x, y) \mid x = -2\}$.

same first entry. To illustrate, the relation $R_1 = \{(x, y) \mid y = x^2 - 1\}$, whose graph appears in Fig. 1.15, is a function. The relations whose graphs appear in Figs. 1.16, 1.17, and 1.19 are also functions. However, the relation $R_{13} = \{(x, y) \mid y^2 = 2x\}$, whose graph G appears in Fig. 1.22, is not a function. Examine the graphs of the functions listed above and observe that the graph of a function is intersected at *most* once by any line perpendicular to the axis on which the domain of the function is graphed. A function that is a relation in Re is referred to as a

Real function   *real function.*

EXERCISES

1. Write the coordinates (they are all integers) of each of the points E, F, G, H, I, and J in Fig. 1.14 and record them in the form $E(4, 2)$.

2. In what quadrant is each of the following points located? $A(-4, 3)$, $B(6, 5)$, $C(-2, -3)$, $D(6, -7)$.

Note. Subsequently, until we study polar coordinates in Chap. 6, when we say "Plot a point in a two-dimensional coordinate system" or "Draw a graph of a relation in Re" we mean to do this on a two-dimensional coordinate system of the type we have just discussed. To accomplish this the student should carefully construct such a coordinate system by drawing and labeling the x axis and y axis on "squared paper" or "graph paper." Also indicate the origin O and label a convenient number of points on each axis.

3. Graph each of the following points on the same coordinate system, and label each point: $P_1(3, 4)$, $P_2(-2, -5)$, $P_3(-4, 6)$, $P_4(5, -7)$, $P_5(0, 7)$, $P_6(-6, 0)$, $P_7(6, 0)$, $P_8(0, -4)$.

4. Explain what is meant by each of the following terms: abscissa, ordinate, quadrant.

5. Observe that

$$P(x_1, y_1) \text{ is in quadrant I} \iff x_1 > 0 \text{ and } y_1 > 0$$

Write similar statements that apply to quadrants II, III, and IV.

6. (*a*) If a point is on the y axis, what is its abscissa?

(*b*) If a point is on the x axis, what is its ordinate?

(*c*) What are the coordinates of the origin?

7. A square whose side has length a has one vertex at the origin, another vertex on the positive x axis, and a third vertex on the positive y axis. What are the coordinates of the vertices of the square?

8. Graph each of the following points on the same coordinate system, and label each point: $P_1(\frac{1}{2}, \frac{3}{4})$, $P_2(-\frac{11}{3}, -\frac{3}{4})$, $P_3(-\frac{7}{2}, \frac{10}{3})$, $P_4(\sqrt{2}, \sqrt{3})$, $P_5(-2\sqrt{3}, 3\sqrt{2})$, $P_6(\frac{7}{3}, \frac{10}{3})$.

9. If the universe is $U = \{1, 2, 3, 4, 5, 6\}$, tabulate and graph each of the following relations:

      (*a*) $R_1 = \{(x, y) \mid y = x\}$ (*b*) $R_2 = \{(x, y) \mid x + y = 6\}$

      (*c*) $R_3 = \{(x, y) \mid y = x + 3\}$ (*d*) $R_4 = \{(x, y) \mid y^2 = x\}$

10. Give the domain and the range of each of the relations of Exercise 9.

In each of Exercises 11–20 the universe is the set of real numbers. Graph each relation and give its domain and range.

11. $R = \{(x, y) \mid x = 3 \text{ and } y < 0\}$

12. $R = \{(x, y) \mid x = 3 \text{ and } -1 < y < 2\}$

13. $R = \{(x, y) \mid y = 2x, x \in [-1; 3]\}$

14. $R = \{(x, y) \mid y < x\}$

15. $R = \{(x, y) \mid y > x\}$

16. $R = \{(x, y) \mid 1 \leqslant x \leqslant 4 \text{ and } y = 3\}$

17. $R = \{(x, y) \mid x = 4\}$

18. $R = \{(x, y) \mid y = 5\}$

19. $R = \{(x, y) \mid x = 4 \text{ and } y = 5\}$

20. $R = \{(x, y) \mid (x - 4)(y - 5) = 0\}$

In each of Exercises 21–26 the universe is the set of real numbers. Graph each equation, and give the domain and the range of the relation specified by the equation.

21. $y = x^2$ **22.** $y = x^3$

23. $y = x^4$ **24.** $y = x^2 - 4$

25. $y = x^2 + 3$ **26.** $y = x^2 - 4x$

27. Graph the equation $y = 1/x$, the universe being the set of real numbers. Observe that y is not defined for $x = 0$. Note that y is positive when x is positive and that y is negative when x is negative.

The domain of the relation specified by the equation $y = 1/x$ is $(-\infty; 0) \cup (0; +\infty)$. What is the range of this relation?

In each of Exercises 28–31 three vertices of a rectangle are given. Find the coordinates of the fourth vertex.

28. $(0, 0), (5, 0), (0, 3)$ **29.** $(1, -2), (5, -2), (5, 4)$

30. $(-4, 4), (-4, -2), (6, -2)$ **31.** $(0, 0), (a, 0), (0, b)$

32. Graph the following points on the same coordinate system, and label each point in the form $P(x, y)$: $P_1(\sqrt{2} + \sqrt{3}, \sqrt{4})$, $P_2(4/\sqrt{3}, 1/\sqrt{2})$, $P_3(1 - \sqrt{5}, -2)$.

33. With the aid of the graph which you constructed in Exercise 21, describe in terms of the union of two graphs, or in terms of the intersection of two graphs, the graph of each of the following relations:

(a) $R_1 = \{(x, y) \mid y = x^2 \text{ or } x = 2\}$

(b) $R_2 = \{(x, y) \mid y = x^2 \text{ and } y = 4\}$

(c) $R_3 = \{(x, y) \mid (y - x^2)(y - 4) = 0\}$

34. With the aid of the graph which you constructed in Exercise 27, describe in terms of the intersection of two graphs, or in terms of the union of two graphs, the graph of each of the following relations:

(a) $R_4 = \{(x, y) \mid y = 1/x \text{ and } y = x\}$

(b) $R_5 = \{(x, y) \mid y = 1/x \text{ and } y = -x\}$

(c) $R_6 = \{(x, y) \mid (y - 1/x)(y - x) = 0\}$

In each of Exercises 35–38 state whether the given relation is a function or not, and give a reason for your answer. Give the domain and the range of each relation, and graph the relation.

35. $R_7 = \{(x, y) \mid y^2 = 4\}$ **36.** $R_8 = \{(x, y) \mid x^2 + y^2 = 25\}$

37. $R_9 = \{(x, y) \mid y = \sqrt{25 - x^2}\}$ **38.** $R_{10} = \{(x, y) \mid y^2 = x^2\}$

39. Is the relation R of Exercise 11 a function? Explain.

40. Is the relation R of Exercise 15 a function? Explain.

2 | THE DISTANCE FORMULA AND THE CIRCLE

2.1 DIRECTED LINES AND PROJECTIONS

Directed line A **directed line** L is a line on which a positive direction is indicated. For example, the x axis and y axis of a two-dimensional coordinate system are directed lines. Let P_1 and P_2 be two distinct points on the line L of Fig. 2.1. If we agree that the direction from P_1 to P_2 is the positive direction on L (indicated by an arrowhead on L), then the direction from P_2 to P_1 is the negative direction on L. If a segment on a directed line L has its end points at P_1 and P_2, then P_1P_2 will be understood

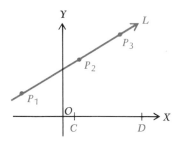

FIGURE 2.1

Directed segment to denote the *directed segment* from P_1 to P_2, which we shall usually refer to simply as the segment P_1P_2.

In Sec. 1.4 we defined directed distance (and undirected distance, or length) on a coordinate axis. Any line segment such as P_1P_2 in Fig. 2.1 is congruent to some line segment CD on the x axis (or on the y axis). (Whenever we consider the distance between two points in a coordinate plane, we assume that the same *Directed distance* unit of length is used on both coordinate axes.) We denote the **directed distance** *from P_1 to P_2* by $\overline{P_1P_2}$ and define it by

$$\overline{P_1P_2} = |CD|$$

when the direction from P_1 to P_2 is the *positive direction*, as in Fig. 2.1. If the direction from P_1 to P_2 is the *negative direction*, then

$$\overline{P_1P_2} = -|CD|$$

Undirected The **undirected distance** *between* P_1 and P_2, or the length of the segment P_1P_2, is *distance* denoted by $|P_1P_2|$ and defined by

$$|P_1P_2| = |CD|$$

We observe that

$$\overline{P_1P_2} = -\overline{P_2P_1}$$

The student should satisfy himself that, for all possible relative positions of the points P_1, P_2, and P_3 on a directed line,

$$\overline{P_1P_3} + \overline{P_3P_2} = \overline{P_1P_2}$$

Let L' be a line and let P be a point not on L'. If we draw a line through P perpendicular to L', this perpendicular will intersect L' in a point P' (see Fig. *Projection of a* 2.2). The point P' is called the **projection on L' of the point** P and is denoted by *point* $\text{Proj}_{L'} P$. If P is on line L', then P is its own projection on L'.

Let P_1P_2 be a (directed) segment on a directed line L, and let P_1' and P_2' be the respective projections on line L' of the points P_1 and P_2 (see Fig. 2.3). The

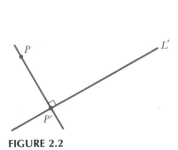

FIGURE 2.2

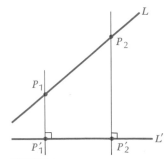

FIGURE 2.3

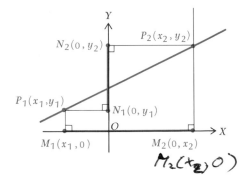

FIGURE 2.4

$M_2(x_2, 0)$

Projection of a   segment $P_1'P_2'$ is the **projection on L' of the segment** P_1P_2; this projection is
segment   denoted by $\text{Proj}_{L'} P_1P_2$.

If P_1 has coordinates (x_1, y_1), observe that its projection on the x axis is the
point $M_1(x_1, 0)$; that is (see Fig. 2.4),

$$\text{Proj}_{OX} P_1(x_1, y_1) = M_1(x_1, 0)$$

Similarly,

$$\text{Proj}_{OY} P_1(x_1, y_1) = N_1(0, y_1)$$

If $P_1(x_1, y_1)$ and $P_2(x_2, y_2)$ are any two points, then (see Fig. 2.4)

$$\text{Length Proj}_{OX} P_1P_2 = |M_1M_2| = |x_2 - x_1| \tag{1}$$
$$\text{Length Proj}_{OY} P_1P_2 = |N_1N_2| = |y_2 - y_1| \tag{2}$$

2.2 THE DISTANCE FORMULA

One of the most important results in analytic geometry is the formula for the
undirected distance between points P_1 and P_2 in terms of the coordinates of P_1
and P_2; this result we now derive.

Let $P_1(x_1, y_1)$ and $P_2(x_2, y_2)$ be any two distinct points in a coordinate plane
(Fig. 2.5). Construct a right triangle with hypotenuse P_1P_2 by drawing a line
through P_1 perpendicular to the x axis and a line through P_2 perpendicular to the
y axis. Denote the point of intersection of these two lines by Q and observe that

$$|P_2Q| = \text{length Proj}_{OX} P_1P_2 = |x_2 - x_1| \tag{3}$$
$$|P_1Q| = \text{length Proj}_{OY} P_1P_2 = |y_2 - y_2| \tag{4}$$

Recall from plane geometry the theorem of Pythagoras: In any right triangle the
square of the length of the hypotenuse is equal to the sum of the squares of
the lengths of the other two sides. We have then that $|P_1P_2|$, the length of the
segment P_1P_2, is given by

$$|P_1P_2|^2 = |P_2Q|^2 + |P_1Q|^2$$

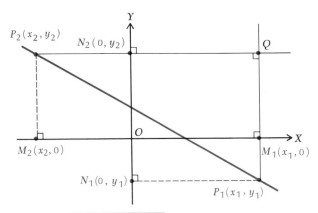

FIGURE 2.5 $|P_1P_2| = \sqrt{(x_2 - x_1)^2 + (y_2 - y_1)^2}.$

Therefore,

$$|P_1P_2|^2 = |x_2 - x_1|^2 + |y_2 - y_1|^2$$

or, since

$$|x_2 - x_1|^2 = (x_2 - x_1)^2 \qquad \text{and} \qquad |y_2 - y_1|^2 = (y_2 - y_1)^2$$

$$|P_1P_2|^2 = (x_2 - x_1)^2 + (y_2 - y_1)^2$$

We have proved the following theorem.

THEOREM 2.1   *If $P_1(x_1, y_1)$ and $P_2(x_2, y_2)$ are any two points in the coordinate plane, then the undirected distance $|P_1P_2|$ is given by*

$$|P_1P_2| = \sqrt{(x_2 - x_1)^2 + (y_2 - y_1)^2} \tag{5}$$

Distance formula

We call (5) the **distance formula** (for plane analytic geometry).

Observe that since $(x_2 - x_1)^2 = (x_1 - x_2)^2$ and $(y_2 - y_1)^2 = (y_1 - y_2)^2$, we may write

$$|P_1P_2| = \sqrt{(x_1 - x_2)^2 + (y_1 - y_2)^2}$$

Consequently, in using the distance formula to find the distance between two points, either point may be designated by (x_1, y_1) and the other designated by (x_2, y_2).

▶   EXAMPLE 1

Find the distance between the points $P_1(-4, -3)$ and $P_2(2, 7)$.

Solution

Using the distance formula, we find that

$$|P_1P_2| = \sqrt{[2 - (-4)]^2 + [7 - (-3)]^2} = \sqrt{36 + 100} = \sqrt{136} = 2\sqrt{34}$$

▶ EXAMPLE 2

Determine whether or not the points $A(3, 7)$, $B(5, -5)$, and $C(-2, 0)$ are the vertices of an isosceles right triangle (Fig. 2.6).

Solution

By the distance formula,

$$|AB| = \sqrt{(5 - 3)^2 + (-5 - 7)^2} = \sqrt{148}$$
$$|AC| = \sqrt{(-2 - 3)^2 + (0 - 7)^2} = \sqrt{74}$$
$$|BC| = \sqrt{(-2 - 5)^2 + (0 + 5)^2} = \sqrt{74}$$

Observe that

$$|AC|^2 + |BC|^2 = 74 + 74 = 148 = |AB|^2$$

Recall the converse of the theorem of Pythagoras: If for the triangle with vertices at A, B, and C, $|AC|^2 + |BC|^2 = |AB|^2$, then ABC is a right triangle with the right angle at C. Therefore, triangle ABC of this example is a right triangle with the right angle at C. Further, we found that $|AC| = |BC|$, and it follows that triangle ABC is an isosceles right triangle.

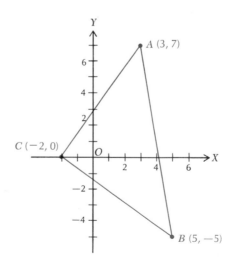

FIGURE 2.6

2.3 PROPERTIES OF DISTANCE. THE TRIANGLE INEQUALITY

By the use of formula (5) in Sec. 2.2 we can associate with any two points P_1 and P_2 a nonnegative real number which we call the "distance" between the points and which we denote by $|P_1P_2|$. Thus we have defined a *function* whose domain is the set of ordered pairs of points in a coordinate plane and whose range is the set $[0; +\infty)$ of nonnegative real numbers. This function has the following properties (see Fig. 2.7):

(i) $|P_1P_1| = 0$

(ii) $|P_1P_2| > 0,$ whenever $P_1 \neq P_2$

(iii) $|P_1P_2| = |P_2P_1|$

(iv) $|P_1P_3| \leq |P_1P_2| + |P_2P_3|$

Triangle inequality

Properties (i) to (iii) follow directly from the distance formula (5), as the student is asked to show in Exercise 22 of Sec. 2.4. The important property of distance expressed by (iv) is called the *triangle inequality* because it reflects the well-known geometric fact that, for any triangle $P_1P_2P_3$, the length of any one side is not greater than the sum of the lengths of the other two sides (Fig. 2.7). Equality in property (iv) holds only if P_2 lies on the segment joining P_1 and P_3 (see Fig. 2.8). Property (iv) can be proved algebraically; however, we shall not give such a proof here. In Sec. 7.2 we shall give a proof of (iv) using vector notation.

Mathematicians have generalized the concept of distance between points in a coordinate plane and have characterized the concept of "distance" between two members of any set by the use of the idea of a "distance function."

Distance function

If S is a set and if δ is a function whose domain is the set of ordered pairs of members of S and whose range is a subset of the set of nonnegative real numbers, this function δ is called a *distance function* on S if and only if it possesses the

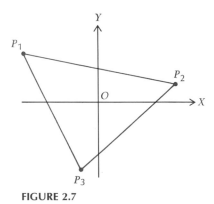

FIGURE 2.7

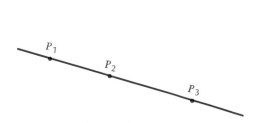

FIGURE 2.8 $|P_1P_3| = |P_1P_2| + |P_2P_3|$.

following properties:

(i)'   For all $a \in S$, $\delta(a, a) = 0$
(ii)'   For all $a, b \in S$, $\delta(a, b) > 0$,   whenever $a \neq b$
(iii)'   For all $a, b \in S$, $\delta(a, b) = \delta(b, a)$
(iv)'   For all $a, b, c \in S$, $\delta(a, c) \leq \delta(a, b) + \delta(b, c)$

Distance   The real number $\delta(a, b)$ which the function δ associates with the ordered pair (a, b) is called the *"distance"* between the "points" a and b in the "space" S.

2.4 THE MIDPOINT OF A LINE SEGMENT

We frequently wish to find the coordinates of the midpoint of a line segment joining two points with given coordinates.

Let $P_1(x_1, y_1)$ and $P_2(x_2, y_2)$ be the end points of a line segment P_1P_2, and let $P_3(x_3, y_3)$ be the midpoint of P_1P_2; that is, let P_1, P_2, and P_3 be points for which $\overline{P_1P_3} = \overline{P_3P_2}$. Through each of P_1, P_3, and P_2 draw lines parallel to the coordinate axes so as to form congruent right triangles P_1QP_3 and P_3RP_2 (see Fig. 2.9). Then $\overline{P_1Q} = \overline{P_3R}$, since $\overline{P_1P_3} = \overline{P_3P_2}$. Now $\overline{P_1Q} = x_3 - x_1$, and $\overline{P_3R} = x_2 - x_3$. Therefore,

$$x_3 - x_1 = x_2 - x_3 \qquad 2x_3 = x_1 + x_2 \qquad x_3 = \frac{x_1 + x_2}{2}$$

Similarly, $\overline{QP_3} = \overline{RP_2}$, and

$$y_3 - y_1 = y_2 - y_3 \qquad 2y_3 = y_1 + y_2 \qquad y_3 = \frac{y_1 + y_2}{2}$$

We have proved the following theorem.

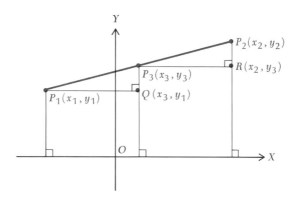

FIGURE 2.9

THEOREM 2.2 *If $P_1(x_1, y_1)$ and $P_2(x_2, y_2)$ are any two points in the coordinate plane, then the coordinates x_3 and y_3 of the midpoint of line segment P_1P_2 are given by*

Midpoint formulas

$$x_3 = \frac{x_1 + x_2}{2} \qquad y_3 = \frac{y_1 + y_2}{2} \tag{6}$$

Similar considerations may be used to derive formulas for the coordinates x_3 and y_3 of the point $P_3(x_3, y_3)$ which has the property that $\overline{P_1P_3}/\overline{P_1P_2} = t$, t being the ratio in which the point P_3 divides the line segment from P_1 to P_2 (see Exercises 17 to 21 at the end of this section).

▶ EXAMPLE 1

Find the coordinates of the midpoints of the sides of the triangle whose vertices are $A(3, 7)$, $B(5, -5)$, and $C(-2, 0)$ (Fig. 2.6).

Solution

Denote the midpoint of BC by A', the midpoint of AC by B', and the midpoint of AB by C'. By Theorem 2.2 the coordinates of A' are

$$x_3 = \frac{5 - 2}{2} = \frac{3}{2} \qquad y_3 = \frac{-5 + 0}{2} = -\frac{5}{2}$$

So A' is the point $(\frac{3}{2}, -\frac{5}{2})$. In a similar manner we find that B' is the point $(\frac{1}{2}, \frac{7}{2})$ and C' is the point $(4, 1)$.

▶ EXAMPLE 2

One end point of a line segment is $P_1(1, -2)$, and the midpoint of this segment is $P_3(4, 3)$. Find the coordinates of the other end point of the segment.

Solution

Let $P_2(x_2, y_2)$ be the other end point. Substituting $x_1 = 1$ and $x_3 = 4$ in the formula $x_3 = \frac{1}{2}(x_1 + x_2)$, we obtain

$$4 = \frac{1 + x_2}{2} \qquad \text{or} \qquad 8 = 1 + x_2 \qquad \text{or} \qquad x_2 = 7$$

Similarly, substituting $y_1 = -2$ and $y_3 = 3$ in the formula $y_3 = \frac{1}{2}(y_1 + y_2)$, we find

$$3 = \frac{-2 + y_2}{2} \qquad \text{or} \qquad 6 = -2 + y_2 \qquad \text{or} \qquad y_2 = 8$$

EXERCISES

In each part of Exercises 1 and 2 give the coordinates of the points M_1 and M_2 which are the respective projections on the x axis of P_1 and P_2. Find $\overline{M_1M_2}$ and $|M_1M_2|$. Similarly, find the coordinates of N_1 and N_2, the respective projections on the y axis of P_1 and P_2. Find $\overline{N_1N_2}$ and $|N_1N_2|$.

1. (*a*) $P_1(3, -2)$; $P_2(4, 5)$ (*b*) $P_1(6, 8)$; $P_2(-3, -1)$

2. (*a*) $P_1(-3, 4)$; $P_2(-8, -9)$ (*b*) $P_1(4, 5)$; $P_2(8, 10)$

3. Find the distance between each of the following pairs of points:
   - (*a*) $(5, 8)$ and $(-3, 2)$ (*b*) $(2, -3)$ and $(3, 3)$
   - (*c*) $(10, 2)$ and $(-2, -2)$ (*d*) $(3, 4)$ and $(9, 11)$
   - (*e*) $(1, 3)$ and $(-5, 5)$ (*f*) $(0, 0)$ and $(a - b, a + b)$

4. Find the perimeter of the triangle whose vertices are the following points:
   - (*a*) $(6, 2), (4, 3), (0, 1)$ (*b*) $(3, 1), (7, 3), (5, 9)$
   - (*c*) $(0, 2), (2, 0), (5, -4)$ (*d*) $(-3, 4), (2, -1), (5, 3)$

5. Determine in each part whether the triangle whose vertices are given is scalene, isosceles, or equilateral.
   - (*a*) $(4, 4), (4, -2), (-4, -2)$
   - (*b*) $(2, 6), (-3, -3), (6, 2)$
   - (*c*) $(-2, -2), (2, 2), (2\sqrt{3}, -2\sqrt{3})$
   - (*d*) $(-3, -2), (7, 4), (1, 14)$
   - (*e*) Which of these are right triangles?

6. (*a*) Find the coordinates of the midpoints of the sides of the triangle whose vertices are $(1, 3), (-2, -4)$, and $(1, -2)$.
   (*b*) Find the lengths of the medians of this triangle.

7. Verify that $(4, 3)$ is the center of the circle that goes through the points $(9, 3), (4, -2)$, and $(8, 6)$.

8. One end point of a line segment is $(1, -9)$ and the midpoint of the segment is $(-1, -2)$. Find the coordinates of the other end point of the segment.

9. Show that the diagonals of the parallelogram whose vertices are $(-2, -3)$, $(5, -4), (4, 1)$, and $(-3, 2)$ bisect each other.

10. Show that the points $(4, 6), (2, -2), (-11, -1)$, and $(-13, -9)$ are the vertices of a parallelogram, and show that the diagonals of this parallelogram bisect each other.

11. By use of the distance formula show that the three points $(2, 6), (0, 2)$, and $(-3, -4)$ are collinear (that is, that they lie on the same straight line).

12. By use of the distance formula show that the three points $(-2, 1), (\frac{1}{2}, -2)$, and $(3, -5)$ are collinear.

In each of Exercises 13–16 use the triangle inequality to determine whether the three given points lie on the same line. Draw a figure to check your work.

13. $P_1(-2, -2)$; $P_2(-5, 1)$; $P_3(-4, 5)$ **14.** $P_1(3, 1)$; $P_2(3, 4)$; $P_3(3, -2)$

15. $P_1(-5, 6)$; $P_2(-1, 3)$; $P_3(7, -3)$ **16.** $P_1(4, 5)$; $P_2(1, -4)$; $P_3(-2, -3)$

17. Prove the theorem: If $P_1(x_1, y_1)$ and $P_2(x_2, y_2)$ are any two points in the coordinate plane, then the coordinates of the point $P_3(x_3, y_3)$ that divides the segment P_1P_2 in the ratio $t = \overline{P_1P_3}/\overline{P_1P_2}$ are given by

$$x_3 = x_1 + t(x_2 - x_1) \qquad y_3 = y_1 + t(y_2 - y_1)$$

Show that for $t = \frac{1}{2}$ these formulas may be written in the form $x_3 = \frac{1}{2}(x_1 + x_2)$, $y_3 = \frac{1}{2}(y_1 + y_2)$.

18. Given $P_1(-2, -5)$ and $P_2(6, 9)$, use the results of Exercise 17 to find the coordinates of the point $P_3(x_3, y_3)$ which divides the segment P_1P_2 in the ratio $t = 3$.

19. Given $P_1(-10, 2)$ and $P_2(10, 7)$, find the coordinates of the point P_3 that divides the segment P_1P_2 in the ratio $t = \frac{3}{5}$.

20. Find the coordinates of the point P_3 that lies four-fifths of the way from $P_1(-7, -7)$ to $P_2(9, 9)$.

21. Find the coordinates of the points P_3 and P_4 that divide the segment joining $P_1(-7, -5)$ and $P_2(8, 8)$ into three equal parts.

22. Prove properties (i) to (iii) of Sec. 2.3 by use of the distance formula (5).

2.5 THE AREA OF A TRIANGLE. DETERMINANTS

Let $P_1(x_1, y_1)$, $P_2(x_2, y_2)$, $P_3(x_3, y_3)$ be the vertices of a triangle selected in such a way that in moving around the perimeter of the triangle from P_1 to P_2 to P_3 and back to P_1 the interior of the triangle is on the left (see Fig. 2.10). When the vertices of a triangle are so selected we say that they are *positively oriented* with respect to the interior of the triangle. We shall obtain a compact expression for the area of a triangle whose vertices are positively oriented.

As shown in Fig. 2.10, construct a rectangle that is circumscribed about the triangle $P_1P_2P_3$ by drawing lines through each of the vertices parallel to each of the coordinate axes. The area of the triangle $P_1P_2P_3$ is equal to the area of the rectangle $SRTP_3$, less the sum of the areas of the three triangles RP_2P_1, P_2TP_3, P_1P_3S. We see that

$$\text{Area } SRTP_3 = (x_3 - x_1)(y_3 - y_2)$$
$$\text{Area } RP_2P_1 = \tfrac{1}{2}(x_2 - x_1)(y_1 - y_2)$$
$$\text{Area } P_2TP_3 = \tfrac{1}{2}(x_3 - x_2)(y_3 - y_2)$$
$$\text{Area } P_1P_3S = \tfrac{1}{2}(x_3 - x_1)(y_3 - y_1)$$

Therefore,

$$\text{Area } P_1P_2P_3 = (x_3 - x_1)(y_3 - y_2)$$
$$- \tfrac{1}{2}[(x_2 - x_1)(y_1 - y_2) + (x_3 - x_2)(y_3 - y_2) + (x_3 - x_1)(y_3 - y_1)]$$

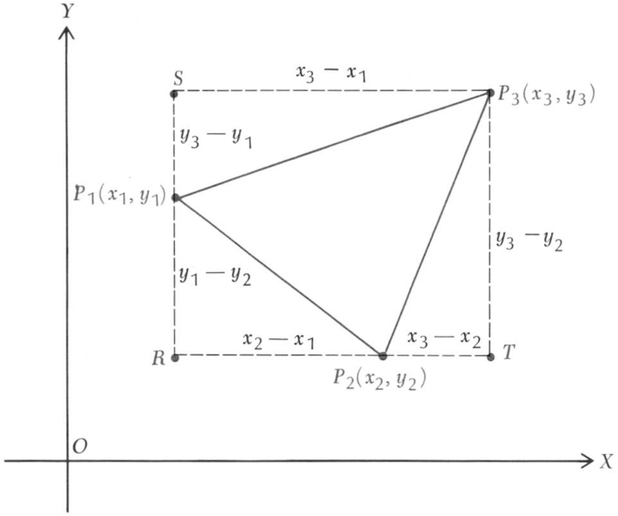

FIGURE 2.10

Upon expanding the products and collecting like terms we have

$$\text{Area } P_1P_2P_3 = \tfrac{1}{2}(x_1y_2 - x_1y_3 - y_1x_2 + y_1x_3 + x_2y_3 - x_3y_2) \tag{7}$$

Formula (7) holds for any triangle in any position on the coordinate plane provided the vertices are positively oriented. The formula is much more easily remembered in determinant form.

With the array (or matrix) of real numbers

$$A_2 = \begin{bmatrix} a & b \\ c & d \end{bmatrix} \tag{8}$$

Determinant we associate the real number $ad - bc$, and we call $ad - bc$ the **determinant** of A_2. We denote this determinant by either $det(A_2)$, or $|A_2|$, or $\begin{vmatrix} a & b \\ c & d \end{vmatrix}$, so

$$det(A_2) = |A_2| = \begin{vmatrix} a & b \\ c & d \end{vmatrix} = ad - bc \tag{9}$$

To illustrate,

$$\begin{vmatrix} 1 & 2 \\ 3 & 4 \end{vmatrix} = 1 \cdot 4 - 2 \cdot 3 = 4 - 6 = -2$$

$$\begin{vmatrix} 1 & -2 \\ 3 & -4 \end{vmatrix} = 1 \cdot (-4) - (-2) \cdot 3 = -4 + 6 = 2$$

If $\mathscr{A}_2$ denotes the set of all arrays (2 × 2 matrices) like (8), observe that *det*, as defined by (9), is a function whose domain is $\mathscr{A}_2$ and whose range is *Re*; *det* is
Determinant
function sometimes called the *determinant function*.

With the array (or matrix) or real numbers

$$A_3 = \begin{bmatrix} a_1 & b_1 & c_1 \\ a_2 & b_2 & c_2 \\ a_3 & b_3 & c_3 \end{bmatrix} \tag{10}$$

we associate a real number which we denote by $det(A_3)$, or $|A_3|$, or $\begin{vmatrix} a_1 & b_1 & c_1 \\ a_2 & b_2 & c_2 \\ a_3 & b_3 & c_3 \end{vmatrix}$

and which we call the *determinant* of A_3. We define $det(A_3)$ by the following equation:

$$det(A_3) = |A_3| = \begin{vmatrix} a_1 & b_1 & c_1 \\ a_2 & b_2 & c_2 \\ a_3 & b_3 & c_3 \end{vmatrix} = a_1 \begin{vmatrix} b_2 & c_2 \\ b_3 & c_3 \end{vmatrix} - b_1 \begin{vmatrix} a_2 & c_2 \\ a_3 & c_3 \end{vmatrix} + c_1 \begin{vmatrix} a_2 & b_2 \\ a_3 & b_3 \end{vmatrix} \tag{11}$$

The student is asked to show that (11) and (9) may be combined to give

$$det(A_3) = a_1 b_2 c_3 - a_1 b_3 c_2 - a_2 b_1 c_3 + a_3 b_1 c_2 + a_2 b_3 c_1 - a_3 b_2 c_1 \tag{12}$$

Using results (7) and (12), the student is asked to complete the proof of the following theorem.

THEOREM 2.3   *The area of the triangle with positively oriented vertices $P_1(x_1, y_1)$, $P_2(x_2, y_2)$, $P_3(x_3, y_3)$ is given by*

$$\text{Area } P_1 P_2 P_3 = \frac{1}{2} \begin{vmatrix} x_1 & y_1 & 1 \\ x_2 & y_2 & 1 \\ x_3 & y_3 & 1 \end{vmatrix} \tag{13}$$

When we evaluate the determinant of a matrix like (10), we do not usually use the result (12). Rather, we first use the definition (11) and then use the definition (9). This procedure is illustrated in the following example.

◆   EXAMPLE

Construct the triangle with vertices $P_1(7, -6)$, $P_2(5, 4)$, and $P_3(-2, 3)$ and observe that the vertices are positively oriented. Find the area of triangle $P_1 P_2 P_3$.

Solution

The construction of the triangle is left to the student. We have, by (13),

$$\text{Area } P_1 P_2 P_3 = \frac{1}{2} \begin{vmatrix} 7 & -6 & 1 \\ 5 & 4 & 1 \\ -2 & 3 & 1 \end{vmatrix}$$

By use of (11) and then (9) we find

$$\begin{vmatrix} 7 & -6 & 1 \\ 5 & 4 & 1 \\ -2 & 3 & 1 \end{vmatrix} = 7\begin{vmatrix} 4 & 1 \\ 3 & 1 \end{vmatrix} - (-6)\begin{vmatrix} 5 & 1 \\ -2 & 1 \end{vmatrix} + 1\begin{vmatrix} 5 & 4 \\ -2 & 3 \end{vmatrix}$$

$$= 7(4-3) + 6(5+2) + 1(15+8) = 72$$

Therefore

$$\text{Area } P_1P_2P_3 = \tfrac{1}{2}(72) = 36$$

2.6 PROVING THEOREMS ANALYTICALLY

Some theorems of elementary plane geometry may be proved *analytically*, that is, by using the ideas and methods of analytic geometry. The following example illustrates the procedures.

♦   EXAMPLE

Prove analytically that the diagonals of a parallelogram bisect each other.

Solution

We are given a parallelogram, and to use the methods of analytic geometry we must place this parallelogram on a two-dimensional coordinate system. To make the determination of the coordinates of the vertices as simple as possible, we place one vertex of the parallelogram at the origin and place one side, whose length we call a, along the positive x axis. Then one vertex is $O(0, 0)$ and another is $A(a, 0)$. A third vertex B will lie at some point in the plane not on the x axis. The coordinates of B are determined by the given parallelogram, and we denote them by (b, c), as shown in Fig. 2.11. Let the fourth vertex be designated by C. Since $AOBC$ is a parallelogram, the side BC is parallel to and equal in length to the segment OA. Therefore, the ordinate of C must be the same as the ordinate

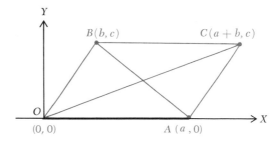

FIGURE 2.11

of B, and the abscissa of C must be a units greater than the abscissa of B; so the coordinates of C are $(a + b, c)$.

By Theorem 2.2 we find that

The coordinates of the midpoint of OC are $\left(\dfrac{a+b}{2}, \dfrac{c}{2}\right)$.

The coordinates of the midpoint of AB are $\left(\dfrac{a+b}{2}, \dfrac{c}{2}\right)$.

This proves that the midpoints of OC and AB are the same point, and the theorem stated in the example is proved.

In proving geometric theorems analytically, care must be taken in placing the figure on a coordinate system so as not to assume more than is given. In particular, we must be careful not to assume the truth of the conclusion when drawing the figure.

EXERCISES

In each of Exercises 1–4 construct the triangle with the given vertices and observe that these vertices are positively oriented. Find the area of the triangle $P_1P_2P_3$.

1. $P_1(6, -5)$; $P_2(11, 6)$; $P_3(-5, 0)$ **2.** $P_1(0, 0)$; $P_2(4, -1)$; $P_3(2, 6)$

3. $P_1(3, -2)$; $P_2(7, 3)$; $P_3(4, 6)$ **4.** $P_1(3, -3)$; $P_2(0, 4)$; $P_3(-4, 0)$

5. Using the result (13), show that if the vertices $O(0, 0)$, $P_1(x_1, y_1)$, and $P_2(x_2, y_2)$ of a triangle are positively oriented, then

$$\text{Area } OP_1P_2 = \tfrac{1}{2}(x_1y_2 - x_2y_1) = \frac{1}{2} \begin{vmatrix} x_1 & y_1 \\ x_2 & y_2 \end{vmatrix}$$

6. Using the formula of Exercise 5, find the area of the triangle whose vertices are O, $P_1(-2, 4)$, and $P_2(-5, -1)$.

In each of Exercises 7 and 8 find the area of the quadrilateral with the given vertices.

7. $P_1(2, -2)$; $P_2(1, 6)$; $P_3(-1, 3)$; $P_4(-3, -4)$. *Hint:* Draw the diagonal P_1P_3 to divide the quadrilateral into triangles $P_1P_2P_3$ and $P_1P_3P_4$.

8. $P_1(0, -4)$; $P_2(5, -3)$; $P_3(1, 3)$; $P_4(-2, -1)$

9. State how formula (13) may be used to find the area of any polygon when the coordinates of its vertices are given.

10. Show that the points $P_1(1, -5)$, $P_2(2, 1)$, and $P_3(3, 7)$ lie on the same line by showing that the area of the triangle $P_1P_2P_3$ is zero.

11. Use the method of Exercise 10 to determine whether the points $P_1(1, 2)$, $P_2(2, 3)$, and $P_3(-3, 4)$ lie on the same line.

12. For the triangle of Fig. 2.10 let M_1, M_2, M_3 be the respective projections on the x axis of P_1, P_2, and P_3. Observe that

$$\text{Area } P_1P_2P_3 = \text{area } M_1M_3P_3P_1 - \text{area } M_1M_2P_2P_1 - \text{area } M_2M_3P_3P_2$$

Each of the figures $M_1M_3P_3P_1$, $M_1M_2P_2P_1$, and $M_2M_3P_3P_2$ is a trapezoid. Recalling that the area of a trapezoid is equal to one-half the product of its altitude and the sum of its bases, prove Theorem 2.3.

13. Characterize *det* defined by formula (12) as a function, specifying its domain and range.

14. Let the triangle $P_1P_2P_3$ have vertices $P_1(x_1, y_1)$, $P_2(x_2, y_2)$, and $P_3(x_3, y_3)$ which are positively oriented. With area $P_1P_2P_3$ defined by (13), characterize *area* as a function and specify its domain and range.

In each of Exercises 15–18 prove analytically the theorem stated.

15. The midpoint of the hypotenuse of a right triangle is equidistant from the three vertices.

16. The diagonals of a rectangle are equal.

17. The line segment joining the midpoints of two sides of a triangle is one-half as long as the third side and is parallel to the third side.

18. The sum of the squares of the lengths of the diagonals of a parallelogram is equal to the sum of the squares of the lengths of the four sides.

2.7 THE CENTER-RADIUS FORM OF AN EQUATION OF A CIRCLE

Recall that a *circle* is the set of all points in a plane that are equidistant from a fixed point called the *center* of the circle. The distance between the center and any point of the circle is called the *radius* of the circle. Let the center of the circle be the point $C(h, k)$ and denote the radius by r, a positive number. A point $P(x, y)$ is on this circle if and only if the distance between $P(x, y)$ and $C(h, k)$ is equal to r. In other words, the circle with center at $C(h, k)$ and radius r is the graph of the relation

$$\{(x, y) \mid |PC| = r\}$$

or, by (5),

$$\{(x, y) \mid \sqrt{(x - h)^2 + (y - k)^2} = r\}$$

or

$$\{(x, y) \mid (x - h)^2 + (y - k)^2 = r^2\}$$

We have proved the following theorem.

THEOREM   *The circle with center at $C(h, k)$ and with radius $r > 0$ is the*
2.4   *graph of the equation*

$$(x - h)^2 + (y - k)^2 = r^2 \tag{14}$$

Center-radius   We call (14) the **center-radius form** of an equation of a circle. If the center C is
form   at the origin, then $h = 0$ and $k = 0$, and Eq. (14) becomes

$$x^2 + y^2 = r^2 \tag{15}$$

Recalling from Sec. 1.8 the definition of the graph of an equation, we see that
Theorem 2.4 means:

(i)   If a point $P(a, b)$ is on the circle with center at $C(h, k)$ and with radius r,
then the ordered pair (a, b) satisfies Eq. (14).
(ii) If a point $Q(c, d)$ is *not* on the circle with center at $C(h, k)$ and with radius
r, then the ordered pair (c, d) does *not* satisfy Eq. (14).

♦   EXAMPLE

Find an equation of the circle which has the points $A(-4, 6)$ and $B(2, 0)$ as the
end points of a diameter. Graph this circle.

Solution

Denote the center of the circle whose equation we are to find by $C(h, k)$ and its
radius by r. Since the center $C(h, k)$ is the midpoint of the segment joining $(-4, 6)$
and $(2, 0)$, we use Theorem 2.2 to find h and k, obtaining

$$h = \frac{-4 + 2}{2} = -1 \qquad k = \frac{6 + 0}{2} = 3$$

Since r is the distance between $C(-1, 3)$ and either end point of the given
diameter, say the end point $B(2, 0)$, we use Theorem 2.1 to find r, and have

$$r = |CB| = \sqrt{(2 + 1)^2 + (3)^2} = \sqrt{9 + 9} = \sqrt{18}$$

We are now in a position to use the center-radius form of an equation of a
circle,

$$(x - h)^2 + (y - k)^2 = r^2$$

Substituting the values $h = -1$, $k = 3$, and $r = \sqrt{18}$ in this equation, we obtain

$$(x + 1)^2 + (y - 3)^2 = 18 \tag{16}$$

as the desired equation.

To graph the circle of this example we first plot the center $(-1, 3)$ of the circle. Then with the use of a compass we draw a circle with center $(-1, 3)$ and with radius $r = \sqrt{18} = 3\sqrt{2}$. It is sufficient in this construction to take $r \doteq 3(1.4) = 4.2$. (We use the symbol $\doteq$ to mean "approximately equal to.") The graph is shown in Fig. 2.12.

x intercept   If a graph G contains a point P on the x axis, the x coordinate of P is called an
y intercept   *x intercept* of G; that is, a number a is an x intercept of a graph G if $P(a, 0) \in G$. Similarly, a *y intercept* of a graph G is a number b for which $P(0, b) \in G$. Since each point on the x axis has 0 for its y coordinate, the x intercepts of a graph may be obtained by replacing y by 0 in the equation of the graph and solving the resulting equation for x. Similarly, the y intercepts of a graph may be obtained by replacing x by 0 in the equation of the graph and solving for y. A given graph may have several x intercepts, or one, or none, and it may have several y intercepts, or one, or none.

To illustrate, the circle with center at the origin and radius 5 has $x^2 + y^2 = 25$ for an equation. This circle has -5 and 5 for x intercepts, and it has -5 and 5 for y intercepts (see Fig. 2.13).

To find the x intercepts of the circle with Eq. (16), we replace y by 0 in (16) and obtain $(x + 1)^2 + 9 = 18$; so $x + 1 = \pm 3$. Therefore, the x intercepts of this circle are -4 and 2. To find the y intercepts, we replace x by 0 in (16) and obtain $1 + (y - 3)^2 = 18$, or $y - 3 = \pm\sqrt{17}$. Therefore, the y intercepts of this circle are $3 + \sqrt{17}$ and $3 - \sqrt{17}$.

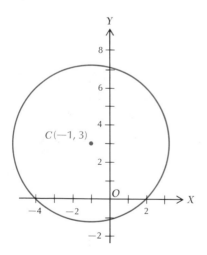

FIGURE 2.12   Graph of $(x + 1)^2 + (y - 3)^2 = 18$.

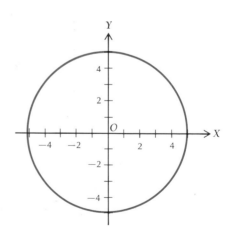

FIGURE 2.13   Graph of $x^2 + y^2 = 25$.

2.8 PARAMETRIC EQUATIONS OF A CIRCLE

Let us consider a circle with center at the point $C(h, k)$ and with radius r; let L be the line through the center C parallel to the x axis. Choose $P(x, y)$ to be any point on the circle and let $M(x, k)$ be the projection on L of P. Figure 2.14 shows four such constructions. We shall agree that the positive direction on the line L is to the right and that the positive direction on the line through P and M is upward. Let $t(0 \leqslant t \leqslant 2\pi)$ denote the measure (in radians) of the positive (or zero) angle

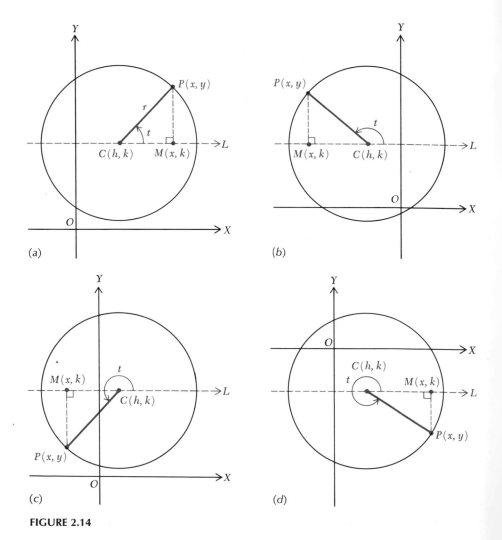

FIGURE 2.14

formed by the portion of L to the right of C and the line segment CP. (Recall that a positive angle is one generated by a counterclockwise rotation.)

Recalling from trigonometry the definitions of the sine and cosine of an angle t, and recalling from Sec. 1.4 that $\overline{P_1P_2}$ denotes the directed distance from P_1 to P_2, we observe that

$$\cos t = \frac{\overline{CM}}{r} \qquad \sin t = \frac{\overline{MP}}{r}$$

Since $\overline{CM} = x - h$ and $\overline{MP} = y - k$, we can write these equations as

$$\cos t = \frac{x-h}{r} \qquad \sin t = \frac{y-k}{r}$$

or

$$\begin{aligned} x - h &= r \cos t \\ y - k &= r \sin t \end{aligned} \tag{17}$$

We have shown that, for any point $P(x, y)$ on a circle with center $C(h, k)$ and radius r, the coordinates x and y are given by (17) or by

$$\begin{aligned} x &= h + r \cos t \\ y &= k + r \sin t \end{aligned} \tag{18}$$

where $0 \le t \le 2\pi$, and t is the measure in radians of the angle described in the preceding paragraph. If h, k, and r in Eqs. (17) or (18) are given constants, then as the variable t increases from 0 to 2π the point $P(x, y)$ whose coordinates are

Parameter

specified by Eqs. (17) or by Eqs. (18) traverses the circle with center $C(h, k)$ and

Parametric equations of a circle

radius r in a counterclockwise sense beginning at the point $(h + r, k)$. We call the variable t a *parameter* and we call Eqs. (17) or (18) **parametric equations** of the circle. [Sometimes each of the two pairs of equations (17) and (18) is called

Parametric representation

a **parametric representation** of the circle.]

From the parametric equations (17) we get

$$(x - h)^2 + (y - k)^2 = r^2(\cos^2 t + \sin^2 t)$$

or

$$(x - h)^2 + (y - k)^2 = r^2$$

since $\cos^2 t + \sin^2 t = 1$ for all values of t. This result, of course, agrees with the center-radius form of the equation of the circle [Eq. (14)].

If the center of the circle is at the origin, that is, if $h = 0$ and $k = 0$, Eqs. (18) become

$$\begin{aligned} x &= r \cos t \\ y &= r \sin t \end{aligned} \tag{19}$$

So, for $0 \le t \le 2\pi$, Eqs. (19) are parametric equations for a circle with center at the origin and radius r.

The student should verify that

$$x = h + r \sin t$$
$$y = k + r \cos t$$

where $0 \leqslant t \leqslant 2\pi$, are also parametric equations of the circle with center (h, k) and radius r. If the center of the circle is at the origin, these equations become

$$x = r \sin t$$
$$y = r \cos t$$

The circle with center $C(h, k)$ and radius r is the graph of the relation

$$\{(x, y) \mid (x - h)^2 + (y - k)^2 = r^2\}$$

and it follows from the above discussion that the circle is also the graph of

$$\{(x, y) \mid x = h + r \cos t, \, y = k + r \sin t, \, t \in [0; 2\pi]\}$$

In other words,

$$\{(x, y) \mid (x - h)^2 + (y - k)^2 = r^2\}$$
$$= \{(x, y) \mid x = h + r \cos t, \, y = k + r \sin t, \, t \in [0; 2\pi]\}$$

We can use the idea of parametric equations to determine relations whose graphs are portions of circles. To illustrate, the graph of

$$\{(x, y) \mid x = 2 + 3 \cos t, \, y = 4 + 3 \sin t, \, t \in [0; \pi]\}$$

is the top half of the circle with center $C(2, 4)$ and radius 3 (see Fig. 2.15). The graph of

$$\{(x, y) \mid x = -3 + 4 \cos t, \, y = 2 + 4 \sin t, \, t \in [\tfrac{1}{6}\pi; \tfrac{3}{2}\pi]\}$$

is the portion of the circle with center $C(-3, 2)$ and radius 4 shown in Fig. 2.16.

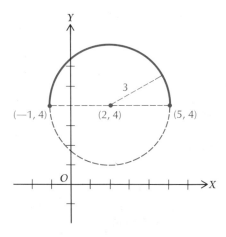

FIGURE 2.15

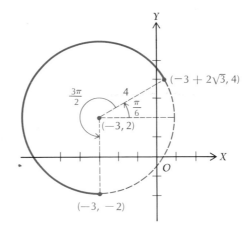

FIGURE 2.16

2.9 THE GENERAL FORM OF AN EQUATION OF A CIRCLE

Up to now we have used an equation of a circle in the form $(x - h)^2 + (y - k)^2 = r^2$. There are other forms in which an equation of a circle can be written; in particular, we wish to study a form known as the general form of an equation of a circle. In order to discuss different forms of equations for the same set of points we need to have the concept of equivalent equations.

Two equations

$$E_1(x, y) = 0 \quad \text{and} \quad E_2(x, y) = 0$$

are said to be *equivalent* if they are satisfied by the same set of ordered pairs of numbers, and therefore if they have the same graphs. To illustrate, any two of the equations

$$x^2 + y^2 = 25 \qquad 2x^2 + 2y^2 = 50 \qquad \tfrac{1}{2}x^2 + \tfrac{1}{2}y^2 = \tfrac{25}{2}$$

are equivalent. From a given equation we may readily obtain any number of equivalent equations by adding a specified real number c to both sides of the given equation, or by multiplying both sides of the given equation by a specified real number $c \neq 0$. These statements are in accordance with the properties of real numbers as expressed by

$$a = b \iff a + c = b + c$$

and, if $c \neq 0$,

$$a = b \iff ac = bc$$

The equations $x^2 + y^2 = 25$ and $x^2 + y^2 + 5 = 30$ are equivalent since the second can be obtained by adding 5 to both sides of the first equation; each ordered pair of numbers that satisfies the first equation will satisfy the second equation, and vice versa. The equations $x^2 + y^2 - 25 = 0$ and $x(x^2 + y^2 - 25) = 0$ are *not* equivalent since there are ordered pairs of numbers, for example, the ordered pair (0, 1), that satisfy the second equation but do not satisfy the first.

When we expand the equation

$$(x - h)^2 + (y - k)^2 = r^2$$

by squaring the binomials $x - h$ and $y - k$, we obtain

$$x^2 - 2hx + h^2 + y^2 - 2ky + k^2 = r^2$$

or

$$x^2 + y^2 + Dx + Ey + F = 0$$

where $D = -2h$, $E = -2k$, and $F = h^2 + k^2 - r^2$. Since the last equation is equivalent to the original equation, the following theorem has been proved.

THEOREM 2.5 *Any circle is the graph of an equation of the form*

$$x^2 + y^2 + Dx + Ey + F = 0 \tag{20}$$

General form of equation of a circle

We call (20) the **general form** of an equation of a circle.

Now consider the question: Is the graph of an equation of the form (20) always a circle?

To answer this question we add $-F$ to both sides of (20) and complete the square in each of x and y, obtaining

$$(x^2 + Dx + \tfrac{1}{4}D^2) + (y^2 + Ey + \tfrac{1}{4}E^2) = \tfrac{1}{4}D^2 + \tfrac{1}{4}E^2 - F$$

or

$$(x + \tfrac{1}{2}D)^2 + (y + \tfrac{1}{2}E)^2 = \frac{D^2 + E^2 - 4F}{4} \tag{21}$$

It should be clear that Eqs. (20) and (21) are equivalent.

If $D^2 + E^2 - 4F > 0$, then Eq. (21) is of the form $(x - h)^2 + (y - k)^2 = r^2$. Consequently (21), and therefore (20), has for its graph a circle with a positive real number r for radius, where

$$r^2 = \tfrac{1}{4}(D^2 + E^2 - 4F)$$

If $D^2 + E^2 - 4F = 0$, then (21), and therefore (20), has for its graph the single point $(-\tfrac{1}{2}D, -\tfrac{1}{2}E)$.

If $D^2 + E^2 - 4F < 0$, then (21), and therefore (20), has for its graph the null set. We have proved the following result.

THEOREM 2.6   *To determine the graph of the equation*

$$x^2 + y^2 + Dx + Ey + F = 0 \qquad (22)$$

write this equation in the equivalent form

$$(x + \tfrac{1}{2}D)^2 + (y + \tfrac{1}{2}E)^2 = s \qquad (23)$$

where $s = \tfrac{1}{4}(D^2 + E^2 - 4F)$.

(i)   *If $s > 0$, then the graph is a circle with $(-\tfrac{1}{2}D, -\tfrac{1}{2}E)$ for center and with radius equal to $\sqrt{s}$.*

(ii) *If $s = 0$, then the graph is the single point $(-\tfrac{1}{2}D, -\tfrac{1}{2}E)$.*

(iii) *If $s < 0$, then the graph is the null set.*

◆   EXAMPLE 1

Determine whether the graph of each of the following equations is a circle, a point, or the null set. If the graph is a circle, give its center and radius.

a. $5x^2 + 5y^2 - 14x + 7y - 24 = 0$

b. $x^2 + y^2 + 6x - 2y + 10 = 0$

c. $x^2 + y^2 + 8x - 10y + 50 = 0$

Solution

a. The equation

$$5x^2 + 5y^2 - 14x + 7y - 24 = 0$$

is not in the general form (20) of an equation of a circle, but we may put it in that form by dividing through by 5. Doing this, we obtain

$$x^2 + y^2 - \tfrac{14}{5}x + \tfrac{7}{5}y - \tfrac{24}{5} = 0$$

which is equivalent to the given equation. We might compute $D^2 + E^2 - 4F$ for this equation to determine the type of graph in accordance with Theorem 2.6, but it is more natural to proceed as follows. Adding $\tfrac{24}{5}$ to both sides of the latter equation and completing the squares in x and y, we have

$$(x^2 - \tfrac{14}{5}x + \tfrac{49}{25}) + (y^2 + \tfrac{7}{5}y + \tfrac{49}{100}) = \tfrac{24}{5} + \tfrac{49}{25} + \tfrac{49}{100}$$

or
$$(x - \tfrac{7}{5})^2 + (y + \tfrac{7}{10})^2 = \tfrac{29}{4}$$

Since this equation is of the form (23) with $s = \tfrac{29}{4} > 0$, the graph of the given equation is a circle with center $(\tfrac{7}{5}, -\tfrac{7}{10})$ and radius $\tfrac{1}{2}\sqrt{29}$.

b. By writing the given equation in the equivalent form

$$(x + 3)^2 + (y - 1)^2 = 0$$

we see that its graph is the point $(-3, 1)$.
c. By writing the given equation in the equivalent form

$$(x + 4)^2 + (y - 5)^2 = -9$$

we see that its graph is the null set.

◗   EXAMPLE 2

Describe in terms of the union of two graphs, or in terms of the intersection of two graphs, the graphs of each of the following relations:
a. $R_1 = \{(r \quad , x^2 + y^2 = 25 \text{ or } x = 3\}$
b. $R_2 = \{(x, y) \mid x^2 + y^2 = 25 \text{ and } x = 3\}$
c. $R_3 = \{(x, y) \mid x^2 + y^2 = 25 \text{ or } y = 4\}$
d. $R_4 = \{(x, y) \mid x^2 + y^2 = 25 \text{ and } y = 4\}$
e. $R_5 = \{(x, y) \mid x^2 + y^2 = 25 \text{ and } x = 6\}$
List the ordered pairs that are members of the relations R_2, R_4, and R_5.

Solution

Here we make use of the statements

$$\{(x, y) \mid S_{xy} \text{ and } T_{xy}\} = \{(x, y) \mid S_{xy}\} \cap \{(x, y) \mid T_{xy}\}$$

and $\quad \{(x, y) \mid S_{xy} \text{ or } T_{xy}\} = \{(x, y) \mid S_{xy}\} \cup \{(x, y) \mid T_{xy}\}$

which were discussed in Sec. 1.8.
a. Since R_1 is the union of

$$\{(x, y) \mid x^2 + y^2 = 25\} \quad \text{and} \quad \{(x, y) \mid x = 3\} \tag{24}$$

the graph of R_1 consists of the circle shown in Fig. 2.13 and the straight line 3 units to the right of the y axis and parallel to it.
b. Since R_2 is the intersection of the relations (24), the graph of R_2 consists of the points $(3, 4)$ and $(3, -4)$, which are the points the graphs of the relations (24) have in common; verify this statement. Hence $R_2 = \{(3, 4), (3, -4)\}$.
c. Since R_3 is the union of the relations

$$\{(x, y) \mid x^2 + y^2 = 25\} \quad \text{and} \quad \{(x, y) \mid y = 4\} \tag{25}$$

the graph of R_3 consists of the circle shown in Fig. 2.13 and the straight line 4 units above the x axis and parallel to it.
d. Since R_4 is the intersection of the relations (25), the graph of R_4 consists of the points $(3, 4)$ and $(-3, 4)$, which are the points the graphs of the relations (25) have in common; verify this statement. Hence $R_4 = \{(3, 4), (-3, 4)\}$.

e. Since R_5 is the intersection of the relations

$$\{(x, y) \mid x^2 + y^2 = 25\} \quad \text{and} \quad \{(x, y) \mid x = 6\}$$

the graph of R_5 consists of the points that the circle of Fig. 2.13 and the straight line 6 units to the right of the y axis and parallel to it have in common. Clearly there are no such points. Hence R_5 is the null set and in this case we can list no ordered pairs of R_5.

EXERCISES

In each of Exercises 1–4 graph the given equation. Give the domain and the range of the relation determined by the given equation, and give the x intercepts and the y intercepts of the graph.

1. $(x + 1)^2 + (y + 2)^2 = 4$ **2.** $x^2 + (y - 3)^2 = 9$

3. $x^2 + y^2 = 5$ **4.** $(x - 2)^2 + y^2 = 16$

5. Using the graph of the equation in Exercise 3, describe in terms of the union of two graphs, or in terms of the intersection of two graphs, the graph of each of the following relations:

    (a) $R_1 = \{(x, y) \mid x^2 + y^2 = 5 \text{ or } x = 1\}$
    (b) $R_2 = \{(x, y) \mid x^2 + y^2 = 5 \text{ and } x = 1\}$
    (c) $R_3 = \{(x, y) \mid x^2 + y^2 = 5 \text{ or } y = 2\}$
    (d) $R_4 = \{(x, y) \mid x^2 + y^2 = 5 \text{ and } y = 2\}$
    (e) $R_5 = \{(x, y) \mid x^2 + y^2 = 5 \text{ and } x = \sqrt{5}\}$
    (f) $R_6 = \{(x, y) \mid x^2 + y^2 = 5 \text{ and } x = 3\}$

List the ordered pairs that are members of the relations R_2, R_4, R_5, and R_6.

In each of Exercises 6–12 find an equation of the circle that satisfies the given conditions. Write this equation in the center-radius form (14) and in the general form (20).

    6. Center $(2, -3)$; radius 4   **7.** Center $(5, 0)$; radius 2

    8. Center $(2, -2)$; radius $\sqrt{2}$ **9.** Center $(-3, -4)$; radius $\frac{2}{3}$

    10. Center $(3, 6)$; passing through the point $(4, 9)$

    11. Center $(-2, 3)$; passing through the point $(4, 4)$

    12. With the points $A(-3, -4)$ and $B(7, -4)$ as the end points of a diameter

In each of Exercises 13–20 determine whether the graph of the given equation is a circle, a point, or the null set. If the graph is a circle, give its center and radius.

    13. $x^2 + y^2 + 10y - 75 = 0$ **14.** $x^2 + y^2 - 14x - 6y + 63 = 0$

    15. $3x^2 + 3y^2 + 5x - 6y + 1 = 0$ **16.** $2x^2 + 2y^2 - 6x - 10y - 1 = 0$

17. $x^2 + y^2 - 8x + 6y + 29 = 0$ **18.** $x^2 + y^2 - 10x - 24y = 0$

19. $3x^2 + 3y^2 - x - 2y - 1 = 0$ **20.** $4x^2 + 4y^2 - 4x + 8y + 5 = 0$

21. Find an equation of the circle that passes through the points $A(4, -2)$, $B(-5, 1)$, and $C(2, 2)$. What are the center and the radius of this circle? *Hint:* Use the general form of an equation of a circle. Since the circle is to pass through each of the three given points, the coordinates of each of these points must satisfy the equation of the circle.

22. Find an equation of the circle that passes through the points $A(0, 0)$ $B(1, 0)$, and $C(0, 1)$. What are the center and the radius of this circle?

23. Find an equation of the circle that has the same center as the circle whose equation is $x^2 + y^2 - 4x - 4y + 7 = 0$, and has radius 4.

24. Find an equation of the set of points G which has the property that for each point $P \in G$ the sum of the squares of the distances of P from $(3, 0)$ and $(-3, 0)$ is 68. If this set is a circle, give its center and radius.

25. Find an equation of the set of points G which has the property that for each point $P \in G$ the distance between P and $(6, -2)$ is 9.

26. Find an equation of the set of points G which has the property that for each point $P \in G$ the sum of the squares of the distances of P from $(3, 5)$ and $(-4, 2)$ is equal to 30. If this set is a circle, give its center and radius.

27. (*a*) What are the x intercepts of the graph of Exercise 13?

(*b*) What are the y intercepts of this graph?

In each of Exercises 28–31 graph the relation R and give the domain and the range of R. Is R a function? Explain. (Recall that π radians = 180 degrees.)

28. $R = \{(x, y) \mid x = 5 \cos t, y = 5 \sin t, t \in [0; \pi]\}$

29. $R = \{(x, y) \mid x = 5 \cos t, y = 5 \sin t, t \in [0; \tfrac{3}{2}\pi]\}$

30. $R = \{(x, y) \mid x = 10 \cos t, y = 10 \sin t, t \in [\tfrac{1}{4}\pi; \tfrac{2}{3}\pi]\}$

31. $R = \{(x, y) \mid x = 10 \cos t, y = 10 \sin t, t \in [\tfrac{2}{3}\pi; \tfrac{4}{3}\pi]\}$

32. For the parametric representation in Exercise 28, "eliminate" the parameter t by squaring both x and y and adding the results. Thus obtain a representation of the relation R of Exercise 28 in the form $R = \{(x, y) \mid S_{xy}\}$, where S_{xy} is a sentence involving only the variables x and y.

33. For the parametric representation in Exercise 30, repeat the computations of Exercise 32.

34. (*a*) Graph the equation $y = \sqrt{4 - x^2}$. What is the domain and what is the range of the relation $R_1 = \{(x, y) \mid y = \sqrt{4 - x^2}\}$ determined by this equation?

(b) Graph the equation $y = -\sqrt{4 - x^2}$. What is the domain and what is the range of the relation $R_2 = \{(x, y) \mid y = -\sqrt{4 - x^2}\}$ determined by this equation?

(c) How is the graph of $R_3 = \{(x, y) \mid x^2 + y^2 = 4\}$ related to the graphs of R_1 and R_2? Give the domain and the range of R_3. Is R_1 a function? Is R_2 a function? Is R_3 a function?

35. Show that

$$x = 3 + 4 \sin v \qquad y = 4 - 4 \cos v$$

are parametric equations of a circle. Give a geometric interpretation of the parameter v.

2.10 SUBSETS OF THE PLANE BOUNDED BY CIRCLES

Associated with the circle K that is the graph of the relation

$$S_1 = \{(x, y) \mid (x - h)^2 + (y - k)^2 = r^2\}$$

are the graphs of the relations

$$S_2 = \{(x, y) \mid (x - h)^2 + (y - k)^2 < r^2\}$$
$$S_3 = \{(x, y) \mid (x - h)^2 + (y - k)^2 > r^2\}$$
$$S_4 = \{(x, y) \mid (x - h)^2 + (y - k)^2 \leqslant r^2\}$$
$$S_5 = \{(x, y) \mid (x - h)^2 + (y - k)^2 \geqslant r^2\}$$

If an ordered pair (a, b) belongs to S_2, then $(a - h)^2 + (b - k)^2 < r^2$; hence the distance between the point $P(a, b)$ and the point $C(h, k)$ is less than r. This means that $P(a, b)$ lies inside the circle K of radius r and center (h, k). Therefore, the graph of S_2 consists of all points in the plane that are *inside* the circle K. By similar analyses the student should be able to convince himself that the graph of S_3 consists of all points of the plane that are *outside* the circle K. Also, the graph of S_4 consists of all points of the plane that are inside or on the circle K; the graph of S_5 consists of all points of the plane which are outside or on the circle K.

Observe that $S_2 \cap S_3 = \emptyset$, $S_2 \cap S_4 = S_2$, and $S_3 \cap S_5 = S_3$.

EXAMPLE 1

Graph the following relations and give the domain and range of each:

a. $R_1 = \{(x, y) \mid x^2 + y^2 < 9\}$
b. $R_2 = \{(x, y) \mid x^2 + y^2 \leqslant 9\}$
c. $R_3 = \{(x, y) \mid x^2 + y^2 > 9\}$
d. $R_4 = \{(x, y) \mid x^2 + y^2 \geqslant 4 \text{ and } x^2 + y^2 \leqslant 9\}$

Solution

a. The graph of R_1 is the set of points inside the circle $x^2 + y^2 = 9$. This graph is indicated by the shaded portion of Fig. 2.17. For this relation,

$$\text{Domain of } R_1 = (-3; 3) \qquad \text{Range of } R_1 = (-3; 3)$$

b. The graph of R_2 is the set of points on or inside the circle with equation $x^2 + y^2 = 9$. For this relation,

$$\text{Domain of } R_2 = [-3; 3] \qquad \text{Range of } R_2 = [-3; 3]$$

c. The graph of R_3 is the set of points outside the circle with equation $x^2 + y^2 = 9$. It should be clear that

$$\text{Domain of } R_3 = (-\infty; +\infty) \qquad \text{Range of } R_3 = (-\infty; +\infty)$$

Although the domain of R_3 and the range of R_3 are each *Re*, R_3 is not all of *Re* × *Re*. Why?

d. The relation R_4 is the intersection of the relations

$$\{(x, y) \mid x^2 + y^2 \geq 4\} \qquad \text{and} \qquad \{(x, y) \mid x^2 + y^2 \leq 9\}$$

The graph of the first one of these relations is the set of all points on or outside the circle with equation $x^2 + y^2 = 4$, and the graph of the second is the set of all points on or inside the circle with equation $x^2 + y^2 = 9$. The graph of R_4 is the set of points common to these graphs and is, therefore, the set of points on or between the circles with equations $x^2 + y^2 = 4$ and $x^2 + y^2 = 9$ (Fig. 2.18). From this discussion of R_4 it follows that

$$\text{Domain of } R_4 = [-3; 3] \qquad \text{Range of } R_4 = [-3; 3]$$

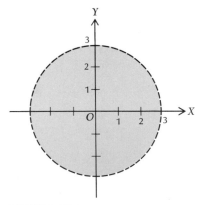

FIGURE 2.17

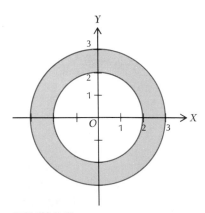

FIGURE 2.18

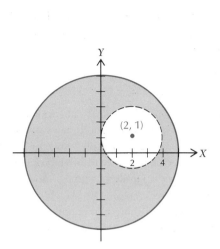

FIGURE 2.19   **FIGURE 2.20**

▶ EXAMPLE 2

Graph the following relations:
  a. $R_1 = \{(x, y) \mid (x - 2)^2 + (y - 1)^2 > 4 \text{ and } x^2 + y^2 \leqslant 25\}$
  b. $R_2 = \{(x, y) \mid (x + 1)^2 + (y - 3)^2 \leqslant 4 \text{ or } (x - 2)^2 + (y + 2)^2 \geqslant 25\}$

Solution

  a. The graph of R_1 is the *intersection* of the set of points outside the circle with equation $(x - 2)^2 + (y - 1)^2 = 4$ and the set of points on or inside the circle with equation $x^2 + y^2 = 25$. The graph of R_1 is shown as the shaded region in Fig. 2.19.
  b. The graph of R_2 is the *union* of the set of points on or inside the circle with equation $(x + 1)^2 + (y - 3)^2 = 4$ and the set of points on or outside the circle with equation $(x - 2)^2 + (y + 2)^2 = 25$. The graph of R_2 is shown as the shaded region in Fig. 2.20.

2.11 FAMILIES OF CIRCLES

Recall that a circle is determined by three points P_1, P_2, and P_3 that are not on a straight line. If the coordinates of P_1, P_2, and P_3 are known, they can be used to find the values of D, E, and F in the general equation of a circle, $x^2 + y^2 + Dx +$

$Ey + F = 0$, that will produce an equation of the circle determined by P_1, P_2, and P_3.

Suppose that we are asked to find an equation of the circle C_3, which passes through a point P_1 and through the points P_2 and P_3 of intersection of the two circles C_1 and C_2 with respective equations

$$x^2 + y^2 + D_1x + E_1y + F_1 = 0$$
$$x^2 + y^2 + D_2x + E_2y + F_2 = 0$$

This problem may be attacked by solving the pair of equations of C_1 and C_2 to find the coordinates of P_2 and P_3, then using the coordinates of the three points P_1, P_2, and P_3 as described in the preceding paragraph. However, this procedure is tedious and time consuming. A much easier way to solve problems of the type just discussed is to use the concept of a family of curves, more particularly, a family of circles. This concept is now explained.

Suppose that $E_1(x, y) = 0$ and $E_2(x, y) = 0$ are two equations in two variables. Let k_1 and k_2 be two real numbers, not both zero, and consider the equation

$$k_1E_1(x, y) + k_2E_2(x, y) = 0 \qquad (26)$$

If an ordered pair (x_1, y_1) satisfies both of the equations $E_1(x, y) = 0$ and $E_2(x, y) = 0$, then the pair (x_1, y_1) will satisfy Eq. (26). Interpreted geometrically, this means that if a point $P_1(x_1, y_1)$ is a point of intersection of the graphs of $E_1(x, y) = 0$ and $E_2(x, y) = 0$, then $P_1(x_1, y_1)$ will be a point on the graph of (26). In other words, the graph of Eq. (26) contains the points of intersection (if there are any) of the graphs of $E_1(x, y) = 0$ and $E_2(x, y) = 0$.

Sometimes we shall find it convenient to indicate that a set G of points is the graph of the equation $E(x, y) = 0$ by writing

$$G: E(x, y) = 0$$

Let us consider the two circles

$$C_1: x^2 + y^2 + D_1x + E_1y + F_1 = 0$$
and
$$C_2: x^2 + y^2 + D_2x + E_2y + F_2 = 0$$
Then
$$k_1(x^2 + y^2 + D_1x + E_1y + F_1) + k_2(x^2 + y^2 + D_2x + E_2y + F_2) = 0 \qquad (27)$$

is an equation of a curve that passes through the points of intersection (if any) of C_1 and C_2. If $k_1 + k_2 \neq 0$, then Eq. (27) can be put in the form

$$x^2 + y^2 + Dx + Ey + F = 0$$

by dividing each side of (27) by $k_1 + k_2$. Therefore (see Theorem 2.6), if $k_1 + k_2 \neq 0$, the graph of Eq. (27) is a circle, a point, or the null set. If the circles C_1 and C_2 have two points of intersection P_1 and P_2, we can assign values to k_1 and k_2 (subject to the condition $k_1 + k_2 \neq 0$), and for each such choice of the real numbers k_1 and k_2 we get from (27) a circle which passes through the points of

Family of circles

intersection P_1 and P_2 of the circles C_1 and C_2. We call the set of all circles that can be so obtained a **family** of circles, and we record our conclusions in Theorem 2.7.

THEOREM 2.7   *If $E_1(x, y) = 0$ and $E_2(x, y) = 0$ are the general forms of the equations of two circles C_1 and C_2, respectively, and if C_1 and C_2 have two points of intersection, then, for each choice of the real numbers k_1 and k_2 with $k_1 + k_2 \neq 0$, the equation*

$$k_1 E_1(x, y) + k_2 E_2(x, y) = 0 \qquad (28)$$

represents a circle through the points of intersection of C_1 and C_2. Equation (28) is called an equation of the family of circles through the points of intersection of C_1 and C_2.

The case for which $k_1 + k_2 = 0$ in (28) will be considered in Sec. 3.5.

The use of Theorem 2.7 in finding an equation of the circle passing through the points of intersection of two given circles and through another given point is illustrated in part **b** of the following example.

▶ EXAMPLE

   a. A family of circles has the equation

$$k_1(x^2 + y^2 - 1) + k_2(x^2 + y^2 + 2x) = 0 \qquad (29)$$

Graph the member of this family for which $k_1 = 4$ and $k_2 = 1$.

   b. Find an equation of the circle which passes through the point $P(3, 2)$ and through the points of intersection of the circles

$$C_1:\ x^2 + y^2 = 1$$

and

$$C_2:\ x^2 + y^2 + 2x = 0$$

Solution

   a. We recognize $x^2 + y^2 - 1 = 0$ as an equation of the circle C_1 with center $(0, 0)$ and radius 1. Similarly, $x^2 + y^2 + 2x = 0$ is an equation of the circle C_2 with center $(-1, 0)$ and radius 1 (see Fig. 2.21). Substituting 4 for k_1 and 1 for k_2 in Eq. (29), we get

$$5x^2 + 5y^2 + 2x - 4 = 0$$

or

$$(x + \tfrac{1}{5})^2 + y^2 = \tfrac{21}{25}$$

This is an equation of the circle C_3, with center $(-\tfrac{1}{5}, 0)$ and radius $\tfrac{1}{5}\sqrt{21} \doteq 0.9$, shown in Fig. 2.21.

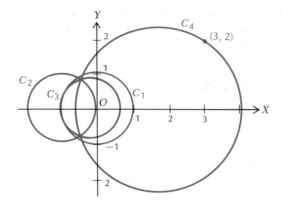

FIGURE 2.21

b. We know that every equation of the form (29) with $k_1 + k_2 \neq 0$ passes through the points of intersection of C_1 and C_2. Therefore, in order to obtain an equation of the desired circle, we wish to determine values for k_1 and k_2 that will make the graph of (29) pass through the point $P(3, 2)$. If $P(3, 2)$ is to lie on the graph of (29), the coordinates $(3, 2)$ must satisfy Eq. (29); that is, k_1 and k_2 must have values so that

$$k_1[(3)^2 + (2)^2 - 1] + k_2[(3)^2 + (2)^2 + 2(3)] = 0$$

or
$$12k_1 + 19k_2 = 0$$

Observe that $k_1 = 19$ and $k_2 = -12$ are values that will make this equation true. Using these values in (29), we get

$$19(x^2 + y^2 - 1) - 12(x^2 + y^2 + 2x) = 0 \qquad (30)$$

which is an equation of the desired circle. The student should note that for *any* *nonzero* real number c, the values

$$k_1 = 19c \qquad k_2 = -12c$$

will satisfy the equation $12k_1 + 19k_2 = 0$ and so, for any choice of $c \neq 0$,

$$19c(x^2 + y^2 - 1) - 12c(x^2 + y^2 + 2x) = 0 \qquad (31)$$

is an equation of the desired circle. Since $c \neq 0$ we see that Eq. (31) is equivalent to Eq. (30). Note that Eq. (31) is an equation of a particular circle, and not an equation of a family of circles.

To draw the graph of Eq. (30), we can obtain the following equations, each of which is equivalent to (30):

$$7x^2 + 7y^2 - 24x - 19 = 0$$

or
$$(x - \tfrac{12}{7})^2 + y^2 = \tfrac{277}{49}$$

Therefore the desired circle has center $(\frac{12}{7}, 0)$ and radius $\frac{1}{7}\sqrt{277} \doteq 2.4$. This circle is shown as C_4 in Fig. 2.21.

EXERCISES

In each of Exercises 1–4 graph the given relation. Give the domain and the range of each relation

1. $R = \{(x, y) \mid x^2 + y^2 < 9\}$ **2.** $R = \{(x, y) \mid x^2 + y^2 = 9 \text{ or } x \leqslant 0\}$

3. $R = \{(x, y) \mid x^2 + y^2 \geqslant 1 \text{ and } x^2 + y^2 \leqslant 16\}$

4. $R = \{(x, y) \mid x^2 + y^2 = 4 \text{ or } y > 2\}$

5. Designate each of the following sets in the manner $\{(x, y) \mid S_{xy}\}$, where S_{xy} is a quadratic equation or inequality:

(*a*) The circle with center at the origin and radius 7

(*b*) The set of points inside the circle with center at the origin and radius 7

(*c*) The set of points outside the circle with center at the origin and radius 7

(*d*) The set of points outside the circle with center at the point (3, 4) and radius 6

6. Graph the relation $R = \{(x, y) \mid x^2 + y^2 \leqslant 25 \text{ and } x \geqslant 3\}$ and give its domain and its range.

7. Graph $R = \{(x, y) \mid x^2 + y^2 \leqslant 25 \text{ and } 3 \leqslant x \leqslant 4\}$ and give its domain and its range.

8. Graph $R = \{(x, y) \mid x^2 + y^2 > 4 \text{ and } x^2 + y^2 - 2x + 4y \leqslant 31\}$.

9. Graph $R = \{(x, y) \mid (x-1)^2 + y^2 \leqslant 4 \text{ or } x^2 + y^2 + 4x - 4y > 41\}$.

10. Graph $R = \{(x, y) \mid x^2 + y^2 \leqslant 4 \text{ and } (x-2)^2 + y^2 \leqslant 1\}$.

11. On the same coordinate system graph the two circles

$$C_1\colon x^2 + y^2 - 2x = 0 \quad \text{and} \quad C_2\colon x^2 + y^2 - 2y = 0$$

A family of circles has the equation

$$k_1(x^2 + y^2 - 2x) + k_2(x^2 + y^2 - 2y) = 0$$

Find the center-radius form of an equation of the member of this family for which $k_1 = 2$ and $k_2 = 1$. Graph this circle on the same coordinate system with C_1 and C_2.

12. On the same coordinate system graph the circles $C_1\colon x^2 + y^2 + 8x - 9 = 0$ and $C_2\colon x^2 + y^2 - 4x - 12 = 0$ and the members of the family with equation

$$k_1(x^2 + y^2 + 8x - 9) + k_2(x^2 + y^2 - 4x - 12) = 0$$

for which $k_1 = 1, k_2 = 2; k_1 = 2, k_2 = 2$.

In each of Exercises 13–16 find an equation of the circle C through the given point P_1 and through the points of intersection of the circles C_1 and C_2 whose equations are given. In each case check your work by graphing C_1, C_2, and C on the same coordinate system.

13. $P_1(-3, -2)$; C_1: $x^2 + y^2 + 7x + 4y - 30 = 0$; C_2: $x^2 + y^2 + 4x - 3y - 30 = 0$

14. $P_1(6, -3)$; C_1: $3x^2 + 3y^2 - 5x + 2y + 1 = 0$; C_2: $2x^2 + 2y^2 + 7x - 5y + 3 = 0$

15. $P_1(-1, 2)$; C_1: $x^2 + y^2 + 3x - 5y = 0$; C_2: $x^2 + y^2 + x - 4y + 1 = 0$

16. $P_1(2, 4)$; C_1: $2x^2 + 2y^2 - 3x + 6y - 10 = 0$; C_2: $2x^2 + 2y^2 + 19x - 30y + 42 = 0$

3 | THE STRAIGHT LINE

3.1 THE SLOPE AND INCLINATION OF A LINE

In the discussion of circles in the preceding chapter it was natural to describe a particular circle by giving its center and radius. In considering a straight line, one of its most obvious characteristics is its "direction" or orientation. In this section we shall consider a way in which a number may be associated with a line to describe its orientation quantitatively.

Let L be a straight line that is not parallel to the y axis. Let $P_1(x_1, y_1)$ and $P_2(x_2, y_2)$ be any two distinct points on L, and consider the number m defined by the equality

$$m = \frac{y_2 - y_1}{x_2 - x_1}$$

In this equality $x_2 \neq x_1$ since the line is not parallel to the y axis. To obtain an idea of the relation of the ratio m to the orientation of the line L, consider the following positions of P_2 relative to P_1:

  (i) P_2 above and to the right of P_1 (Fig. 3.1)
  (ii) P_2 below and to the left of P_1 (Fig. 3.2)

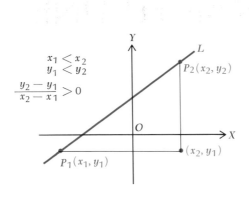

FIGURE 3.1

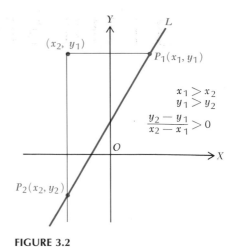

FIGURE 3.2

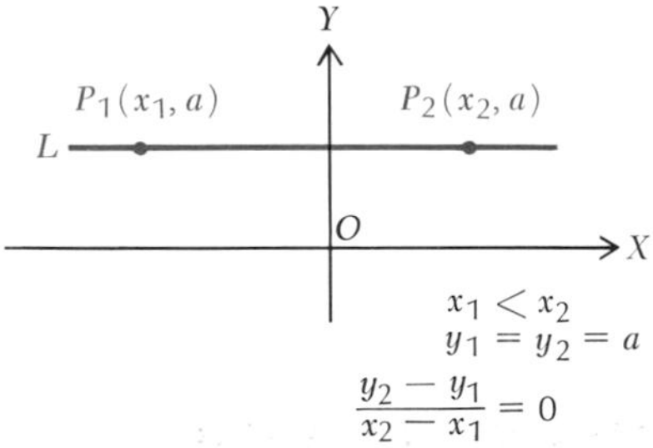

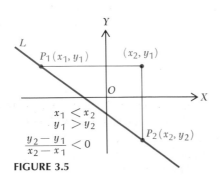

FIGURE 3.3

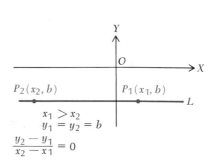

FIGURE 3.4

FIGURE 3.5

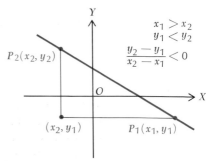

FIGURE 3.6

(iii) P_2 to the right of P_1 with the same y coordinate (Fig. 3.3)
(iv) P_2 to the left of P_1 with the same y coordinate (Fig. 3.4)
(v) P_2 below and to the right of P_1 (Fig. 3.5)
(vi) P_2 above and to the left of P_1 (Fig. 3.6)

In cases (i) and (ii) the point with the larger x coordinate lies *above* the other point, the line slopes upward to the right (or downward to the left), and $(y_2 - y_1)/(x_2 - x_1) = 0$.

In cases (iii) and (iv), the points lie on a horizontal line, so $y_2 = y_1$ and $(y_2 - y_1)/(x_2 - x_1) = 0$.

In cases (v) and (vi), the point with the larger x coordinate lies *below* the other point, the line slopes downward to the right (or upward to the left), and $(y_2 - y_1)/(x_2 - x_1) < 0$.

Thus the sign of the ratio $m = (y_2 - y_1)/(x_2 - x_1)$ indicates whether the line slopes upward to the right, is horizontal, or slopes downward to the right. Further, the magnitude of the ratio m indicates the "steepness" of the line since

$$\left| \frac{y_2 - y_1}{x_2 - x_1} \right| = \frac{|y_2 - y_1|}{|x_2 - x_1|} = \frac{\text{vertical distance between } P_1 \text{ and } P_2}{\text{horizontal distance between } P_1 \text{ and } P_2}$$

By the use of similar triangles we can readily show that if $P_1'(x_1', y_1')$ and $P_2'(x_2', y_2')$ are any two distinct points other than $P_1(x_1, y_1)$ and $P_2(x_2, y_2)$ on L (see Fig. 3.7), then

$$m = \frac{y_2 - y_1}{x_2 - x_1} = \frac{y_2' - y_1'}{x_2' - x_1'}$$

Thus we see that the equality $m = (y_2 - y_1)/(x_2 - x_1)$ associates with each line L that is not parallel to the y axis a unique number m. We call

$$m = \frac{y_2 - y_1}{x_2 - x_1} \qquad (x_1 \neq x_2) \tag{1}$$

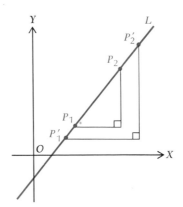

FIGURE 3.7

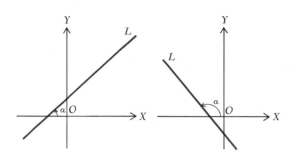

FIGURE 3.8

Slope   the **slope** of the line through the points $P_1(x_1, y_1)$ and $P_2(x_2, y_2)$. *Note that a line parallel to the y axis does not have a slope.*

For a given line L let the angle α be defined as the smallest nonnegative angle from the positive x axis to L, as shown in Fig. 3.8. (A nonnegative angle is an angle measured in a counterclockwise direction.) Then, if L is not parallel to the y axis,

$$m = \tan \alpha \tag{2}$$

and $$0° \leqslant \alpha < 180° \tag{3}$$

If a line is parallel to the x axis, or coincident with it, then $m = 0$ and $\alpha = 0°$. If a line is parallel to the y axis, or coincident with it, then $\alpha = 90°$, and neither $\tan \alpha$ nor the slope of the line is defined.

Inclination of a line   The angle α as defined is called the **inclination** of the line L.

Since, unless specifically stated otherwise, we take the x axis to be horizontal,

Horizontal line
Vertical line   a line parallel to the x axis will be called a *horizontal line* and a line parallel to the y axis will be called a *vertical line*. A horizontal line has inclination 0 degrees and slope 0, and a vertical line has inclination 90 degrees and no slope.

▶ EXAMPLE 1

In each of the following determine the slope m and the inclination α of the line that passes through the two points given:

a. $P_1(2, 1)$, $P_2(4, 3)$ **b.** $P_1(0, 0)$, $P_2(1, \sqrt{3})$
c. $P_1(1, 1)$, $P_2(-2, 4)$ **d.** $P_1(3, 4)$, $P_2(4, 1)$

Solution

a. Using Eq. (1), we find the slope m to be given by

$$m = \frac{3 - 1}{4 - 2} = \frac{2}{2} = 1$$

Hence tan $\alpha = 1$, and since $0° \leqslant \alpha < 180°$ we conclude that $\alpha = 45°$.

b. Here $m = \sqrt{3}$, and $\alpha = 60°$.

c. In this case $m = -1$, and tan $\alpha = -1$. Since tan α is negative and since $0° \leqslant \alpha < 180°$, α must be a second-quadrant angle. Now the second-quadrant angle whose tangent is equal to -1 is 135 degrees, for tan $135° = $ tan $(180° - 45°) = -$tan $45° = -1$. So $\alpha = 135°$.

d. Here

$$m = \frac{1-4}{4-3} = \frac{-3}{1} = -3$$

So tan $\alpha = -3$, and α is obtuse. To find α, use tan $(180° - \alpha) = -$tan $\alpha = 3$. From the Appendix at the end of this book we find that the acute angle whose tangent is 3 is 72 degrees (to the nearest degree). Therefore, $180° - \alpha \doteq 72°$ and $\alpha \doteq 180° - 72° = 108°$ (to the nearest degree).

◆ EXAMPLE 2

Graph the line through the point $P_1(2, 1)$:

a. With slope $\frac{3}{4}$ **b.** With slope $-\frac{3}{4}$

Solution

a. Formula (1) states that the slope of a nonvertical line is equal to the difference in the ordinates of two points on the line divided by the difference in the abscissas of those points taken in the same order. Therefore, we can go from the given point $P_1(2, 1)$ to a second point P_2 on the line by going 4 units to the right of P_1 and then going upward 3 units. Thus we locate a second point $P_2(6, 4)$ on the line (Fig. 3.9). The desired graph is the line that contains P_1P_2 as a segment, since this line passes through $P_1(2, 1)$ and has the proper slope. Note that we can readily verify that this line does have the desired slope: $m = (4-1)/(6-2) = \frac{3}{4}$.

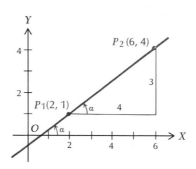

FIGURE 3.9

b. We locate a second point P_2 on the line through $P_1(2, 1)$ by going 4 units to the right of P_1 and then going downward 3 units (Fig. 3.10). The second point so located is $(6, -2)$. Observe that we would have arrived at the same point P_2 by first going downward 3 units from P_1 and then going to the right 4 units. As a check we find the slope m of the line through P_1 and P_2: $m = (-2 - 1)/(6 - 2) = -\frac{3}{4}$.

Two distinct lines either intersect in one point or are parallel. The concept of the slope of a line can be used to determine whether lines intersect or are parallel. It should be clear that two lines are parallel if and only if their inclinations are the same. This fact is used in establishing Theorem 3.1.

THEOREM 3.1 *Two nonvertical lines L_1 and L_2 are parallel if and only if their slopes m_1 and m_2 are equal:*

$$L_1 \parallel L_2 \iff m_1 = m_2 \qquad (4)$$

Proof

First let us prove that $L_1 \parallel L_2 \Rightarrow m_1 = m_2$. If the lines L_1 and L_2 are parallel, their inclinations α_1 and α_2 are equal (Fig. 3.11). Hence $\tan \alpha_1 = \tan \alpha_2$, or $m_1 = m_2$.

Next we are to prove that $m_1 = m_2 \Rightarrow L_1 \parallel L_2$. From $m_1 = m_2$, we conclude that $\tan \alpha_1 = \tan \alpha_2$. Must $\alpha_1 = \alpha_2$? Yes, because the inclination α of a line is restricted so that $0° \leqslant \alpha < 180°$, and there is exactly one angle satisfying this inequality which has a given real number m for its tangent. Since $\alpha_1 = \alpha_2$, then $L_1 \parallel L_2$.

Often it is significant to determine whether two lines are perpendicular. Again the concept of slope provides an easy way to determine perpendicularity. The

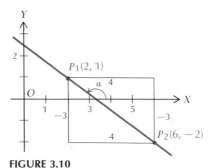

FIGURE 3.10

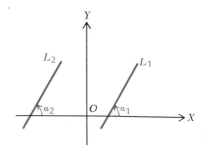

FIGURE 3.11

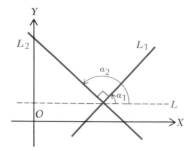

FIGURE 3.12

fact that two lines are perpendicular if and only if their inclinations differ by 90 degrees can be used to establish Theorem 3.2.

THEOREM 3.2 *Two nonvertical lines L_1 and L_2 are perpendicular if and only if the product of their slopes m_1 and m_2 is equal to -1:*

$$L_1 \perp L_2 \iff m_1 m_2 = -1 \tag{5}$$

Proof

First, assume that L_1 and L_2 are perpendicular lines with respective inclinations α_1 and α_2, and suppose that the subscripts are chosen so that $\alpha_2 > \alpha_1$ (Fig. 3.12). Draw a line L through the point of intersection of L_1 and L_2 and parallel to the x axis. Then α_1 and α_2 are the angles as represented in Fig. 3.12 with

$$\alpha_2 = \alpha_1 + 90°$$

and, consequently,

$$\tan \alpha_2 = \tan (\alpha_1 + 90°)$$

Now

$$\tan (\alpha_1 + 90°) = -\cot \alpha_1 \tag{6}$$

Therefore

$$\tan \alpha_2 = -\cot \alpha_1 = -\frac{1}{\tan \alpha_1}$$

or

$$m_1 = -\frac{1}{m_2} \quad \text{or} \quad m_1 m_2 = -1$$

and we have proved that $L_1 \perp L_2 \Rightarrow m_1 m_2 = -1$.

Next, we assume that the lines L_1 and L_2 with respective inclinations α_1 and α_2 and slopes m_1 and m_2 do satisfy the condition $m_1 m_2 = -1$. We want to prove that $m_1 m_2 = -1 \Rightarrow L_1 \perp L_2$, or, alternatively stated, that

$$\tan \alpha_1 \tan \alpha_2 = -1 \quad \Rightarrow \quad L_1 \perp L_2 \tag{7}$$

Under the assumption that $m_1 m_2 = -1$, one of the numbers $m_1 = \tan \alpha_1$ and $m_2 = \tan \alpha_2$ is positive and the other is negative. Suppose that the lines are labeled so that $\tan \alpha_1 > 0$ and $\tan \alpha_2 < 0$. Then

$$0° < \alpha_1 < 90° \quad \text{and} \quad 90° < \alpha_2 < 180° \tag{8}$$

From (7)

$$\tan \alpha_2 = -\frac{1}{\tan \alpha_1} = -\cot \alpha_1 \tag{9}$$

From (6) and (9) we have

$$\tan (\alpha_1 + 90°) = \tan \alpha_2 \tag{10}$$

From (8) and (10) it follows that

$$\alpha_2 = \alpha_1 + 90° \quad \text{or} \quad \alpha_2 - \alpha_1 = 90°$$

so $L_1 \perp L_2$.

The fact that the product of two numbers is equal to -1 is often expressed by saying that the two numbers are *negative reciprocals* and that either is the negative reciprocal of the other. So the result of Theorem 3.2 can be written as

$$L_1 \perp L_2 \quad \Longleftrightarrow \quad m_1 \text{ is the negative reciprocal of } m_2$$

▶ EXAMPLE 3

Show that the line L_1 with slope m_1 through $P_1(-3, -4)$ and $P_2(2, 7)$ is parallel to the line L_2 with slope m_2 through $P_3(1, -9)$ and $P_4(6, 2)$.

Solution

Using Eq. (1), we find that

$$m_1 = \frac{7+4}{2+3} = \frac{11}{5} \quad \text{and} \quad m_2 = \frac{-9-2}{1-6} = \frac{11}{5}$$

Since $m_1 = m_2$, $L_1 \parallel L_2$ by Theorem 3.1.

▶ EXAMPLE 4

Show that the line L_1 with slope m_1 through $P_1(-2, -4)$ and $P_2(1, 3)$ is perpendicular to the line L_2 with slope m_2 through $P_3(3, 2)$ and $P_4(-4, 5)$.

Solution

In this example, $m_1 = \frac{7}{3}$ and $m_2 = -\frac{3}{7}$. Since m_1 and m_2 are negative reciprocals, $L_1 \perp L_2$ by Theorem 3.2.

♦   EXAMPLE 5

Find the slope m_2 of a line L_2 which is perpendicular to the line L_1 that passes through the points $P_1(-2, 1)$ and $P_2(3, 5)$.

Solution

Let m_1 be the slope of line L_1. Then using Eq. (1) we find that $m_1 = \frac{4}{5}$. By Theorem 3.2, m_2 must be the negative reciprocal of m_1; therefore, $m_2 = -\frac{5}{4}$.

EXERCISES

1. Using the Appendix at the end of this book, find α if:
   (*a*) $\tan \alpha = 0.325$ (*b*) $\tan \alpha = -0.325$

In each of Exercises 2–7 find the slope and the inclination (to the nearest degree) of the line which passes through the two given points.

2. (0, 0); (2 $\sqrt{3}$, 2)   **3.** (3, 2); (5, 6)

4. (0, 0); (−2 $\sqrt{3}$, 2)   **5.** (−2, 5); (−1, 3)

6. (−3, 4); (5, 4)   **7.** (2, −5); (−3, −1)

In each of Exercises 8–11 the line determined by P_1 and P_2 and the line determined by P_3 and P_4 are either parallel or perpendicular. Determine which is the case.

8. $P_1(2, 0)$; $P_2(-3, 2)$; $P_3(0, \frac{3}{4})$; $P_4(-\frac{3}{10}, 0)$

9. $P_1(1, 6)$; $P_2(-1, 2)$; $P_3(-7, 0)$; $P_4(1, -4)$

10. $P_1(6, 2)$; $P_2(8, 1)$; $P_3(4, 9)$; $P_4(2, 5)$

11. $P_1(3, 0)$; $P_2(0, 2)$; $P_3(6, 0)$; $P_4(0, 4)$

In each of Exercises 12–17 graph the line with the specified slope through the given point, without finding its inclination.

12. (3, 4); $m = \frac{2}{3}$ **13.** (−2, 3); $m = 0$

14. (3, 4); $m = -\frac{2}{3}$ **15.** (−3, −2); $m = \frac{4}{5}$

16. (0, 5); $m = 2$ **17.** (4, 0); $m = -3$

In each of Exercises 18–21 show, by the use of slopes, that the three given points are collinear.

18. $P_1(-6, 0)$; $P_2(-1, 3)$; $P_3(4, 6)$. *Hint:* Show that the slope of the line through P_1 and P_2 is equal to the slope of the line through P_2 and P_3.

19. $(4, -13)$; $(2, -7)$; $(-1, 2)$ **20.** $(0, -1)$; $(\frac{1}{2}, 0)$; $(6, 11)$

21. $(2, 5)$; $(7, 3)$; $(-3, 7)$

22. Show that the point $(-5, 3)$ is on the perpendicular bisector of the segment whose end points are $(-3, -4)$ and $(2, 5)$.

23. By the use of slopes verify that the points $(-6, -4)$, $(3, 5)$, and $(10, -2)$ are the vertices of a right triangle.

24. By the use of slopes verify that the points $(-13, -9)$, $(-11, -1)$, $(2, -2)$, and $(4, 6)$ are the vertices of a parallelogram.

25. Is the quadrilateral with the points $(-11, -5)$, $(-2, -19)$, $(12, -10)$, and $(3, 4)$ for vertices a parallelogram? Is it a rectangle?

In each of Exercises 26–29 prove analytically the theorem which is stated.

26. The diagonals of a square are perpendicular.

27. The diagonals of a rhombus bisect each other at right angles.

28. If the diagonals of a rectangle are perpendicular, then the rectangle is a square.

29. The line segments joining the midpoints of adjacent sides of any quadrilateral form a parallelogram.

In each of Exercises 30–33 find the slope of a line that is perpendicular to the line through the two given points.

30. $(-2, 3)$; $(1, -2)$ **31.** $(1, 3)$; $(2, 4)$

32. $(-3, 4)$; $(1, -2)$ **33.** $(2, 1)$; $(-4, -3)$

3.2 THE POINT-SLOPE FORM AND THE GENERAL FORM OF AN EQUATION OF A LINE

In Chap. 2 we found that every circle is the graph of an equation of a certain form and that every equation of a certain type represents a circle. It is natural to ask whether a similar correspondence can be established between lines and a certain type of equation.

First we shall consider the simple cases in which a given line is parallel to either the y axis or the x axis. If a line L is vertical, then every point on L has the same x coordinate. If this x coordinate is x_1, then the point $P(x, y)$ is on L *if and only if*

$$x = x_1 \tag{11}$$

That is, a line parallel to the y axis is the graph of the relation

$$\{(x, y) \mid x = x_1\}$$

If a line L is parallel to the x axis, then every point on L has the same y coordinate. If this y coordinate is y_1, then the point $P(x, y)$ is on L *if and only if*

$$y = y_1$$

That is, a line parallel to the x axis is the graph of the relation

$$\{(x, y) \mid y = y_1\}$$

Thus, the graph of an equation of the form $x = x_1$ or of the form $y = y_1$ is a line that is parallel to one of the coordinate axes.

Now let L be the nonvertical line that passes through the point $P_1(x_1, y_1)$ and has slope m. Suppose that $P(x, y)$ is a point in the plane different from P_1. Then $P(x, y)$ will lie on L *if and only if* the slope of the segment PP_1 is m; that is,

$$P(x, y) \text{ is on } L \iff \text{slope of } PP_1 \text{ is } m$$

or $\qquad P(x, y) \text{ is on } L \iff \dfrac{y - y_1}{x - x_1} = m \tag{12}$

Since L is nonvertical we know that $x \neq x_1$, and for a point $P(x, y)$ different from $P_1(x_1, y_1)$ we may write (12) as

$$P(x, y) \text{ is on } L \iff y - y_1 = m(x - x_1) \tag{13}$$

We note that statement (13) remains valid when the restriction that P is different from P_1 is removed. So statement (13) says that the line L through $P_1(x_1, y_1)$ with slope m is the graph of the relation

$$\{(x, y) \mid y - y_1 = m(x - x_1)\}$$

That is, L is the graph of the equation

$$y - y_1 = m(x - x_1) \tag{14}$$

If the line L is parallel to the x axis, then $m = 0$ and Eq. (14) reduces to

$$y - y_1 = 0 \quad \text{or} \quad y = y_1$$

Point-slope form   We call (14) the **point-slope form** of an equation of a line.

◆   EXAMPLE 1

Find an equation of the line through the point $P_1(-3, 5)$ which has slope $-\frac{3}{4}$.

Solution

Using (14), we obtain

$$y - 5 = -\tfrac{3}{4}[x - (-3)] \qquad \text{or} \qquad 4y - 20 = -3x - 9$$

or

$$3x + 4y - 11 = 0$$

♦ EXAMPLE 2

Find an equation of the line through the points $P_1(4, 6)$ and $P_2(-1, 3)$.

Solution

Using (1), we find the slope of the line to be $\tfrac{3}{5}$. Now using (14) with $m = \tfrac{3}{5}$, $x_1 = 4$, and $y_1 = 6$, we have

$$y - 6 = \tfrac{3}{5}(x - 4) \qquad \text{or} \qquad 5y - 30 = 3x - 12$$

or

$$3x - 5y + 18 = 0$$

We can check this answer by showing that the coordinates of $P_1(4, 6)$ and $P_2(-1, 3)$ satisfy this equation. Thus

$$3(4) - 5(6) + 18 = 12 - 30 + 18 = 0$$

and

$$3(-1) - 5(3) + 18 = -3 - 15 + 18 = 0$$

Any nonvertical line meets the y axis at a point which may be denoted by $B(0, b)$, b being the y intercept of the line (Fig. 3.13). Using (14), we find that an equation of the line L through $B(0, b)$ with slope m is

$$y = mx + b \tag{15}$$

Slope-intercept form   Equation (15) is called the **slope-intercept form** of an equation of a line.

To illustrate, the equation of the line with slope -2 and y intercept 3 is $y = -2x + 3$.

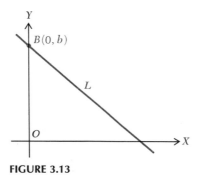

FIGURE 3.13   FIGURE 3.14

Suppose the x intercept of a line L is $a \neq 0$ and the y intercept of L is $b \neq 0$ (Fig. 3.14). Then L passes through the points $A(a, 0)$ and $B(0, b)$. Using (1), we find that $m = -b/a$; then, using (15), we find that an equation of L is $y = -(b/a)x + b$, or $ay = -bx + ab$, or

$$\frac{x}{a} + \frac{y}{b} = 1 \qquad (16)$$

Intercept form   Equation (16) is called the **intercept form** of an equation of a line.

To illustrate, an equation of the line with x intercept 2 and y intercept 3 is

$$\frac{x}{2} + \frac{y}{3} = 1$$

An equation of the form

$$Ax + By + C = 0 \qquad (17)$$

First-degree equation   where A, B, and C are any given real numbers, with A and B not both zero, is called an **equation of the first degree** in the two variables x and y.

THEOREM 3.3   *Every line in the coordinate plane is the graph of an equation of the first degree in two variables.*

Proof

It has been seen that if a line is nonvertical it is the graph of $y = mx + b$. If a line is vertical, it is the graph of $x = x_1$. Each of these equations is an equation of the first degree in x and y, and so the theorem is proved.

THEOREM 3.4   *The graph of any equation of the first degree in two variables, such as*

$$Ax + By + C = 0$$

that is, the graph of the relation

$$\{(x, y) \mid Ax + By + C = 0\}$$

is a line.

Proof

If $B \neq 0$, we can write the equation in the form

$$y = -\frac{A}{B}x - \frac{C}{B}$$

Comparing this with Eq. (15), we recognize it as an equation of a line with slope $-A/B$ and y intercept $-C/B$.

If $B = 0$, then $A \neq 0$, and we can write the equation in the form

$$Ax + C = 0 \qquad \text{or} \qquad x = -\frac{C}{A}$$

This is an equation of a vertical line.

Hence, in both cases, the graph of $Ax + By + C = 0$ is a line.

General form of equation of a line

As a consequence of Theorem 3.4 we call $Ax + By + C = 0$ the **general form** of an equation of a line. All other forms of an equation of a line may be obtained from it. Also, because of Theorem 3.4, an equation of the first degree in two variables is often called a **linear equation.**

Linear equation

Subsequently, we should readily recognize any given equation of the first degree in two variables as an equation of a line. In graphing such an equation it is sufficient, since two points determine a line, to find two ordered pairs of numbers that satisfy the equation, graph these ordered pairs, and draw the line through them. As a matter of caution, we may wish to graph a third ordered pair that satisfies the equation to see whether the three points lie in a line.

▶ EXAMPLE 3

a. Graph the line whose equation is $2x - 3y + 6 = 0$.

b. Write an equation of the line in slope-intercept form, and from this determine the slope of the line.

c. Give the domain and the range of the relation $R = \{(x, y) \mid 2x - 3y + 6 = 0\}$.

Solution

a. It is convenient here to use the intercepts of the line. The x intercept is the number x_0 for which $2x_0 = 3(0) - 6$, or $x_0 = -3$. Similarly, we find the y intercept to be 2. To find a third point, we may replace x by $\frac{3}{2}$, and we find that in this case y must be replaced by 3 to satisfy the equation. We graph the points $P_1(-3, 0)$ and $P_2(0, 2)$, draw the line L determined by them, and observe that $P_3(\frac{3}{2}, 3)$ is on this line (Fig. 3.15).

b. Solving the given equation for y, we find the slope-intercept form to be

$$y = \tfrac{2}{3}x + 2$$

From this we see that the slope is $\frac{2}{3}$, and we note that the y intercept is 2, as we found in part *a*.

c. For the specified relation R we see that

$$\text{Domain of } R = (-\infty; +\infty) \qquad \text{Range of } R = (-\infty; +\infty)$$

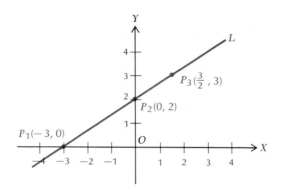

FIGURE 3.15

▶ EXAMPLE 4

Find the point of intersection P of the graphs of the relations

$$R_1 = \{(x, y) \mid 2x - y + 4 = 0\} \quad \text{and} \quad R_2 = \{(x, y) \mid 3x - y + 3 = 0\}$$

Solution

The coordinates of P are obtained by finding the solution of the pair of equations

$$2x - y + 4 = 0 \qquad 3x - y + 3 = 0$$

The solution of this pair of equations is the ordered pair $(1, 6)$. Hence

$$R_1 \cap R_2 = \{(1, 6)\}$$

and the two lines, which are the graphs of R_1 and R_2, respectively, intersect at $P(1, 6)$.

From plane geometry we know that two lines in a plane either intersect in a point, are parallel, or are coincident.

Suppose that we are given the linear equations

$$A_1x + B_1y + C_1 = 0 \quad \text{and} \quad A_2x + B_2y + C_2 = 0$$

with $B_1 \neq 0$ and $B_2 \neq 0$. The graphs of these equations intersect, are parallel, or are coincident. We can determine which is the case by first writing the given equations in the forms

$$y = m_1x + b_1 \quad \text{and} \quad y = m_2x + b_2$$

respectively, and then making the following observations.

(i)   If $m_1 \neq m_2$, then the lines intersect.
(ii) If $m_1 = m_2$ and $b_1 \neq b_2$, then the lines are parallel, since they have equal slopes but different y intercepts.

(iii)   If $m_1 = m_2$ and $b_1 = b_2$, then the lines coincide, since they have equal slopes and equal y intercepts.

◆ EXAMPLE 5

Determine whether the graphs of the equations in each of the following pairs intersect. If they intersect, find the coordinates of their point of intersection.

a. $4x + 3y = 12$	**b.** $4x + 3y = 12$	**c.** $4x + 3y = 12$
$12x + 5y = 60$	$8x + 6y = 18$	$8x + 6y = 24$

Solution

Writing the given equations in the slope-intercept form, we obtain the following results:

a. $y = -\frac{4}{3}x + 4$ **b.** $y = -\frac{4}{3}x + 4$ **c.** $y = -\frac{4}{3}x + 4$

$y = -\frac{12}{5}x + 12$ $y = -\frac{4}{3}x + 3$ $y = -\frac{4}{3}x + 4$

a. In this case $m_1 = -\frac{4}{3}$ and $m_2 = -\frac{12}{5}$, so $m_1 \neq m_2$ and the lines intersect. We solve the given pair of equations using the method of elimination by substitution. Solving $4x + 3y = 12$ for y, we have $y = \frac{1}{3}(12 - 4x)$. Substituting this value of y in $12x + 5y = 60$, we obtain

$$12x + \frac{5}{3}(12 - 4x) = 60 \quad \text{or} \quad 36x + 60 - 20x = 180 \quad \text{or} \quad 16x = 120$$

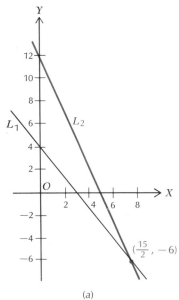

(a)

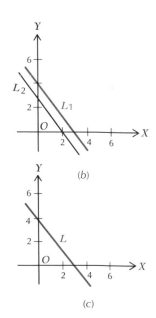

(b)

(c)

FIGURE 3.16

Hence $x = \frac{15}{2}$. Placing this value of x in the equation $y = \frac{1}{3}(12 - 4x)$, we find $y = -6$. That the coordinate pair $(\frac{15}{2}, -6)$ does indeed satisfy both of the given equations can be verified by substitution.

b. Here $m_1 = -\frac{4}{3}$, $m_2 = -\frac{4}{3}$, $b_1 = 4$, and $b_2 = 3$. Therefore, the lines are parallel.

c. In this case the slopes are equal and the y intercepts are equal; hence, the lines coincide.

The graphs are given in Fig. 3.16.

General first-degree function

The **general first-degree function** is

$$F = \{(x, y) \mid y = ax + b\}$$

where a and b are real numbers and $a \neq 0$. Since $y = ax + b$ is the slope-intercept form of an equation of a line, we see that the graph of a first-degree function is a nonvertical line. The domain of a first-degree function is Re and the range of a first-degree function is Re. For this reason it is sometimes said that a first-degree function $F = \{(x, y) \mid y = ax + b\}$ establishes a one-to-one correspondence (or a one-to-one mapping) between the points on the x axis and the points on the y axis.

EXERCISES

In each of Exercises 1–4 give an equation of the line which satisfies the given conditions.

1. Horizontal; y intercept 4
2. Horizontal; y intercept -3
3. Vertical; x intercept -5
4. Vertical; x intercept 7

In each of Exercises 5–8 graph the given relation.

5. $\{(x, y) \mid x + 3 = 0\}$
6. $\{(x, y) \mid y - 4 = 0\}$

7. $\{(x, y) \mid 2x + 5 = 0\}$
8. $\{(x, y) \mid 3y + 7 = 0\}$

In each of Exercises 9–24 find an equation of the line through the given point and with the given slope; or through the given point and with the given inclination; or through the two given points.

9. $(3, -2)$; $m = \frac{2}{3}$
10. $(-3, 5)$; $m = -\frac{3}{2}$

11. $(-1, 2)$; $m = \frac{3}{4}$
12. $(-5, 6)$; $(8, -3)$

13. $(-1, 3)$; $(4, 6)$
14. $(4, 6)$; $m = -3$

15. $(3, 4)$; $\alpha = 120°$
16. $(-5, 1)$; $(-5, 8)$

17. $(10, -1)$; $\alpha = 60°$
18. $(-5, -2)$; $m = \frac{4}{3}$

19. $(-1, 3)$; $(7, 4)$ **20.** $(0, 2)$; $m = \frac{4}{7}$

21. $(-3, 4)$; $(1, -2)$ **22.** $(-4, -3)$; $(2, -3)$

23. $(-4, 5)$; $m = -2$ **24.** $(2, -3)$; $\alpha = 135°$

In each of Exercises 25–30 find the intercepts and the slope of the graph of the given equation and graph that equation.

25. $5x + 2y + 10 = 0$ **26.** $2x - 3y + 4 = 0$

27. $x - 2y + 7 = 0$ **28.** $3x + 2y - 2 = 0$

29. $7x + 3y + 21 = 0$ **30.** $5x - 4y - 20 = 0$

31. Find an equation of the line through the point $(1, 2)$ and parallel to the graph of $3x - 2y + 6 = 0$.

32. Find an equation of the line through the point of intersection of the graphs of $x - 3y + 2 = 0$ and $5x + 6y - 4 = 0$ that is parallel to the graph of $4x + y + 7 = 0$.

33. Find an equation of the line through the points $(-3, -5)$ and $(4, 7)$. Does the point $(\frac{1}{2}, 1)$ lie on this line? Why?

34. A triangle has $5x - 6y + 16 = 0$, $x + 7y + 36 = 0$, and $6x + y - 30 = 0$ for equations of its sides. Find the coordinates of the vertices of the triangle. Find an equation of the perpendicular bisector of each of the sides of the triangle.

In each of Exercises 35–40 determine whether the graphs of the given equations intersect. If they do intersect, find the coordinates of their point of intersection. Graph the equations for each exercise on the same coordinate system.

35. $x + y = 10$
$x - y - 1$

36. $6x - 3y - 2 = 0$
$2x - y = -1$

37. $2x + y = 5$
$x + y = 2$

38. $x - 2y = 4$
$-2x + 4y = -8$

39. $3x - 10y - 4 = 0$
$4x + 6y - 15 = 0$

40. $5x - 2y - 10 = 0$
$3x + y - 17 = 0$

41. (a) Find an equation of the line L_1 through the point $(-1, -3)$ and parallel to the line L_2 which is the graph of $4x - 8y - 5 = 0$.

(b) Find an equation of the line L_3 through the point $(-1, -3)$ and perpendicular to the line L_2 which is the graph of $4x - 8y - 5 = 0$.

(c) Graph the three lines L_1, L_2, and L_3 on the same coordinate system.

42. Designate each of the following sets in the manner $\{(x, y) \mid S_{xy}\}$, where S_{xy} is a first-degree equation:

(a) The points on the line through the point $(2, 3)$ which is parallel to the x axis

(b) The set of points on the line through the point $(3, 4)$ with slope 2

43. Draw a graph of each of the following sets:

(a) $\{(x, y) \mid 3x - 4 = 0\}$ (b) $\{(x, y) \mid 4x + 3y - 12 = 0\}$

44. Find an equation of the line through the point of intersection of the graphs of $2x - 3y = 0$ and $x + 5y - 4 = 0$ and the point $(1, 2)$. Do this exercise two ways, as follows:

(a) Find the coordinates of the point of intersection of the specified graphs by solving the two equations simultaneously, then use the two-point form of an equation of a line.

(b) Use the fact that a line through the point of intersection of the two specified graphs has an equation of the form

$$k_1(2x - 3y) + k_2(x + 5y - 4) = 0$$

Then find the ratio of k_2 to k_1 by requiring that the latter equation be satisfied by the coordinate pair $(1, 2)$.

In each of Exercises 45–50 graph the given equation, and give the intercepts of the graph. *Hint:* In each case factor the given equation, and then proceed as we did with R_{12} in Example 2 of Sec. 1.8.

45. $y^2 - 4x^2 = 0$ **46.** $y^2 = (3x + 1)^2$

47. $y^2 = 9x^2 - 12x + 4$ **48.** $2xy - x^2 = 0$

49. $(x + 3)(x^2 + y^2 - 16) = 0$ **50.** $x^2 - 5xy = 10x$

In each of Exercises 51–54 graph the given relation. Give the domain and the range of the relation.

51. $R = \{(x, y) \mid 2x - 3y = 6 \text{ and } 1 \leqslant x \leqslant 3\}$

52. $R = \{(x, y) \mid x^2 + y^2 = 9 \text{ or } y = 3x\}$

53. $R = \{(x, y) \mid y = x \text{ for } x \leqslant 2, \text{ and } y = 2x \text{ for } x > 2\}$

54. $R = \{(x, y) \mid y = (x^2 - 9)/(x - 3)\}$

55. Find an equation of the set of points G which has the property that point $P \in G$ is equidistant from $P_1(-3, -4)$ and $P_2(2, 5)$. Graph G.

56. Show that the four points $(3, 2)$, $(1, -2)$, $(4, 4)$, and $(-2, -8)$ lie on the same straight line.

57. The vertices of a triangle are $P_1(-2, 0)$, $P_2(4, 0)$, and $P_3(0, 6)$. For this triangle find:

(a) Equations of the sides

(b) Equations of the altitudes

(c) Equations of the medians

(d) Equations of the perpendicular bisectors of the sides

58. For the triangle given in Exercise 57:

(*a*) Show that the three altitudes meet in a point A, and find the coordinates of this point.

(*b*) Show that the three medians meet in a point B, and find the coordinates of this point.

(*c*) Show that the three perpendicular bisectors of the sides meet in a point C, and find the coordinates of this point.

(*d*) Show that the three points A, B, and C lie on a straight line. Find an equation of this line.

(*e*) Graph, on the same coordinate system, the vertices, sides, altitudes, medians, and the perpendicular bisectors of the sides of the triangle of Exercise 57. On the graph indicate the points A, B, and C, and draw the line through these points. This line is called *Euler's line* for the triangle.

59. Denote the three vertices of a triangle by $A(a, 0)$, $B(b, 0)$, and $C(0, c)$, where $a \neq b$ and $c \neq 0$.

(*a*) Find equations of the medians of this triangle, and show analytically that these medians meet in a point D.

(*b*) Find equations of the altitudes of this triangle, and show analytically that these altitudes meet in a point E.

(*c*) Find equations of the perpendicular bisectors of the sides of this triangle, and show analytically that these perpendicular bisectors meet in a point F.

(*d*) Prove analytically that the points D, E, and F lie on a line.

3.3 LINEAR INEQUALITIES IN TWO VARIABLES

We found in the preceding section that any nonvertical line L is the graph of an equation of the form $y = mx + b$, where m is the slope of L and b is the y intercept (Fig. 3.17). Let us consider two points $P_1(x_1, y_1)$ and $P_2(x_1, y_2)$ with the same x coordinate and with $P_2(x_1, y_2)$ on the line L. Aided by Fig. 3.17a, we see that

$$P_1 \text{ is above } L \iff y_1 > y_2$$

or, since $y_2 = mx_1 + b$,

$$P_1 \text{ is above } L \iff y_1 > mx_1 + b$$

Similarly, from Fig. 3.17b we see that

$$P_1 \text{ is below } L \iff y_1 < y_2$$

or

$$P_1 \text{ is below } L \iff y_1 < mx_1 + b$$

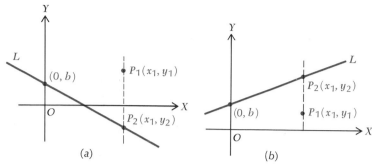

FIGURE 3.17

Of course, from the definition of the graph of an equation we know that

$$P_1 \text{ is on } L \iff y_1 = mx_1 + b$$

By reasoning in this manner, Theorem 3.5 can be established.

THEOREM 3.5   *The point $P_1(x_1, y_1)$ is above the graph of $y = mx + b$ if and only if*

$$y_1 > mx_1 + b$$

The point $P_1(x_1, y_1)$ is below the graph of $y = mx + b$ if and only if

$$y_1 < mx_1 + b$$

EXAMPLE 1

Graph the relation

$$R = \{(x, y) \mid 2x - 3y < 6\}$$

and give the domain and range of the relation.

Solution

Using the familiar properties of inequalities, we see that the inequality

$$2x - 3y < 6$$

is equivalent to the inequality

$$y > \tfrac{2}{3}x - 2$$

so that

$$R = \{(x, y) \mid 2x - 3y < 6\} = \{(x, y) \mid y > \tfrac{2}{3}x - 2\}$$

From Theorem 3.5 it follows that the ordered pair $(x_1, y_1) \in \{(x, y) \mid y > \tfrac{2}{3}x - 2\}$ if and only if the point $P_1(x_1, y_1)$ lies above the graph of $y = \tfrac{2}{3}x - 2$. Hence, the

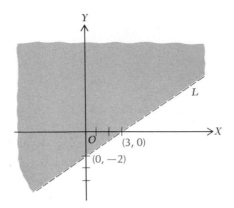

FIGURE 3.18

graph of R consists of the set of points in the coordinate plane that lie above the line L which is the graph of $y = \frac{2}{3}x - 2$; this graph is indicated by the shaded portion in Fig. 3.18.

The domain of R is Re and the range of R is Re.

As a consequence of Theorem 3.5 we see that a nonvertical line L which is the graph of

$$R_1 = \{(x, y) \mid y = mx + b\}$$

divides the coordinate plane into two parts which are the graphs of

$$R_2 = \{(x, y) \mid y > mx + b\} \quad \text{and} \quad R_3 = \{(x, y) \mid y < mx + b\}$$

The graph of R_2 consists of the points lying *above* L, and the graph of R_3 consists of the points lying *below* L. We call the graph of each of R_2 and R_3 a **half plane.**

If L is a vertical line that is the graph of $\{(x, y) \mid x = a\}$, then the half plane to the *right* of L is the graph of $\{(x, y) \mid x > a\}$ and the half plane to the *left* of L is the graph of $\{(x, y) \mid x < a\}$

EXAMPLE 2

Graph the relations
    a. $R_1 = \{(x, y) \mid x^2 + y^2 < 9 \text{ and } x + 2y > 4\}$
    b. $R_2 = \{(x, y) \mid x^2 + y^2 = 9 \text{ and } x + 2y > 4\}$
Give the domain and the range of each relation.

Solution

    a. By the use of (21) of Sec. 1.8 we may write

$$R_1 = \{(x, y) \mid x^2 + y^2 < 9\} \cap \{(x, y) \mid x + 2y > 4\}$$

So the graph of R_1 is the intersection of the graphs of

$$R_3 = \{(x, y) \mid x^2 + y^2 < 9\}$$

and $\qquad R_4 = \{(x, y) \mid x + 2y > 4\} = \{(x, y) \mid y > -\tfrac{1}{2}x + 2\}$

The graph of R_3 consists of all points *within* the circle with center at the origin and radius 3, and the graph of R_4 consists of all points *above* the line with equation $x + 2y - 4 = 0$. The graph of R_1, the intersection of the graphs of R_3 and R_4, is indicated by the shaded portion in Fig. 3.19.

Solving the pair of equations $x^2 + y^2 = 9$ and $x + 2y = 4$, we find that the points of intersection of their graphs are

$$\left(\frac{4 - 2\sqrt{29}}{5}, \frac{8 + \sqrt{29}}{5}\right) \quad \text{and} \quad \left(\frac{4 + 2\sqrt{29}}{5}, \frac{8 - \sqrt{29}}{5}\right)$$

Verify this statement. Using $\sqrt{29} \doteq 5.385$, we obtain

$$(-1.354, 2.677) \quad \text{and} \quad (2.954, 0.523)$$

as approximate coordinates of these points of intersection.

From the results just stated we see that

$$\text{Domain of } R_1 = \left(\frac{4 - 2\sqrt{29}}{5}; \frac{4 + 2\sqrt{29}}{5}\right) \quad \text{Range of } R_1 - \left(\frac{8 - \sqrt{29}}{5}; 3\right)$$

b. By (21) of Sec. 1.8 we may write

$$R_2 = \{(x, y) \mid x^2 + y^2 = 9\} \cap \{(x, y) \mid x + 2y > 4\}$$

Hence, the graph of R_2 is the intersection of the graphs of

$$R_5 = \{(x, y) \mid x^2 + y^2 = 9\}$$

and $\qquad R_4 = \{(x, y) \mid x + 2y > 4\} = \{(x, y) \mid y > -\tfrac{1}{2}x + 2\}$

The graph of R_5 consists of all points *on* the circle with center at the origin and

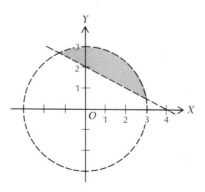

FIGURE 3.19

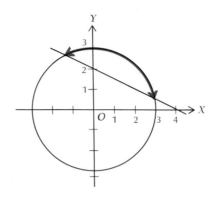

FIGURE 3.20

radius 3, and the graph of R_4 consists of all points *above* the line with equation $x + 2y - 4 = 0$. The graph of R_2, the intersection of R_5 and R_4, is indicated by the heavily drawn arc of Fig. 3.20.

The domain and range of R_2 are the same, respectively, as the domain and range of R_1. However, to each member of the domain of R_1 there correspond several members of the range, while to each member of the domain of R_2 there corresponds only one member of the range. That is, R_1 is a nonfunctional relation, and R_2 is a function.

▶ EXAMPLE 3

Describe the graph of the relation

$$R = \{(x, y) \mid (4x + 3y - 12)(12x + 5y - 60) > 0\}$$

Solution

The sentence

$$(4x + 3y - 12)(12x + 5y - 60) > 0$$

is equivalent to the compound sentence

$$4x + 3y - 12 > 0 \qquad \text{and} \qquad 12x + 5y - 60 > 0$$

$$\text{or}$$

$$4x + 3y - 12 < 0 \qquad \text{and} \qquad 12x + 5y - 60 < 0$$

Therefore

$$R = (R_1 \cap R_2) \cup (R_3 \cap R_4)$$

where

$$R_1 = \{(x, y) \mid 4x + 3y - 12 > 0\} \qquad R_2 = \{(x, y) \mid 12x + 5y - 60 > 0\}$$
$$R_3 = \{(x, y) \mid 4x + 3y - 12 < 0\} \qquad R_4 = \{(x, y) \mid 12x + 5y - 60 < 0\}$$

The graphs of

$$L_1: 4x + 3y = 12 \quad \text{and} \quad L_2: 12x + 5y = 60$$

are given in Fig. 3.16a. The graph of R_1 consists of the points lying *above* L_1 and the graph of R_2 consists of the points lying *above* L_2; therefore, the graph of $R_1 \cap R_2$ consists of the points that lie *above both* L_1 and L_2. Similarly, the graph of R_3 consists of the points lying *below* L_1, and the graph of R_4 consists of the points lying *below* L_2; hence, the graph of $R_3 \cap R_4$ consists of the points that *lie below* both L_1 and L_2. Finally, the graph of R is the union of the graph of $R_1 \cap R_2$ and the graph of $R_3 \cap R_4$; therefore, the graph of R consists of the points that lie above both of L_1 and L_2 or below both of L_1 and L_2. In Exercise 22 of this section the student is asked to construct the graph of R.

EXERCISES

In each of Exercises 1–4 determine by use of Theorem 3.5 whether each of the given points is on, below, or above the given line.

1. $5x - 12y - 26 = 0$; $(-5, 1)$, $(0, -\frac{13}{6})$, $(10, 0)$

2. $3x + 7y - 21 = 0$; $(7, 0)$, $(-2, 4)$, $(6, -2)$

3. $3x + 4y + 8 = 0$; $(0, 0)$, $(-5, -1)$, $(2, 3)$

4. $3x - 4y - 10 = 0$; $(-4, 0)$, $(-\frac{5}{2}, 0)$, $(-2, 1)$

Graph each of the following relations.

5. $R = \{(x, y) \mid 3x + 4y > 12\}$ **6.** $R = \{(x, y) \mid 2x + 3y < 6\}$

7. $R = \{(x, y) \mid 6x - 5y > 30\}$ **8.** $R = \{(x, y) \mid 2x - 7y < 14\}$

9. $R = \{(x, y) \mid 3x + 4y \leq 12\}$ **10.** $R = \{(x, y) \mid 2x + 3y \geq 6\}$

11. $R = \{(x, y) \mid 6x - 5y \leq 30\}$ **12.** $R = \{(x, y) \mid 2x - 7y \geq 14\}$

13. $R = \{(x, y) \mid x^2 + y^2 < 16 \text{ or } 2x + 3y > 6\}$

14. $R = \{(x, y) \mid x^2 + y^2 < 16 \text{ and } 2x + 3y > 6\}$

15. $R = \{(x, y) \mid x^2 + y^2 = 16 \text{ and } 2x + 3y > 6\}$

16. $R = \{(x, y) \mid x^2 + y^2 > 16 \text{ or } 2x + 3y > 6\}$

17. $R = \{(x, y) \mid x^2 + y^2 > 16 \text{ and } 2x + 3y > 6\}$

18. $R = \{(x, y) \mid 2x + y > 5 \text{ or } x + y > 2\}$

19. $R = \{(x, y) \mid 2x + y > 5 \text{ and } x + y > 2\}$

20. $R = \{(x, y) \mid 2x + y = 5 \text{ and } x + y > 2\}$

21. $R = \{(x, y) \mid 2x + y = 5 \text{ and } x + y = 2\}$

22. Construct the graph of the relation R of Example 3.

Construct the graph of each of the following relations.

23. $R = \{(x, y) \mid (x - y)(x + y) \geq 0\}$ **24.** $R = \{(x, y) \mid (x - y)(x + y) \leq 0\}$

25. $R = \{(x, y) \mid (x - y - 2)(2x - y + 1) > 0\}$

26. $R = \{(x, y) \mid (x - y)(x^2 + y^2 - 4) > 0\}$

27. $R = \{(x, y) \mid (x - y)(x^2 + y^2 - 4) < 0\}$

3.4 DISTANCE BETWEEN A POINT AND A LINE

In addition to determining the distance between two points, it is often useful to be able to find the distance between a point and a line.

Any line L in the plane either is vertical (Fig. 3.21), is horizontal (Fig. 3.22), or is not parallel to either coordinate axis. Let d denote the distance $|PM|$ between the point $P(x_1, y_1)$ and the line L, M being the projection on L of the point P. If L is vertical and is the graph of $\{(x, y) \mid x = a\}$, then, as seen from Fig. 3.21,

$$d = |x_1 - a|$$

If L is horizontal and is the graph of $\{(x, y) \mid y = b\}$, then, as seen from Fig. 3.22,

$$d = |y_1 - b|$$

If L is not parallel to either coordinate axis, the following theorem is useful in finding the distance d between the point $P(x_1, y_1)$ and the line L. The student is asked to prove this theorem in Exercise 17 of this section.

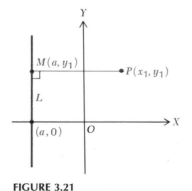

FIGURE 3.21

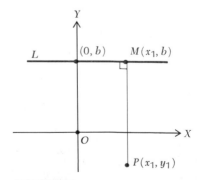

FIGURE 3.22

THEOREM 3.6   *The distance d between the point P(x_1, y_1) and the nonvertical line L with equation*

$$Ax + By + C = 0$$

is given by

$$d = \frac{|Ax_1 + By_1 + C|}{\sqrt{A^2 + B^2}}$$

Distance between a point and a line

The equality involving d in this theorem is called the **formula for the distance between a point and a line.** It can be shown that this formula is true for vertical as well as nonvertical lines.

◆   EXAMPLE

Find the distance between each of the following points and the line L: $3x + 4y - 20 = 0$:

a. $O(0, 0)$ **b.** $B(0, 1)$ **c.** $C(1, -2)$ **d.** $D(6, 4)$

Solution

By Theorem 3.6 the distance between the point (x_1, y_1) and the specified line is given by

$$d = \frac{|3x_1 + 4y_1 - 20|}{5}$$

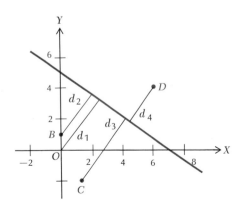

FIGURE 3.23

Let d_1, d_2, d_3, d_4 be the respective distances asked for. These distances are indicated in Fig. 3.23. We have the following results:

a. $d_1 = \dfrac{|3(0) + 4(0) - 20|}{5} = 4$ **b.** $d_2 = \dfrac{|3(0) + 4(1) - 20|}{5} = \dfrac{16}{5}$

c. $d_3 = \dfrac{|3(1) + 4(-2) - 20|}{5} = 5$ **d.** $d_4 = \dfrac{|3(6) + 4(4) - 20|}{5} = \dfrac{14}{5}$

EXERCISES

In each of Exercises 1–8 find the distance between the given point and the graph of the given equation

1. $x + 4 = 0$; $(3, 2)$ **2.** $2x - 5 = 0$; $(-4, -1)$

3. $2y + 7 = 0$; $(2, -3)$ **4.** $y - 5 = 0$; $(-2, -4)$

5. $5x + 12y - 26 = 0$; $(8, 10)$ **6.** $15x - 8y - 102 = 0$; $(-3, -2)$

7. $5x - 12y - 25 = 0$; $(-1, 3)$ **8.** $3x + 4y - 7 = 0$; $(3, -2)$

9. Find the distance between the point of intersection of the graphs of the equations $x - y - 1 = 0$ and $x - 2y + 1 = 0$ and the graph of $5x + 12y - 13 = 0$.

10. Find an equation of the circle with center at $(-1, 4)$ which is tangent to the graph of $3x + 4y - 24 = 0$.

11. Find equations of the bisectors of the angles between the graphs of $3x - 4y - 10 = 0$ and $4x + 3y - 7 = 0$. *Hint:* Use the fact that the points on the bisectors of the angles formed by two lines L_1 and L_2 are equidistant from L_1 and L_2.

12. Find an equation of the circle with center at the intersection of the graphs of $2x - y - 2 = 0$ and $5x - 2y - 1 = 0$ which is tangent to the graph of $4x - 3y - 2 = 0$.

In each of Exercises 13–16 find the distance between the pair of parallel lines whose equations are given.

13. $3x - 4y + 15 = 0$; $3x - 4y + 24 = 0$

14. $5x + 4y - 3 = 0$; $5x + 4y + 2 = 0$

15. $x + 2y - 5 = 0$; $x + 2y + 10 = 0$

16. $2x + 3y - 8 = 0$; $2x + 3y - 10 = 0$

17. Prove Theorem 3.6. *Hint:* First, let the nonvertical line L have $y = mx + b$ for an equation. Find the coordinates of the point of intersection M of L and the line through P perpendicular to L. Then, using the distance formula (see Sec. 2.2), show that

$$d^2 = \frac{(y_1 - mx_1 - b)^2}{m^2 + 1}$$

Using this result, show that if L has

$$Ax + By + C = 0$$

for an equation, then

$$d = \frac{|Ax_1 + By_1 + C|}{\sqrt{A^2 + B^2}}$$

18. Show that the formula for d in Theorem 3.6 holds for a vertical line L. *Hint:* Let L have equation $Ax + C = 0$, and consider the two cases $A > 0$ and $A < 0$.

3.5 THE RADICAL AXIS OF TWO CIRCLES[1]

We recall from Theorem 2.7 of Sec. 2.11 that if the circles

$$C_1: \ x^2 + y^2 + D_1x + E_1y + F_1 = 0$$
$$C_2: \ x^2 + y^2 + D_2x + E_2y + F_2 = 0$$

have points of intersection P_1 and P_2, then, for any real numbers k_1 and k_2 for which $k_1 + k_2 \neq 0$ the equation

$$k_1(x^2 + y^2 + D_1x + E_1y + F_1) + k_2(x^2 + y^2 + D_2x + E_2y + F_2) = 0 \qquad (18)$$

Radical axis

is an equation of a circle through P_1 and P_2. If the real numbers k_1 and k_2 are chosen so that $k_1 + k_2 = 0$, then Eq. (18) simplifies to an equation of the form $Ax + By + C = 0$ and therefore its graph is a line which passes through the points of intersection P_1 and P_2. This line is called the **radical axis** of the two given circles.

If the circles C_1 and C_2 are tangent (have one point in common), and if $k_1 + k_2 = 0$, then the graph of Eq. (18) is a line, still called the radical axis, that is a common tangent line of the circles. If the circles C_1 and C_2 have no points in common, and if $k_1 + k_2 = 0$, then the graph of Eq. (18) is still a line called the radical axis of the two circles.

In all three cases the radical axis of two circles is perpendicular to the line joining the centers of the circles. The student is asked to prove this in Exercise 5 of this section.

In finding the points of intersection of two intersecting circles, it is convenient to determine an equation of the radical axis and then to find the solution of the pair of equations consisting of this equation of the radical axis and an equation of one of the circles. An equation of the radical axis is readily obtained by subtracting the general form of an equation of one circle from the general form of an equation of the other circle; this is equivalent to setting $k_1 = 1$ and $k_2 = -1$ in Eq. (18). To illustrate, consider the circles of the Example in Sec. 2.11:

$$C_1:\ x^2 + y^2 - 1 = 0 \qquad \text{and} \qquad C_2:\ x^2 + y^2 + 2x = 0$$

Subtracting the first equation from the second, we obtain $2x + 1 = 0$, so that

$$x = -\tfrac{1}{2}$$

is an equation of the radical axis of C_1 and C_2. The graphs of C_1 and C_2 are shown in Fig. 2.21, and we observe that the graph of $x = -\tfrac{1}{2}$ passes through the points of intersection of the circles. To find these points of intersection we can solve the pair of equations

$$x = -\tfrac{1}{2}$$
$$x^2 + y^2 - 1 = 0$$

by substituting $x = -\tfrac{1}{2}$ in $x^2 + y^2 - 1 = 0$. We find $y^2 = \tfrac{3}{4}$ so that

$$y = \tfrac{1}{2}\sqrt{3} \qquad \text{or} \qquad y = -\tfrac{1}{2}\sqrt{3}$$

and $P_1(-\tfrac{1}{2}, \tfrac{1}{2}\sqrt{3})$, $P_2(-\tfrac{1}{2}, -\tfrac{1}{2}\sqrt{3})$ are the points of intersection of the circles C_1 and C_2.

♦ EXAMPLE

Graph the relations
   a. $R_1 = \{(x, y) \mid (x + 2)^2 + (y - 4)^2 = 10\}$
   b. $R_2 = \{(x, y) \mid (x - \tfrac{1}{2})^2 + (y - \tfrac{3}{2})^2 = \tfrac{5}{2}\}$
   c. $R_3 = R_1 \cap R_2$

Solution

   a. The graph of R_1 is a circle with center at $(-2, 4)$ and radius $\sqrt{10}$ and is the circle C_1 of Fig. 3.24.
   b. The graph of R_2 is a circle with center at $(\tfrac{1}{2}, \tfrac{3}{2})$ and radius $\sqrt{\tfrac{5}{2}}$ and is the circle C_2 of Fig. 3.24.
   c. Since R_3 is the intersection of the relations R_1 and R_2, the graph of R_3 consists of the two points P_1 and P_2 that circles C_1 and C_2 have in common. The general form of an equation of C_1 is

$$x^2 + y^2 + 4x - 8y + 10 = 0$$

and the general form of an equation of C_2 is

$$x^2 + y^2 - x - 3y = 0$$

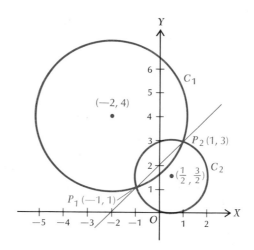

FIGURE 3.24

Subtracting the second of these equations from the first, we obtain

$$5x - 5y + 10 = 0 \quad \text{or} \quad x - y + 2 = 0$$

as an equation of the radical axis. If we solve the pair of equations

$$x - y + 2 = 0 \quad \text{and} \quad x^2 + y^2 - x - 3y = 0$$

we find that $(-1, 1)$ and $(1, 3)$ are solutions. Hence the points $P_1(-1, 1)$ and $P_2(1, 3)$ are the points of intersection of the two circles. These points and the radical axis are shown in Fig. 3.24.

EXERCISES

1. Find an equation of the radical axis L of the circles C_1 and C_2 of Exercise 11 in Sec. 2.11. With the aid of this equation find the points of intersection P_1 and P_2 of the circles. Graph C_1, C_2, and L on the same coordinate system.

2. Do the same as in Exercise 1 for the circles given in Exercise 12 of Sec. 2.11.

In each of Exercises 3 and 4 find the points of intersection of the circles whose equations are given.

3. $x^2 + y^2 - 2x + 2y - 30 = 0$ **4.** $x^2 + y^2 + 3x - 3y = 52$
    $x^2 + y^2 - 4x + 4y - 26 = 0$ $x^2 + y^2 - 2x + 2y = 32$

5. Prove that the radical axis [the graph of Eq. (18) with $k_1 + k_2 = 0$] of two circles is perpendicular to the line joining the centers of the circle.

3.6 DIRECTION ANGLES, DIRECTION COSINES, AND DIRECTION NUMBERS

With each line in a coordinate plane we have associated (Sec. 3.1) a unique angle called the *inclination* of the line. For some purposes [for example, in working with vectors (see Sec. 7.2)] it is advantageous to associate two angles with a line in a coordinate plane. In order to establish this association we first define the concept of the angle between two lines.

Angle between directed lines   If L_1 and L_2 are two *directed* lines intersecting at a point P, the **angle θ between L_1 and L_2** is taken to be the smallest (undirected) angle formed by the positive half lines; this definition is illustrated by Fig. 3.25. If L_1 and L_2 are parallel and have the same direction, then we agree that $\theta = 0$; if L_1 and L_2 are parallel and have opposite directions, then we agree that $\theta = \pi$. From these definitions it follows that the angle between directed lines L_1 and L_2 is equal to the angle between L_2 and L_1, and satisfies the inequality $0 \le \theta \le \pi$.

Angle between undirected lines   If L_1 and L_2 are two *undirected* lines intersecting at a point P, the **angle between L_1 and L_2** is taken to be the smaller of the two angles formed by the two lines; this definition is illustrated by Fig. 3.26. If L_1 and L_2 are undirected and parallel, then $\theta = 0$. We note that the angle θ between two undirected lines satisfies the inequality $0 \le \theta \le \frac{1}{2}\pi$.

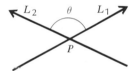

FIGURE 3.25 Angle between directed lines.

FIGURE 3.26 Angle between undirected lines.

If L is a *directed* line we can associate two angles α and β with L by the following definitions (recall that the coordinate axes are *directed* lines):

α = angle between L and the x axis
β = angle between L and the y axis

Direction angles
Direction cosines   The angles α and β so defined are called the **direction angles** of the line L. The cosines of the direction angles are called the **direction cosines** of L. Figures 3.27 to 3.30 illustrate the direction angles for several directed lines. Note that $0 \le \alpha \le \pi$ and $0 \le \beta \le \pi$.

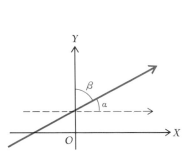

FIGURE 3.27

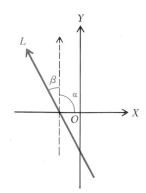

FIGURE 3.28

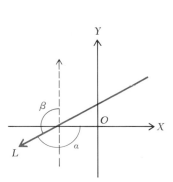

FIGURE 3.29

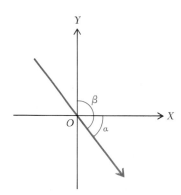

FIGURE 3.30

If L is an undirected line it has two sets of direction angles, one set for each of the two possible choices of direction for L. These two sets of direction angles for an undirected line are illustrated in Fig. 3.31; we observe that if the two sets of direction angles are $\{\alpha_1, \beta_1\}$ and $\{\alpha_2, \beta_2\}$, then

$$\alpha_2 = \pi - \alpha \qquad \text{and} \qquad \beta_2 = \pi - \beta_1$$

Thus, an undirected line has two sets of direction cosines; the members of one set are the negatives of the members of the other set, since $\cos(\pi - \alpha_1) = -\cos \alpha_1$ and $\cos(\pi - \beta_1) = -\cos \beta_1$.

Since two lines that are parallel and have the same direction will have equal direction angles and equal direction cosines, it is sufficient, in studying results about direction angles and direction cosines, to consider lines that pass through the origin. To illustrate, any statement made about the direction angles of the line

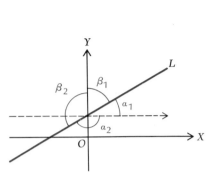

FIGURE 3.31

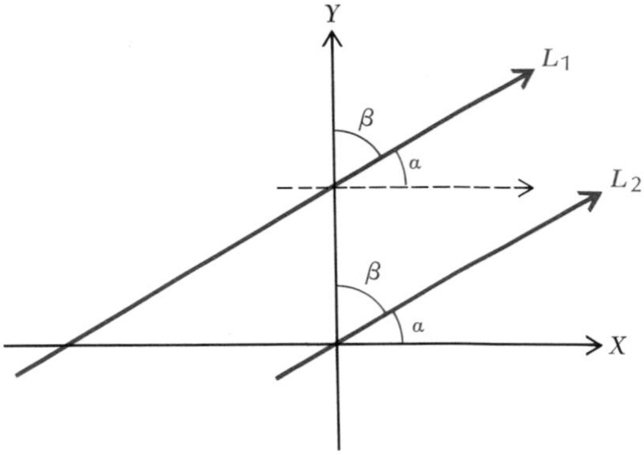

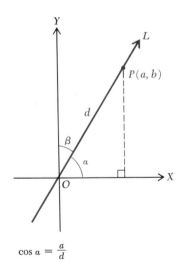

FIGURE 3.32

$$\cos \alpha = \frac{a}{d}$$

$$\cos \beta = \cos \left(\frac{\pi}{2} - \alpha\right) = \sin \alpha = \frac{b}{d}$$

(a)

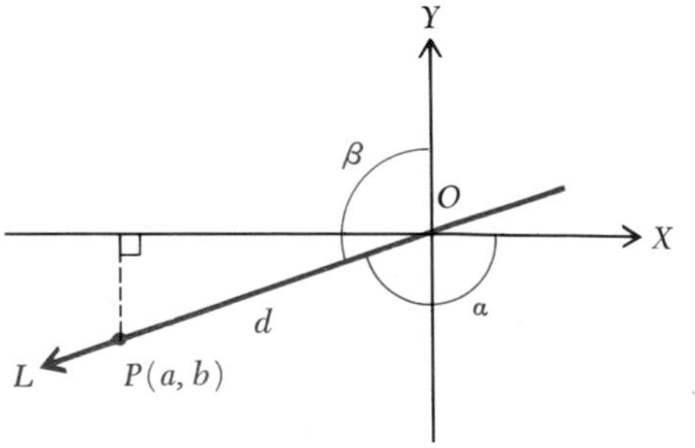

$$\cos \alpha = \frac{a}{d}$$

$$\cos \beta = \cos \left(\frac{3\pi}{2} - \alpha\right)$$

$$= -\sin \alpha = -\left(\frac{-b}{d}\right) = \frac{b}{d}$$

(b)

FIGURE 3.33

L_1 in Fig. 3.32 will be true about the direction angles of L_2, the converse is also true.

Suppose that L is a directed line passing through the origin, and let $P(a, b)$ be a point on L. If we designate the distance $|OP|$ by d, we have (as illustrated in Fig. 3.33)

$$d^2 = a^2 + b^2 \qquad \cos \alpha = \frac{a}{d} \qquad \cos \beta = \frac{b}{d}$$

Hence,
$$\cos^2 \alpha + \cos^2 \beta = \frac{a^2}{d^2} + \frac{b^2}{d^2} = \frac{a^2 + b^2}{d^2}$$

or
$$\cos^2 \alpha + \cos^2 \beta = 1 \tag{19}$$

That is, *the sum of the squares of the direction cosines of a line L is equal to* 1. Figure 3.33 shows the line L when the positive end of L is in the first quadrant and when the positive end is in the third quadrant. The student should draw figures showing L when the positive end of L is in the second quadrant and when it is in the fourth quadrant, and observe that the derivation of Eq. (19) holds in these two cases.

Again taking L to be a directed line through the origin, let $P_1(x_1, y_1)$ and $P_2(x_2, y_2)$ be points on L with the direction from P_1 to P_2 being the direction of L. If we designate by d the distance $|P_1 P_2|$ on L, we have (as illustrated in Fig. 3.34)

$$\cos \alpha = \frac{x_2 - x_1}{d} \qquad \text{and} \qquad \cos \beta = \frac{y_2 - y_1}{d} \tag{20}$$

Figure 3.34 shows the line L when the positive end of L is in the second quadrant and when the positive end is in the fourth quadrant. The student should draw figures showing L when the positive end of L is in the first quadrant and when it is in the third quadrant, and observe that Eqs. (20) hold in these two cases.

Equations (20) enable us to determine the direction cosines of any directed line L when we know the coordinates of two distinct points on L and the direction of L.

When $\cos \alpha$ and $\cos \beta$ are direction cosines of a directed line L, then two real numbers r and s which have the property that, for some *positive* real number k,

$$r = k \cos \alpha \qquad \text{and} \qquad s = k \cos \beta \tag{21}$$

Direction numbers are called **direction numbers** of L. If L is an undirected line, then k may be any *nonzero* real number. When two ordered pairs of numbers (a_1, b_1) and (a_2, b_2) are related in such a way that $a_2 = k a_1$ and $b_2 = k b_1$ for some nonzero real number k, we say that the second pair is *proportional* to the first pair with constant of proportionality k. Thus we say that *an ordered pair (r, s) of real numbers is a set of direction numbers* of a directed line L if (r, s) is proportional to the pair of direction cosines $(\cos \alpha, \cos \beta)$ of L, with a *positive* constant

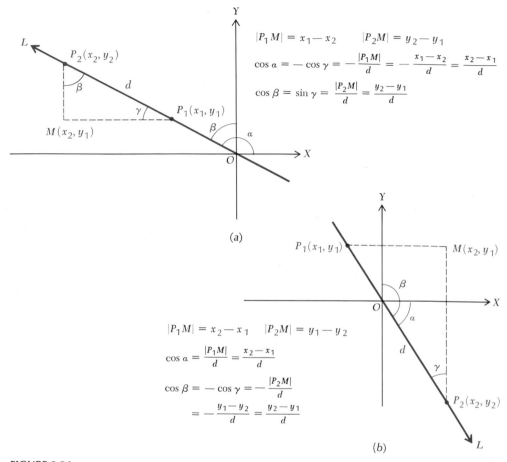

FIGURE 3.34

of proportionality; if the line is undirected the constant of proportionality is simply nonzero.

If (r, s) is a set of direction numbers of a line L, then from (21) we have

$$r^2 + s^2 = k^2(\cos^2 \alpha + \cos^2 \beta)$$

which, by the use of (19), can be written

$$r^2 + s^2 = k^2$$

Therefore,

$$k = \sqrt{r^2 + s^2} \qquad \text{if } L \text{ is a directed line}$$
$$k = \pm\sqrt{r^2 + s^2} \qquad \text{if } L \text{ is an undirected line}$$

Using these results together with Eqs. (21), we find that, if (r, s) is a set of direction numbers of a *directed* line L, then

$$\cos \alpha = \frac{r}{\sqrt{r^2 + s^2}} \qquad \cos \beta = \frac{s}{\sqrt{r^2 + s^2}} \tag{22}$$

For an *undirected* line L, *either* (22) *or*

$$\cos \alpha = \frac{r}{-\sqrt{r^2 + s^2}} \qquad \cos \beta = \frac{s}{-\sqrt{r^2 + s^2}} \tag{23}$$

will be true.

If L is a line directed from $P_1(x_1, y_1)$ to $P_2(x_2, y_2)$, it follows from (20) that the pair (r, s) where

$$r = x_2 - x_1 \qquad \text{and} \qquad s = y_2 - y_1$$

is a set of direction numbers of L. Observe that if L is not parallel to the y axis (and therefore has a slope), then $r = x_2 - x_1 \neq 0$.

♦   EXAMPLE 1

Find the direction cosines of the line L through $P_1(1, 3)$ and $P_2(4, 7)$:
  a. If L is directed from P_1 to P_2
  b. If L is undirected

Solution

Here $r = x_2 - x_1 = 4 - 1 = 3$ and $s = y_2 - y_1 = 7 - 3 = 4$ are direction numbers for L.
  a. Using (22), we find that $\cos \alpha = \frac{3}{5}$ and $\cos \beta = \frac{4}{5}$ for the directed line.
  b. For L undirected, either $\cos \alpha = \frac{3}{5}$ and $\cos \beta = \frac{4}{5}$ or $\cos \alpha = -\frac{3}{5}$ and $\cos \beta = -\frac{4}{5}$.

Theorems 3.7 to 3.9, which follow, give methods for determining the angle between two lines. Recall that the angle between two directed lines and the angle between two undirected lines were defined at the beginning of this section.

THEOREM 3.7   *Let L_1 be a directed line with direction angles α_1 and β_1; let L_2 be a directed line with direction angles α_2 and β_2; let θ be the angle between L_1 and L_2. Then*

$$\cos \theta = \cos \alpha_1 \cos \alpha_2 + \cos \beta_1 \cos \beta_2 \tag{24}$$

Proof

As we have pointed out previously, there will be no loss in generality in taking lines L_1 and L_2 passing through the origin. When this is done we note that $P_1(\cos \alpha_1, \cos \beta_1)$ is a point on L_1 and that $\overline{OP_1} = 1$; similarly, $P_2(\cos \alpha_2, \cos \beta_2)$ is a point on L_2 and $\overline{OP_2} = 1$. The proof can now be completed by applying the law of cosines to the triangle OP_1P_2. The student should draw a figure and carry out these computations.

Theorem 3.8 follows from Theorem 3.7 when we recall the definition of the angle between two undirected lines.

THEOREM 3.8 *If L_1 and L_2 are undirected lines with direction angles α_1, β_2 and α_2, β_2, respectively, and if θ is the angle between L_1 and L_2, then*

$$\cos \theta = |\cos \alpha_1 \cos \alpha_2 + \cos \beta_1 \cos \beta_2| \qquad (25)$$

Using Eqs. (22) in conjunction with Theorems 3.7 and 3.8, we get Theorem 3.9.

THEOREM 3.9 *If (r_1, s_1) is a set of direction numbers of L_1, and (r_2, s_2) is a set of direction numbers of L_2, and if θ is the angle between L_1 and L_2, then*

$$\cos \theta = \frac{r_1 r_2 + s_1 s_2}{\sqrt{r_1^2 + s_1^2} \; \sqrt{r_2^2 + s_2^2}} \qquad \textit{if the lines are directed} \qquad (26)$$

and

$$\cos \theta = \frac{|r_1 r_2 + s_1 s_2|}{\sqrt{r_1^2 + s_1^2} \; \sqrt{r_2^2 + s_2^2}} \qquad \textit{if the lines are undirected} \qquad (27)$$

Using Eq. (27) and the trigonometric identity $\sin^2 \theta = 1 - \cos^2 \theta$, the student should prove that if θ is the angle between undirected lines L_1 and L_2 with respective sets of direction numbers (r_1, s_1) and (r_2, s_2), then

$$\sin \theta = \frac{|r_1 s_2 - r_2 s_1|}{\sqrt{r_1^2 + s_1^2} \; \sqrt{r_2^2 + s_2^2}} \qquad (28)$$

Combining (27) and (28) and making use of the identity

$$\tan \theta = \frac{\sin \theta}{\cos \theta} \qquad \theta \neq \tfrac{1}{2}\pi$$

we can obtain

$$\tan \theta = \left| \frac{r_1 s_2 - r_2 s_1}{r_1 r_2 + s_1 s_2} \right| \qquad (29)$$

If a line L is not parallel to the y axis, we can determine a relationship between the slope m of the line and any pair of direction numbers (r, s). If $P_1(x_1, y_1)$

and $P_2(x_2, y_2)$ are two distinct points on such a line L, then we recall that $m = (y_2 - y_1)/(x_2 - x_1)$ and that $r = x_2 - x_1$ and $s = y_2 - y_1$ are direction numbers of L. Hence we see that $m = s/r$, and we have proved Theorem 3.10.

THEOREM 3.10   *If (r, s) is a set of direction numbers for a line L which has slope m, then*

$$m = \frac{s}{r} \tag{30}$$

The proofs of the next three theorems are left to the student.

THEOREM 3.11   *If a line L has slope m, then $(1, m)$ is a set of direction numbers of L.*

THEOREM 3.12   *If a line L has inclination $\alpha \neq 90°$, then $(1, \tan \alpha)$ is a set of direction numbers of L.*

THEOREM 3.13   *If θ is the angle between two undirected lines with slopes m_1 and m_2, respectively, then*

$$\tan \theta = \left| \frac{m_2 - m_1}{1 + m_1 m_2} \right| \tag{31}$$

Hint: Divide both the numerator and the denominator of the right side of (29) by $r_1 r_2$ and then use Theorem 3.10.

The following theorem is a direct consequence of the definition of direction numbers of a line.

THEOREM 3.14   *If a line L has a set of direction numbers (r, s), then, for any real number k $(k > 0$ if L is directed, $k \neq 0$ if L is undirected), the pair (kr, ks) is a set of direction numbers of L.*

We shall agree that when we speak of a line L, we mean an undirected line unless specifically stated otherwise.

▶   EXAMPLE 2

Line L_1 is determined by $P_1(1, -1)$ and $P_2(-2, -3)$, and line L_2 is determined by $Q_1(1, -2)$ and $Q_2(6, 8)$. If θ is the angle between L_1 and L_2, find $\cos \theta$ by the use of (27) and $\tan \theta$ by the use of (31).

Solution

Here $m_1 = \frac{2}{3}$ and $m_2 = 2$. Hence $(1, \frac{2}{3})$ and $(3, 2)$ are each a set of direction numbers of L_1, and $(1, 2)$ is a set of direction numbers of L_2.

Using (27), we obtain

$$\cos\theta = \left| \frac{3(1) + 2(2)}{\sqrt{9+4}\ \sqrt{4+1}} \right| = \frac{7}{\sqrt{13}\ \sqrt{5}} = \frac{7}{\sqrt{65}}$$

Using (31), we get

$$\tan\theta = \left| \frac{\frac{2}{3} - 2}{1 + (\frac{2}{3})(2)} \right| = \left| \frac{-\frac{4}{3}}{\frac{7}{3}} \right| = \frac{4}{7}$$

These results are in agreement, since the angle between 0 and $\frac{1}{2}\pi$ whose tangent is $\frac{4}{7}$ has cosine equal to $7/\sqrt{65}$ (Fig. 3.35).

▶   EXAMPLE 3

Find the tangent of the angle θ between the lines

$$L_1:\ 4x + 3y = 12 \qquad \text{and} \qquad L_2:\ 12x + 5y = 60$$

of Example 5*a* of Sec. 3.2.

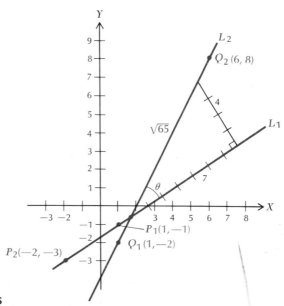

FIGURE 3.35

Solution

In this case $m_1 = -\frac{4}{3}$ and $m_2 = -\frac{12}{5}$. Using (31), we get

$$\tan \theta = \left| \frac{-\frac{12}{5} + \frac{4}{3}}{1 + (-\frac{4}{3})(-\frac{12}{5})} \right| = \left| \frac{-\frac{16}{15}}{\frac{63}{15}} \right| = \frac{16}{63}$$

If L_1 and L_2 are lines and if θ is the angle between them, then

$$L_1 \perp L_2 \iff \theta = 90° \text{ and } \cos \theta = 0 \tag{32}$$
$$L_1 \parallel L_2 \iff \theta = 0° \text{ and } \sin \theta = 0 \tag{33}$$

Using (32) and (27), we get

$$L_1 \perp L_2 \iff r_1 r_2 + s_1 s_2 = 0 \tag{34}$$
$$L_1 \parallel L_2 \iff r_1 s_2 - r_2 s_1 = 0 \tag{35}$$

Note that (35) can be written

$$L_1 \parallel L_2 \iff \begin{vmatrix} r_1 & r_2 \\ s_1 & s_2 \end{vmatrix} = 0$$

The student should reconcile the results (34) and (35) with the results (5) and (4), respectively.

EXERCISES

In each of Exercises 1–4 find the direction cosines of the directed line through P_1 and P_2, directed from P_1 to P_2.

1. $P_1(1, 2); P_2(2, 4)$ **2.** $P_1(2, 3); P_2(-3, 5)$

3. $P_1(1, 0); P_2(-7, 5)$ **4.** $P_1(a, 0); P_2(0, b)$

    5. Find a set of direction numbers and one set of direction cosines for the line that is the graph of $Ax + By + C = 0$.

    6. With the use of your result in Exercise 5, show that (A, B) is a set of direction numbers for any line that is perpendicular to the line with $Ax + By + C = 0$ for an equation. *Hint:* Use Theorems 3.2 and 3.10.

    7. We know that the system of equations

$$a_1 x + b_1 y = c_1 \qquad a_2 x + b_2 y = c_2 \tag{*}$$

has a unique solution if and only if the lines

$$L_1: a_1 x + b_1 y = c_1 \quad \text{and} \quad L_2: a_2 x + b_2 y = c_2$$

are neither parallel nor coincident (Sec. 3.2). Using your result in Exercise 5 and

(35), prove that the system (*) has a unique solution if and only if

$$a_1 b_2 - a_2 b_1 = \begin{vmatrix} a_1 & b_1 \\ a_2 & b_2 \end{vmatrix} \neq 0$$

8. Show that the unique solution of the system (*) of equations in Exercise 7 is given by

$$x = \frac{\begin{vmatrix} c_1 & b_1 \\ c_2 & b_2 \end{vmatrix}}{\begin{vmatrix} a_1 & b_1 \\ a_2 & b_2 \end{vmatrix}} \qquad y = \frac{\begin{vmatrix} a_1 & c_1 \\ a_2 & c_2 \end{vmatrix}}{\begin{vmatrix} a_1 & b_1 \\ a_2 & b_2 \end{vmatrix}}$$

In each of Exercises 9–12 use the result of Exercise 7 to determine whether or not the given system has a unique solution. If the system does have a unique solution, use the result of Exercise 8 as an aid in finding it.

9. $x - y = 2$
   $x + y = 2$
10. $3x - 5y = 12$
   $6x - 10y = 21$
11. $x - 2y = 1$
   $7x - 14y = 7$
12. $x - 2y = 4$
   $3x - y = 17$

13. If L has inclination 90 degrees, give a pair of direction numbers of L.
14. A line L has slope $m = \frac{3}{5}$. Give a pair of direction numbers of L.

In each of Exercises 15–18 find the angle between L_1 and L_2 by use of (31).

15. L_1: $3x - 2y = 0$; L_2: $2x + 3y = 0$

16. L_1: $3x - 7y = 9$; L_2: $6x - 14y = 4$

17. L_1 determined by $P_1(1, 1)$ and $P_2(4, 5)$; L_2 determined by $Q_1(4, 5)$ and $Q_2(5, -2)$
18. L_1 determined by $P_1(3, 2)$ and $P_2(7, 7)$; L_2 determined by $Q_1(5, -3)$ and $Q_2(9, 2)$
19. By use of Theorem 3.13 show that $P_1(4, 3)$, $P_2(0, -3)$, and $P_3(-1, 2)$ are the vertices of an isosceles triangle.
20. By the use of Theorem 3.13 show that $P_1(8, -1)$, $P_2(-6, 1)$, and $P_3(2, -7)$ are the vertices of a right triangle.

In each of Exercises 21 and 22 find the tangent of the angle between L_1 and L_2 by use of (31).

21. L_1: $2x - 3y - 1 = 0$; L_2: $x + 5y - 1 = 0$

22. L_1: $4x - y - 5 = 0$; L_2: $x - 2y - 1 = 0$

23. For the triangle whose vertices are $P_1(-8, -3)$, $P_2(3, -10)$, and $P_3(8, 5)$, find the tangent of each of the interior angles.

24. Find, to the nearest degree, the angles of the triangle whose vertices are $P_1(-5, -2)$, $P_2(-3, 7)$, and $P_3(6, 2)$.

3.7 PARAMETRIC EQUATIONS OF A LINE

There is one and only one line through a given point with a given set of direction numbers; therefore, the specification of a point $P_1(x_1, y_1)$ and a set of direction numbers (r, s) determines a unique line.

Let L be the line through $P_1(x_1, y_1)$ with (r, s) as a set of direction numbers, and let $P(x, y)$ be a point in the plane distinct from $P_1(x_1, y_1)$. The line L' through P and P_1 will coincide with the line L if and only if each set of direction numbers of L' is proportional to each set of direction numbers of L. Since $x - x_1$ and $y - y_1$ are direction numbers of the line through $P(x, y)$ and $P_1(x_1, y_1)$, we find that

$$P \in L \iff x - x_1 = tr \text{ and } y = y_1 = ts$$

where t is a nonzero real number. This means that, if $P(x, y)$ is a point on L distinct from $P_1(x_1, y_1)$, then there is a nonzero real number t for which

$$x = x_1 + tr \qquad y = y_1 + ts \qquad (36)$$

and, if t is any nonzero real number, then the point $P(x, y)$ whose coordinates are given by (36) is on the line L. If we take $P(x, y)$ to coincide with $P_1(x_1, y_1)$, then clearly (36) holds with $t = 0$. Consequently, when in Eqs. (36) x_1, y_1, r, and s are given constants and t is a variable whose universe is Re, then Eqs. (36) associate with each value of the variable t the coordinates (x, y) of a point on L; conversely, with each point $P(x, y)$ on L, the equations associate a value of the variable t. We call the variable t a *parameter* and we call Eqs. (36) **parametric equations** of the line L, which has (r, s) as a set of direction numbers and which passes through the point $P_1(x_1, y_1)$. Frequently, the pair of equations (36) is called a **parametric representation** of the line L. To illustrate, if L passes through $P_1(2, 3)$ and has direction numbers -4, 5, then parametric equations of L are

Parametric equations of a line

$$x = 2 - 4t \qquad y = 3 + 5t \qquad (37)$$

From (37) we find coordinates of other points on L by assigning values to t: $t = -1$ gives the point $P_2(6, -2)$, $t = \frac{1}{2}$ gives the point $P_3(0, \frac{11}{2})$, $t = 3$ gives $P_4(-10, 18)$.

Parametric equations of a line are especially helpful in problems such as the one in the following example.

◆ EXAMPLE

Find the point of intersection of the line L_1 determined by $P_1(1, 2)$ and $P_2(3, 1)$ and the line L_2: $2x + 3y = 6$.

Solution

Rather than finding an equation of the form $Ax + By + C = 0$ for L_1 and then finding the solution of the pair of equations representing lines L_1 and L_2, it is more convenient to make use of parametric equations for L_1.

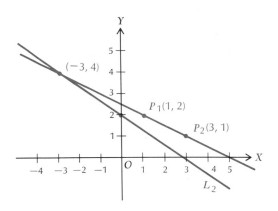

FIGURE 3.36

Since $x_2 - x_1$ and $y_2 - y_1$ are direction numbers of the line through $P_1(x_1, y_1)$ and $P_2(x_2, y_2)$, by using (36) we have that

$$x = x_1 + (x_2 - x_1)t \qquad y = y_1 + (y_2 - y_1)t \qquad (38)$$

are parametric equations of the line through $P_1(x_1, y_1)$ and $P_2(x_2, y_2)$. Using (38), with $(x_1, y_1) = (1, 2)$ and $(x_2, y_2) = (3, 1)$, we obtain

$$x = 1 + 2t \qquad y = 2 - t \qquad (39)$$

as paramatric equations of L_1. Since the point $P(x, y)$ with coordinates given by (39) must lie on L_1, we should like to determine a value of the variable t for which the point $P(x, y)$ will also lie on

$$L_2: \ 2x + 3y = 6$$

That is, we wish to find a value of t for which

$$2(1 + 2t) + 3(2 - t) = 6$$

Solving this equation, we find that $t = -2$ is the value of the parameter that corresponds to the point which is on both L_1 and L_2. Substituting -2 for t in (39), we find $x = -3$, $y = 4$, so $P(-3, 4)$ is the point of intersection of L_1 and L_2 (see Fig. 3.36).

EXERCISES

In each of Exercises 1–4 find parametric equations of the line through the given two points.

1. $P_1(2, 3)$; $P_2(5, 7)$

2. $P_1(1, -6)$; $P_2(-1, 1)$

3. $P_1(3, 0)$; $P_2(0, 4)$

4. $P_1(4, -2)$; $P_2(-3, -2)$

In each of Exercises 5–8 parametric equations of a line L are given. Find a pair of direction numbers of L, find a point on L, and graph L.

5. $x = 8 - 6t$; $y = -2 + 9t$

6. $x = -5 + 2t$; $y = 3 + t$

7. $x = 2$; $y = t$

8. $x = 7 + 3t$; $y = 4 - 3t$

9. Give the slope (if it exists) of the line:

(a) L of Exercise 5

(b) L of Exercise 6

(c) L of Exercise 7

(d) L of Exercise 8

In each of Exercises 10–12 eliminate the parameter t to obtain an equation of the form $Ax + By + C = 0$.

10. $x = 1 \quad 2t$; $y = 3 - t$

11. $x = 2 + 4t$; $y = -1 + 3t$

12. $x = t$; $y = 5 - 2t$

In each of Exercises 13–16 find the point P of intersection of the lines L_1 and L_2. Graph L_1 and L_2, and on this graph indicate P.

13. L_1: $x = -5 + 2t$, $y = 4 + t$; L_2: $x + y = 2$

14. L_1: $x = -5 + 2t$, $y = 4 + t$; L_2: $x = 2$, $y = t$

15. L_1, the line of Exercise 3; L_2: $2x + 3y = 6$

16. L_1, the line of Exercise 3; L_2, the line of Exercise 4

17. If θ is the angle between the line of Exercise 5 and the line of Exercise 6, find $\cos\theta$, $\sin\theta$, and $\tan\theta$ by use of (27), (28), and (29), respectively.

3.8 THE DETERMINANT FORM OF AN EQUATION OF A LINE. CONCURRENT LINES

If $P_1(x_1, y_1)$ and $P_2(x_2, y_2)$ are two distinct points on a line L which is not parallel to the y axis (so that $x_1 \neq x_2$), then the slope of L is

$$m = \frac{y_2 - y_1}{x_2 - x_1}$$

Using the point-slope form (14) of an equation of a line, we obtain

$$y - y_1 = \frac{y_2 - y_1}{x_2 - x_1}(x - x_1) \tag{40}$$

By carrying out appropriate algebraic operations, the student should verify that Eq. (40) is equivalent to the equation

$$(x - x_1)(y_2 - y_1) - (y - y_1)(x_2 - x_1) = 0$$

and that this equation is equivalent to the equation

$$\begin{vmatrix} x & y & 1 \\ x_1 & y_1 & 1 \\ x_2 & y_2 & 1 \end{vmatrix} = 0 \tag{41}$$

If the points $P(x, y)$, $P_1(x_1, y_1)$, and $P_2(x_2, y_2)$ lie on a straight line, the triangle formed by these points has zero area. Thus the result (41) could be obtained from an application of Theorem 2.3.

If L is a line parallel to the y axis so that $x_2 = x_1$, then (41) becomes

$$\begin{vmatrix} x & y & 1 \\ x_1 & y_1 & 1 \\ x_1 & y_2 & 1 \end{vmatrix} = 0$$

which is equivalent to

$$x(y_1 - y_2) + x_1(y_2 - y_1) = 0 \qquad \text{or} \qquad x - x_1 = 0$$

Of course $x = x_1$ is an equation of the vertical line through $P_1(x_1, y_1)$ and $P_2(x_1, y_2)$. Therefore Eq. (41) represents the line through the points $P_1(x_1, y_1)$ and $P_2(x_2, y_2)$ regardless of whether the line is parallel to the y axis or not. We record this result in Theorem 3.15.

THEOREM 3.15 *The line L through the two distinct points $P_1(x_1, y_1)$ and $P_2(x_2, y_2)$ has*

$$\begin{vmatrix} x & y & 1 \\ x_1 & y_1 & 1 \\ x_2 & y_2 & 1 \end{vmatrix} = 0 \tag{41}$$

for an equation.

Determinant form of equation of a line

We call Eq. (41) the **determinant form** of an equation of a line.

◆ EXAMPLE

Find an equation of the line through the points $P_1(-2, 3)$ and $P_2(1, -2)$.

Solution

Using Theorem 3.15, we get

$$\begin{vmatrix} x & y & 1 \\ -2 & 3 & 1 \\ 1 & -2 & 1 \end{vmatrix} = 0 \quad \text{or} \quad 5x + 3y + 1 = 0$$

for the desired equation.

Concurrent lines   If two or more lines have a point in common they are said to be **concurrent.** A necessary condition for three lines to be concurrent is given in Theorem 3.16.

THEOREM 3.16   *If the three lines*

$$L_1: A_1x + B_1y + C_1 = 0$$
$$L_2: A_2x + B_2y + C_2 = 0$$
$$L_3: A_3x + B_3y + C_3 = 0$$

are concurrent, then

$$\Delta = \begin{vmatrix} A_1 & B_1 & C_1 \\ A_2 & B_2 & C_2 \\ A_3 & B_3 & C_3 \end{vmatrix} = 0 \qquad (42)$$

Outline of proof

Since L_1, L_2, and L_3 are concurrent, they have a point P in common. P must be either (i) the point of intersection of L_1 and L_2, in case L_1 and L_2 are not parallel, or (ii) any point on L_1 and L_2 if these lines coincide. For case (i), the unique solution of the equations for L_1 and L_2 is given by Exercise 8 of Sec. 3.6. The student can show that if this solution also satisfies $A_3x + B_3y + C_3 = 0$, then (42) holds. For case (ii), there is some nonzero real number k for which $A_2 = kA_1$, $B_2 = kB_1$, $C_2 = kC_1$. (Why?) The student can show that these three conditions imply that $\Delta = 0$.

The converse of Theorem 3.16 is *not* true. That is, the condition that $\Delta = 0$ is not sufficient to ensure that the lines are concurrent. To illustrate, $\Delta = 0$ when the three lines are parallel and do not coincide, and therefore are not concurrent.

EXERCISES

In each of Exercises 1–8 use Theorem 3.15 to find an equation of the line through P_1 and P_2.

1. $P_1(2, 4)$; $P_2(1, 3)$ **2.** $P_1(2, 6)$; $P_2(-1, 1)$

3. $P_1(-1, 4)$; $P_2(0, 0)$ **4.** $P_1(-3, -5)$; $P_2(4, 7)$

5. $P_1(4, 3)$; $P_2(2, 7)$ **6.** $P_1(-5, 1)$; $P_2(7, 9)$

7. $P_1(-3, 8)$; $P_2(2, -5)$ **8.** $P_1(-5, 6)$; $P_2(7, -2)$

In each of Exercises 9 and 10 show that the three lines are concurrent.

9. L_1: $2x + 3y - 8 = 0$; L_2: $6x - 7y + 8 = 0$; L_3: $3x - 5y + 7 = 0$

10. L_1: $x - y - 2 = 0$; L_2: $3x + y - 2 = 0$; L_3: $4x + 7y + 3 = 0$

In each of Exercises 11 and 12 determine all the values of k for which the lines having the given equations are concurrent.

11. $x + 2y - 3 = 0$; $4x - y - 3 = 0$; $kx + y + 7 = 0$

12. $x + 2y + 3 = 0$; $2x + y + k = 0$; $kx - y + 4 = 0$

13. Find an equation of each diagonal of the rectangle whose sides are the lines

$$L_1: x + 3y + 2 = 0 \qquad L_2: x + 3y - 5 = 0$$
$$L_3: 3x - y + 7 = 0 \qquad L_4: 3x - y - 1 = 0$$

14. For the triangle whose vertices are $(12, -4)$, $(-4, 12)$, and $(-2, -2)$, find an equation of each of its sides.

15. For the triangle of Exercise 14, find an equation for each perpendicular bisector of a side.

16. Show that the perpendicular bisectors whose equations you found in Exercise 15 are concurrent.

3.9 FAMILIES OF LINES

From considerations like those in the first paragraph of Sec. 2.11, we can see that if

$$L_1: A_1x + B_1y + C_1 = 0 \qquad \text{and} \qquad L_2: A_2x + B_2y + C_2 = 0 \qquad (43)$$

are two intersecting lines (so that $A_1B_2 - A_2B_1 \neq 0$), then, for k_1 and k_2 real numbers that are not both zero, the graph of the equation

$$k_1(A_1x + B_1y + C_1) + k_2(A_2x + B_2y + C_2) = 0 \qquad (44)$$

is a curve through the point P of intersection of L_1 and L_2. Since Eq. (44) is of the first degree, its graph is a line through P. If the coordinates of the point P of intersection are (x_1, y_1) and if in Eq. (44) we replace x by x_1 and y by y_1, we have

$$k_1(0) + k_2(0) = 0$$

which holds for all values of k_1 and k_2. Hence Eq. (44) represents *all* lines through $P_1(x_1, y_1)$, the intersection of L_1 and L_2. In particular, for $k_1 \neq 0$ and $k_2 = 0$, we obtain an equation of L_1; for $k_1 = 0$ and $k_2 \neq 0$, we obtain an equation of L_2.

Family of lines   We call the set of all lines that can be obtained from Eq. (44) a **family** of lines, and Eq. (44) is called an equation of the family of lines through the point of intersection of L_1 and L_2.

If $k_1 \neq 0$ in (44), we can divide each side by k_1 and replace k_2/k_1 by t to find that

$$A_1x + B_1y + C_1 + t(A_2x + B_2y + C_2) = 0 \qquad (45)$$

is an equation of the family of all lines, except L_2, through the intersection of L_1 and L_2. L_2 is not included in the family of lines with Eq. (45) because no value can be assigned to t to produce an equation equivalent to

$$A_2x + B_2y + C_2 = 0$$

♦   EXAMPLE 1

Find an equation of the line L which passes through the point P_1 of intersection of

$$L_1: \ x + 3y + 9 = 0 \qquad \text{and} \qquad L_2: \ 4x - 3y - 4 = 0$$

and through the point $P_2(2, 3)$.

Solution

From (45) we have that

$$x + 3y + 9 + t(4x - 3y - 4) = 0 \qquad (46)$$

is an equation of the family of lines (except L_2) through the point P_1 of intersection of L_1 and L_2. We wish to determine the one member of the family (46) which passes through the point $P_2(2, 3)$. Hence we wish to find the value of t for which the ordered pair (2, 3) will satisfy Eq. (46). Replacing x by 2 and y by 3, we get

$$2 + 9 + 9 + t(8 - 9 - 4) = 0 \qquad \text{or} \qquad t = 4$$

Substituting $t = 4$ in (46) we find that

$$17x - 9y - 7 = 0$$

is the desired equation.

Recall that it requires *two (independent) conditions* to specify a unique line. A family of lines is the set of all lines that satisfy *one* condition. Equation (44) represents the family of lines through the intersection of two given lines. Another type of family is illustrated in Example 2.

♦ EXAMPLE 2

Find an equation of the line L that is parallel to L_1: $2x - y = 4$ and that passes through the point $P_1(1, 2)$.

Solution

The line L_1 has slope 2. We note that for each choice of the real number t, the equation

$$2x - y = t \tag{47}$$

represents a line with slope 2, and each line with slope 2 has an equation of the form (47). Therefore (47) is an equation of the family of all lines parallel to L_1. To determine the value of t for which the graph of (47) will pass through $P_1(1, 2)$, we substitute 1 for x and 2 for y in (47) and get

$$2 - 2 = t \quad \text{or} \quad t = 0$$

Thus the desired equation is

$$2x - y = 0$$

EXERCISES

In each of Exercises 1–4 find an equation of the line which passes through the point of intersection of L_1 and L_2 and through the point P_1.

1. L_1: $2x + 3y + 4 = 0$; L_2: $4x - y + 3 = 0$; $P_1(3, 4)$

2. L_1: $x + y + 1 = 0$; L_2: $3x - 5y - 10 = 0$; $P_1(2, 1)$

3. L_1: $3x - 4y - 2 = 0$; L_2: $2x - 3y + 2 = 0$; $P_1(0, 0)$

4. L_1: $x + y + 3 = 0$; L_2: $11x - 9y + 13 = 0$; $P_1(7, -4)$

5. Give an equation of the family of lines all of which have -3 for slope.

6. Find an equation of the member of the family of Exercise 5 that goes through the point $P_1(2, 3)$.

7. Give an equation of the family of lines all of which have 2 for x intercept.

8. Find an equation of the member of the family of Exercise 7 that goes through the point $(4, 5)$.

9. Give an equation of the family of lines all of which pass through the point $(3, 4)$.

10. Find an equation of the member of the family of Exercise 9 that passes through the point $(6, 2)$.

4 | THE PARABOLA, ELLIPSE, AND HYPERBOLA

In Chap. 2 we studied the correspondence between circles and equations of a certain form and in Chap. 3 we studied the correspondence between lines and equations of another form. The study of such correspondences between equations and sets of points in a coordinate plane is the major concern of plane analytic geometry. In this chapter we shall consider three types of curves in the coordinate plane and determine equations for these curves.

4.1 THE PARABOLA

Parabola   A **parabola** is a set K of points in a plane which has the property that a point P belongs to K if and only if P is equidistant from a fixed point F and a fixed line *Focus* D in the plane. The fixed point F is called the **focus** of the parabola and the fixed *Directrix*   line D is called the **directrix** of the parabola (Fig. 4.1). The line FA through F and *Axis*   perpendicular to D is called the **axis** of the parabola.

Suppose P is a point not on the directrix D (Fig. 4.2). Denote by M the point of intersection of D and a line through P perpendicular to D. Then, if K is the

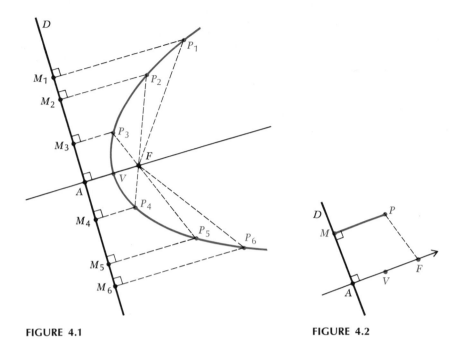

FIGURE 4.1   FIGURE 4.2

parabola determined by the focus F and the directrix D,

$$P \in K \iff |PF| = |PM| \tag{1}$$

The midpoint V of the segment AF is a point on the parabola, since $|VF| = |VA|$. The point V is called the **vertex** of the parabola.

Vertex

To find an equation of a parabola we must introduce a coordinate system in the plane. We choose the x axis to be the axis of the parabola and place the origin of the coordinate system at the vertex of the parabola. In addition, we denote the directed distance from A to F by $2p$; that is,

$$2p = \overline{AF} \quad \text{or} \quad p = \overline{VF}$$

Then the coordinates of F are $(p, 0)$ and the coordinates of A are $(-p, 0)$, and the directrix is the graph of $\{(x, y) \mid x = -p\}$. If p is positive, the focus is on the positive x axis, with the parabola opening toward the right (Fig. 4.3a); if p is negative, the focus is on the negative x axis, with the parabola opening toward the left (Fig. 4.3b).

Let the parabola be designated by K, and let $P(x, y)$ be a point in the plane. Then by (1) we know

$$P(x, y) \in K \iff |PM| = |PF|$$

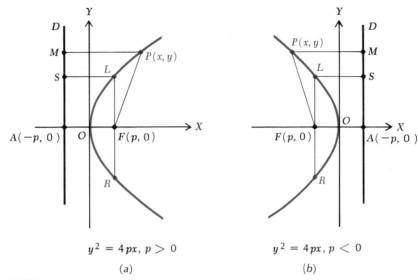

$$y^2 = 4px, \ p > 0$$

(a)

$$y^2 = 4px, \ p < 0$$

(b)

FIGURE 4.3

Since $|PM| = |x - (-p)| = |x + p|$ and $|PF| = \sqrt{(x-p)^2 + y^2}$, we have

$$P(x, y) \in K \iff |x + p| = \sqrt{(x-p)^2 + y^2} \qquad (2)$$

By direct algebraic manipulation we can see that the equation in (2) is equivalent to the equation

$$y^2 = 4px$$

So $\qquad\qquad P(x, y) \in K \iff y^2 = 4px$

and we have proved Theorem 4.1.

THEOREM 4.1   *The parabola K whose vertex is at the origin, whose focus is $(p, 0)$, and whose directrix is the graph of $\{(x, y) \mid x = -p\}$ is the graph of*

$$y^2 = 4px \qquad (3)$$

That is, K is the graph of the relation

$$\{(x, y) \mid y^2 = 4px\}$$

Similarly we may prove Theorem 4.2 (see Fig. 4.4*a* and *b*).

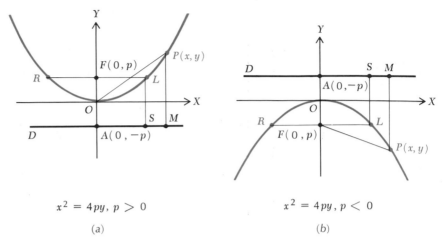

$$x^2 = 4py, \ p > 0$$

(a)

$$x^2 = 4py, \ p < 0$$

(b)

FIGURE 4.4

THEOREM 4.2 *The parabola K whose vertex is at the origin, whose focus is $(0, p)$, and whose directrix is the graph of $\{(x, y) \mid y = -p\}$ is the graph of*

$$x^2 = 4py \qquad (4)$$

That is, K is the graph of the relation

$$\{(x, y) \mid x^2 = 4py\}$$

Latus rectum

The segment RL cut off by the parabola from the line through the focus and perpendicular to the axis is called the **latus rectum** of the parabola (Figs. 4.3 and 4.4). Let S be the foot of the perpendicular from L on the directrix D. Then, from the definition of the parabola, $|LF| = |LS|$. Now $|LS| = |FA| = |2p|$, so $|LF| = |2p|$, and

$$|RL| = |4p| \qquad (5)$$

In graphing a parabola the result (5) is useful in determining the coordinates of the end points of the latus rectum.

⬧ EXAMPLE

Find the vertex, focus, and end points of the latus rectum, and an equation of the directrix of the parabola with equation $y^2 = -8x$, and graph this parabola. Give the domain and the range of the relation $S = \{(x, y) \mid y^2 = -8x\}$.

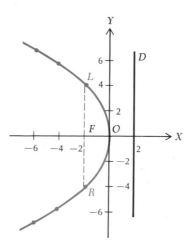

FIGURE 4.5

Solution

The equation $y^2 = -8x$ is of the form $y^2 = 4px$, with $p = -2$. So the vertex is at the origin, the focus is $F(-2, 0)$, and an equation of the directrix is $x = 2$. From Eq. (5) we find that the length $|RL|$ of the latus rectum is $|-8| = 8$. Hence $|FL| = |FR| = 4$, and the end points of the latus rectum are $L(-2, 4)$ and $R(-2, -4)$. We know that the parabola opens to the left and that $O(0, 0)$, $L(-2, 4)$, and $R(-2, -4)$ are points on the parabola. Additional points may be obtained as desired. To illustrate, replacing x by -4 in the given equation, we obtain $y^2 = 32$; replacing x by -6, we obtain $y^2 = 48$. From these results it follows that the points $(-4, 4\sqrt{2})$, $(4, -4\sqrt{2})$, $(-6, 4\sqrt{3})$, and $(-6, -4\sqrt{3})$ are on the parabola, which is shown in Fig. 4.5. From the figure it should be clear that

$$\text{Domain of } S = (-\infty; 0] \qquad \text{Range of } S = (-\infty; +\infty)$$

4.2 SYMMETRY IN RECTANGULAR COORDINATES

In determining the graph of a given equation, it is frequently helpful to make use of the concept of symmetry about a line or about a point. This concept is defined and its use in graphing is illustrated in this section.

Line of symmetry   A curve C is **symmetric with respect to a line** L, called a **line of symmetry,** if, whenever a point A is on the curve C, then the point B, located so that L is the perpendicular bisector of the segment AB, is also on the curve C (Fig. 4.6). A

Center of   curve C is **symmetric with respect to a point** P, called a **center of symmetry,** if, *symmetry*   whenever a point A is on the curve C, then the point B, located so that P is the midpoint of the segment AB, is also on the curve C (Fig. 4.7).

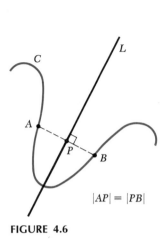

$|AP| = |PB|$

FIGURE 4.6

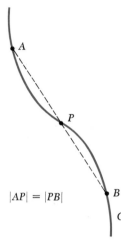

$|AP| = |PB|$

FIGURE 4.7

With the aid of appropriate figures, the student should convince himself of the following facts:

The x axis is the perpendicular bisector of the segment joining $A(a, b)$ and $B(a, -b)$.

The y axis is the perpendicular bisector of the segment joining $A(a, b)$ and $B(-a, b)$.

The origin is the midpoint of the segment joining $A(a, b)$ and $B(-a, -b)$.

Therefore, if C is the graph of an equation $E(x, y) = 0$, the following conclusions can be drawn:

(i)   If the equation $E(x, -y) = 0$ is equivalent to the equation $F(x, y) = 0$, then C is symmetric with respect to the x axis.

(ii) If the equation $E(-x, y) = 0$ is equivalent to the equation $E(x, y) = 0$, then C is symmetric with respect to the y axis.

(iii) If the equation $E(-x, -y) = 0$ is equivalent to the equation $E(x, y) = 0$, then C is symmetric with respect to the origin.

Using these conclusions, the student should prove Theorem 4.3.

THEOREM 4.3   *If a curve C is symmetric with respect to both the x axis and the y axis, then C is symmetric with respect to the origin.*

We now give some illustrations regarding symmetry.

The parabola of the Example in Sec. 4.1 is symmetric with respect to the x axis. But it is not symmetric with respect to the y axis, nor with respect to the origin.

The graph of $y^2 - 4px = 0$ $(p > 0)$ shown in Fig. 4.3a is symmetric with respect to the x axis, since the equation

$$(-y)^2 - 4px = 0$$

is equivalent to the equation

$$y^2 - 4px = 0$$

that is,

$$\{(x, y) \mid y^2 - 4px = 0\} = \{(x, y) \mid (-y)^2 - 4px = 0\}$$

However, this graph is not symmetric with respect to the y axis nor with respect to the origin.

Similarly, the graph of $x^2 - 4py = 0$ $(p > 0)$ shown in Fig. 4.4a is symmetric with respect to the y axis, since the equation

$$(-x)^2 - 4py = 0$$

is equivalent to the equation

$$x^2 - 4py = 0$$

that is,

$$\{(x, y) \mid x^2 - 4py = 0\} = \{(x, y) \mid (-x)^2 - 4py = 0\}$$

But this graph is not symmetric with respect to the x axis nor with respect to the origin.

Consider the graph of $x^2 + y^2 - r^2 = 0$. Note that

$$\{(x, y) \mid x^2 + y^2 - r^2 = 0\} = \{(x, y) \mid x^2 + (-y)^2 - r^2 = 0\}$$
$$\{(x, y) \mid x^2 + y^2 - r^2 = 0\} = \{(x, y) \mid (-x)^2 + y^2 - r^2 = 0\}$$
and $\qquad \{(x, y) \mid x^2 + y^2 - r^2 = 0\} = \{(x, y) \mid (-x)^2 + (-y)^2 - r^2 = 0\}$

So the graph of $x^2 + y^2 - r^2 = 0$ is symmetric with respect to the x axis, the y axis, and the origin. The graph is, of course, a circle with center at the origin.

EXERCISES

In each of Exercises 1–8 the equation of a parabola is specified. For this parabola give the vertex, focus, end points of the latus rectum, and an equation of the directrix. Identify any line of symmetry of the parabola. Graph the parabola. Give the domain and the range of the relation determined by the given equation.

1. $y^2 = 16x$ **2.** $x^2 = -16y$ **3.** $x^2 = 10y$

4. $y^2 = 7x$ **5.** $3x^2 + 5y = 0$ **6.** $5x^2 - 2y = 0$

7. $y^2 + 6x = 0$ **8.** $x^2 = 11y$

In each of Exercises 9–16 find an equation of the parabola with vertex at the origin which satisfies the given condition. Graph the parabola.

9. With focus at $(7, 0)$
10. Passing through the point $(2, 4)$ and with focus on the x axis
11. With length of latus rectum 8 and with focus on the positive y axis
12. With focus at $(0, 5)$
13. Passing through $(-2, -4)$ and with focus on the x axis
14. With the graph of $x - 3 = 0$ for its directrix
15. With the graph of $y + 4 = 0$ for its directrix
16. Passing through $(6, 8)$ and with focus on the y axis

17. Show that lines through the end points of the latus rectum and through the point of intersection of the axis of a parabola with its directrix are perpendicular.

18. Find an equation of the circle which has as a diameter the latus rectum of the parabola with equation $y^2 = 10x$.

19. Using the definition of a parabola, find an equation of the parabola with the graph of $y - 3 = 0$ for directrix and with $(0, -3)$ for focus.

20. Using the definition of a parabola, find an equation of the parabola whose directrix is the graph of $y = 3$ and whose focus is the point $(0, -5)$.

21. Prove that if a curve C is symmetric with respect to any two of the x axis, the y axis, and the origin, then it is symmetric with respect to the third of these.

4.3 SUBSETS OF THE PLANE BOUNDED BY PARABOLAS

Associated with the parabola K which is the graph of the relation

$$S_1 = \{(x, y) \mid y^2 = 4px, \, p > 0\}$$

are the graphs of the relations

$$S_2 = \{(x, y) \mid y^2 > 4px, \, p > 0\} \quad \text{and} \quad S_3 = \{(x, y) \mid y^2 < 4px, \, p > 0\}$$

To determine the graph of S_2 we reason as follows.
    Observe that

$$y^2 > 4px \iff x < \frac{y^2}{4p} \tag{6}$$

so the graph of S_2 is the portion of the plane to the *left* of the graph of $x = y^2/4p$ (which is the same as the graph of $y^2 = 4px$). That is, the graph of S_2 is the *shaded*

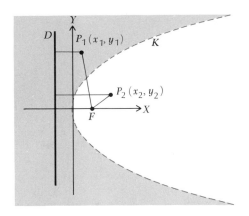

FIGURE 4.8

region shown in Fig. 4.8. We say that the graph of S_2 consists of all points *outside* the parabola K.

Analogous to (6) we have

$$y^2 < 4px \iff x > \frac{y^2}{4p}$$

so the graph of S_3 is the portion of the plane to the *right* of the graph of $x = y^2/4p$. Hence, the graph of S_3 is the *unshaded* region of Fig. 4.8, and we say that it consists of all points *inside* the parabola K.

◆   EXAMPLE

Graph the following relations:
  a. $R_1 = \{(x, y) \mid y^2 = 4x \text{ and } y = -2x + 2\}$
  b. $R_2 = \{(x, y) \mid y^2 < 4x \text{ and } y < -2x + 2\}$
Give the domain and range of each relation.

Solution

  a. By the use of (21) of Sec. 1.8 we may write

$$R_1 = \{(x, y) \mid y^2 = 4x\} \cap \{(x, y) \mid y = -2x + 2\}$$

So the graph of R_1 is the intersection of the parabola K which is the graph of $\{(x, y) \mid y^2 = 4x\}$ and the line L which is the graph of $\{(x, y) \mid y = -2x + 2\}$. Hence

$$R_1 = \left\{\left(\frac{3 - \sqrt{5}}{2}, -1 + \sqrt{5}\right), \left(\frac{3 + \sqrt{5}}{2}, -1 - \sqrt{5}\right)\right\}$$

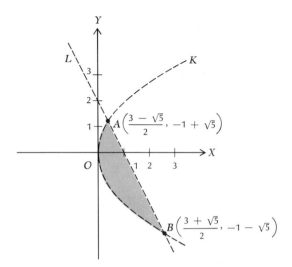

FIGURE 4.9

as the reader should verify. From this tabulation of R_1 we see that

$$\text{Domain of } R_1 = \left\{ \frac{3 - \sqrt{5}}{2}, \frac{3 + \sqrt{5}}{2} \right\} \qquad \text{Range of } R_1 = \{-1 + \sqrt{5}, -1 - \sqrt{5}\}$$

The two points $A\{(3 - \sqrt{5})/2, -1 + \sqrt{5}\}$ and $B\{(3 + \sqrt{5})/2, -1 - \sqrt{5}\}$, which constitute the graph of R_1, are shown in Fig. 4.9.

  b. We see that

$$R_2 = \{(x, y) \mid y^2 < 4x\} \cap \{(x, y) \mid y < -2x + 2\}$$

so the graph of R_2 is the intersection of the graphs of $R_3 = \{(x, y) \mid y^2 < 4x\}$ and $R_4 = \{(x, y) \mid y < -2x + 2\}$. The graph of R_3 consists of the points inside the parabola K of part a. The graph of R_4 consists of the points below the line L of part a. The set of points common to the graphs of R_3 and R_4, which constitutes the graph of R_2, is indicated by the shaded portion of Fig. 4.9. From the graph, and knowing the coordinates of A and B from part a, we conclude that

$$\text{Domain of } R_2 = \left(0; \frac{3 + \sqrt{5}}{2}\right) \qquad \text{Range of } R_2 = (-1 - \sqrt{5}; -1 + \sqrt{5})$$

EXERCISES

In each exercise graph the given relation. Give the domain and range of each relation.

  1. $R = \{(x, y) \mid y^2 > 2x\}$ **2.** $R = \{(x, y) \mid y^2 < 2x\}$

3. $R = \{(x, y) \mid y^2 = 2x \text{ or } y = x - 4\}$

4. $R = \{(x, y) \mid y^2 = 2x \text{ and } y = x - 4\}$

5. $R = \{(x, y) \mid y^2 < 2x \text{ and } y > x - 4\}$

6. $R = \{(x, y) \mid y^2 < 2x \text{ and } y < x - 4\}$

7. $R = \{(x, y) \mid y^2 \geqslant 9x\}$ **8.** $R = \{(x, y) \mid y^2 \leqslant 9x\}$

9. $R = \{(x, y) \mid y^2 = 9x \text{ and } y = 3x\}$

10. $R = \{(x, y) \mid y^2 < 9x \text{ and } y > 3x\}$

11. $R = \{(x, y) \mid x^2 > 16y\}$ **12.** $R = \{(x, y) \mid x^2 < 16y\}$

4.4 TRANSLATION OF COORDINATE AXES

It is often convenient to introduce a new coordinate system in addition to the coordinate system originally given in a problem. We shall suppose that both coordinate systems are rectangular, that the units of distance in both systems are the same, and that the original coordinate axes are labeled as the x axis and the y axis, with origin O, while the new set of axes are labeled as the x' axis and the y' axis with origin O'. If the x' axis is parallel to and has the same direction as the x axis, and if the y' axis is parallel to and has the same direction as the y axis, it is often said that the $x'O'y'$ coordinate system is obtained from the xOy system by a *translation of axes.* Figure 4.10 shows such a configuration of axes.

A point P in the plane will have coordinates with respect to both sets of axes. Suppose that P has coordinates (x_1, y_1) with respect to the xOy system and

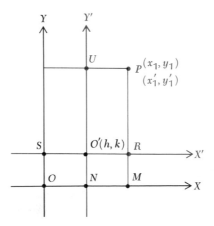

FIGURE 4.10

coordinates (x_1', y_1') with respect to the $x'O'y'$ system. In addition, suppose that the coordinates of O' with respect to the xOy system are (h, k). Referring to Fig. 4.10, we see that

$$x_1 = \overline{OM} = \overline{NM} + \overline{ON} = \overline{O'R} + \overline{ON} = x_1' + h$$

and
$$y_1 = \overline{MP} = \overline{RP} + \overline{MR} = \overline{O'U} + \overline{OS} = y_1' + k$$

Since we have made use of directed distances, this argument is valid for any selection of the origin O' of the new system and any selection of the point P in the plane. Therefore, if the coordinate system $x'O'y'$ is obtained from the system xOy by a translation of axes with O' *having coordinates* (h, k) *with respect to the xOy system*, and if a point has coordinates (x, y) in the xOy system and (x', y') in the $x'O'y'$ system, then

Translation formulas

$$x = x' + h \qquad y = y' + k \qquad (7)$$

or
$$x' = x - h \qquad y' = y - k \qquad (8)$$

If a set of points is the graph of an equation $E(x, y) = 0$ with respect to the xOy coordinate system, the set will be the graph of an equation $E'(x', y') = 0$ with respect to the $x'O'y'$ system. Equations (7) and (8) may be used to obtain the equation $E'(x', y') = 0$ from the equation $E(x, y) = 0$.

◆ EXAMPLE 1

A circle C is the graph of

$$(x + 1)^2 + (y - 3)^2 = 18$$

in a given xOy coordinate system. Translate the coordinate system so that the origin O' of the new system has coordinates $(-1, 3)$ in the xOy system and find an equation of the circle with respect to the new coordinate system.

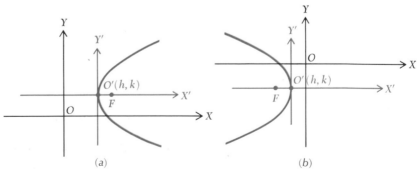

(a)   (b)

FIGURE 4.11

Solution

In this example h is -1 and k is 3. Using these values in Eqs. (8), we have

$$x' = x + 1 \qquad y' = y - 3$$

Making these substitutions in the given equation, we obtain

$$x'^2 + y'^2 = 18$$

as an equation of the circle with respect to the $x'O'y'$ system. The circle is shown in Fig. 2.12.

THEOREM 4.4   *A parabola with vertex at (h, k), with axis parallel to the x axis, and with the directed distance from the vertex to the focus given by p is the graph of*

$$(y - k)^2 = 4p(x - h) \qquad (9)$$

If the axis of the parabola is parallel to the y axis, then the parabola is the graph of

$$(x - h)^2 = 4p(y - k) \qquad (10)$$

Proof

First, consider the parabola with vertex at (h, k) and with axis parallel to the x axis, as shown in Fig. 4.11u for $p > 0$ and in Fig. 4.11b for $p < 0$. Construct a new coordinate system $x'O'y'$ with O' at the vertex of the parabola and the x' axis parallel to the x axis. Then from Theorem 4.1 we know that the parabola has equation

$$y'^2 = 4px' \qquad (11)$$

with respect to the $x'O'y'$ system. However, since O' has coordinates (h, k) with respect to the xOy system, we have from Eqs. (8) that

$$x' = x - h \qquad \text{and} \qquad y' = y - k$$

Making these substitutions in (11), we obtain

$$(y - k)^2 = 4p(x - h)$$

as an equation of the parabola with respect to the xOy system.

   In a similar way we can establish Eq. (10) for a parabola with axis parallel to the y axis.

   In each case the length of the latus rectum is $|4p|$ so that the ends of the latus rectum lie at a distance $|2p|$ from the focus.

♦ EXAMPLE 2

Find an equation of the parabola whose vertex is (−3, 4) and whose focus is (−5, 4). Find the coordinates of the end points of the latus rectum and an equation of the directrix of this parabola, and graph the parabola.

Solution

Since the vertex and the focus of a parabola lie on its axis, and since for the specified parabola these points have the same ordinate 4, it follows that the axis is horizontal. Therefore, by Theorem 4.4, an equation of the parabola is of the form

$$(y - k)^2 = 4p(x - h) \tag{12}$$

Since in general $p = \overline{VF}$, in this case

$$p = -5 - (-3) = -2$$

Replacing h by −3, k by 4, and p by −2 in (12), we obtain

$$(y - 4)^2 = -8(x + 3)$$

as an equation of the parabola. Since $|2p| = 4$, the end points of the latus rectum are 4 units above and below the focus (−5, 4); so the end points of the latus rectum are $R(-5, 0)$ and $L(-5, 8)$. The directrix is vertical and is 2 units to the right of the vertex $V(-3, 4)$; hence, an equation of the directrix is $x = -1$. The graph is shown in Fig. 4.12.

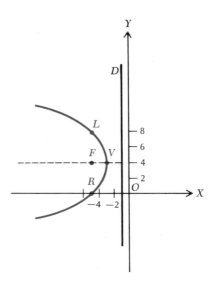

FIGURE 4.12

THEOREM 4.5 *The graph of*

$$Ay^2 + Dx + Ey + F = 0 \qquad A \neq 0, D \neq 0 \qquad (13)$$

is a parabola with axis parallel to or coincident with the x axis.

Proof

Theorem 4.5 will be proved if we show that Eq. (13) is equivalent to an equation of the form $(y - k)^2 = 4p(x - h)$. Since $A \neq 0$, we may write (13) in the equivalent forms

$$y^2 + \frac{E}{A} y = -\frac{D}{A} x - \frac{F}{A}$$

$$y^2 + \frac{E}{A} y + \left(\frac{E}{2A}\right)^2 = -\frac{D}{A} x - \frac{F}{A} + \frac{E^2}{4A^2}$$

$$\left(y + \frac{E}{2A}\right)^2 = -\frac{D}{A}\left[x - \left(\frac{E^2}{4AD} - \frac{F}{D}\right)\right]$$

The last equation is in the desired form.

THEOREM 4.6 *The graph of*

$$Bx^2 + Dx + Ey + F = 0 \qquad B \neq 0, E \neq 0 \qquad (14)$$

is a parabola with axis parallel to or coincident with the y axis.

The student is asked to prove Theorems 4.6 to 4.8 in Exercises 26 to 28, respectively, at the end of this section.

THEOREM 4.7 *The graph of*

$$Ay^2 + Ey + F = 0 \qquad A \neq 0$$

is either two distinct lines parallel to the x axis, two coincident lines parallel to the x axis, or the null set.

THEOREM 4.8 *The graph of*

$$Bx^2 + Dx + F = 0 \qquad B \neq 0$$

is either two distinct lines parallel to the y axis, two coincident lines parallel to the y axis, or the null set.

The general second-degree function, or *quadratic function*, is

$$\{(x, y) \mid y = ax^2 + bx + c\}$$

where a, b, and c are constants and $a \neq 0$. An equation of the form (14) can be written in the form

$$y = ax^2 + bx + c \qquad a \neq 0 \tag{15}$$

and by Theorem 4.6 the graph of (15) is a parabola with axis parallel to or coincident with the y axis. Writing (15) in the form (10), we obtain

$$\left(x + \frac{b}{2a}\right)^2 = \frac{1}{a}\left(y + \frac{b^2}{4a} - c\right)$$

From this result and Theorem 4.4, Theorem 4.9 follows.

THEOREM 4.9 *The graph of the quadratic function,*

$$\{(x, y) \mid y = ax^2 + bx + c, a \neq 0\}$$

is a parabola with axis parallel to or coincident with the y axis and with vertex $(-b/2a, c - b^2/4a)$.

If $a > 0$, the parabola opens upward (Fig. 4.13a) and the vertex is the lowest point on the curve; if $a < 0$, the parabola opens downward (Fig. 4.13b) and the vertex is the highest point on the curve.

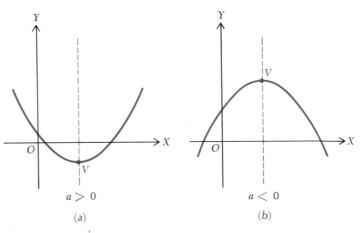

$$a > 0$$

$$(a)$$

$$a < 0$$

$$(b)$$

FIGURE 4.13 Graph of $\{(x, y) \mid y = ax^2 + bx + c, a \neq 0\}$.

EXERCISES

In each of Exercises 1–6 put the given equation in the form

$$(y - k)^2 = 4p(x - h) \quad \text{or} \quad (x - h)^2 = 4p(y - k)$$

and find the vertex, the focus, and the end points of the latus rectum for the parabola which is the graph of the given equation. Give an equation of the directrix and an equation of the axis of the parabola, and graph the parabola.

1. $y^2 + 2y - 4x + 9 = 0$ **2.** $x^2 - 6x - 16y + 73 = 0$

3. $x^2 + 20y - 40 = 0$ **4.** $y^2 - 10y + 12x + 37 = 0$

5. $3x^2 - 4x - 6y + 8 = 0$ **6.** $3y^2 - 60y - 24x + 388 = 0$

7. A parabola has its axis vertical and passes through the points $(0, 0)$, $(1, 0)$, and $(3, 6)$. Find an equation for it.

8. Find an equation of the parabola with vertex at $(-2, 0)$ and with focus at $(-\frac{3}{2}, 0)$, and graph the parabola. Give an equation of the directrix of this parabola.

9. Find an equation of the parabola with $(3, 1)$ for its focus and with the graph of $y - 3 = 0$ for its directrix.

10. Find an equation of the parabola with $(3, 1)$ and $(3, 5)$ for end points of the latus rectum, and with focus to the right of the vertex.

In each of Exercises 11–14 find the points of intersection of the graphs of the given pair of equations, graph these two parabolas on the same coordinate system, and indicate on the graph the points of intersection.

11. $y^2 = 4x; \ x^2 = 4y$ **12.** $y^2 = -9x; \ 3x^2 = 8y$

13. $y = x^2 - 2; \ y = 6 - x^2$ **14.** $x = y^2 - 10; \ x = 8 - y^2$

15. Making use of the graph you constructed in Exercise 11, give a description of the graph of each of the following relations:
   (a) $R_1 = \{(x, y) \mid y^2 = 4x \text{ or } x^2 = 4y\}$
   (b) $R_2 = \{(x, y) \mid y^2 = 4x \text{ and } x^2 = 4y\}$
   (c) $R_3 = \{(x, y) \mid y^2 > 4x \text{ or } x^2 < 4y\}$
   (d) $R_4 = \{(x, y) \mid y^2 > 4x \text{ and } x^2 < 4y\}$

16. Making use of the graph you constructed in Exercise 13, give a description of the graph of each of the following relations:
   (a) $R_1 = \{(x, y) \mid y = 6 - x^2 \text{ or } y = x^2 - 2\}$
   (b) $R_2 = \{(x, y) \mid y = 6 - x^2 \text{ and } y = x^2 - 2\}$
   (c) $R_3 = \{(x, y) \mid y < 6 - x^2 \text{ or } y > x^2 - 2\}$
   (d) $R_4 = \{(x, y) \mid y < 6 - x^2 \text{ and } y > x^2 - 2\}$

17. Using the definition of a parabola, find an equation of the parabola with the graph of $2x + y - 10 = 0$ for directrix and the origin $O(0, 0)$ for focus. Give an equation of the axis of this parabola. What are the coordinates of its vertex? Of the end points of its latus rectum? What is the length of the latus rectum? Find the x intercepts and the y intercepts of the parabola. Graph the parabola.

In each of Exercises 18–23 find an equation of the form $y = ax^2 + bx + c$ whose graph passes through the given three points, and graph the equation.

18. $(1, -1), (2, 1), (-3, -11)$ **19.** $(-3, -7), (-1, 1), (0, 2)$

20. $(0, -3), (2, -3), (4, 5)$ **21.** $(-2, 9), (0, 1), (3, 4)$

22. $(-3, -6), (0, 6), (1, 2)$ **23.** $(2, -1), (4, 7), (-2, 7)$

24. We have 400 feet of fence and desire to fence in a rectangular lot, which has one side along a high rock wall so that no fence is needed on that side. Find the dimensions of the largest rectangular lot which can be enclosed with the given 400 feet of fence, using the rock wall just described.

Hint: One side of the lot is perpendicular to the wall; let x represent the dimension of that side. Express the area y of the lot in terms of x. Note that this equation, which gives y in terms of x, is of the form $y = ax^2 + bx + c$, with $a < 0$. Therefore, its graph is like that in Fig. 4.13b, and the desired value of x is the abscissa of the vertex of the graph of this equation.

25. A vertical section of a particular trough is a portion of a parabola 8 feet across the top and 4 feet deep. Find an equation of this parabola. *Hint:* Let the origin be at the vertex of the parabola and the y axis be the axis of the parabola.

26. Prove Theorem 4.6.

27. Prove Theorem 4.7.

28. Prove Theorem 4.8.

29. If $y = 24x - 2x^2$, find the greatest value of y. Graph this equation and give the coordinates of the highest point on this graph.

30. If $y = 4x - x^2$, find the greatest value of y. Graph this equation and give the coordinates of the highest point on this graph.

31. If $y = x^2 - 6x + 13$, find the least value of y. Graph this equation and give the coordinates of the lowest point on this graph.

32. Find two numbers whose sum is 16 and whose product is as large as possible.

4.5 THE ELLIPSE

Ellipse Let two points F_1 and F_2 and a number (which we denote by $2a$) be given such that $2a > 0$ and $2a > |F_1 F_2|$. An **ellipse** is a set K of points in a plane with the property that a point P belongs to K if and only if the sum of the distances $|PF_1|$ and $|PF_2|$ between P and the fixed points F_1 and F_2 is equal to $2a$ (Fig. 4.14).

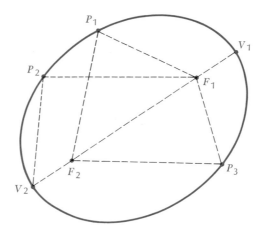

FIGURE 4.14

That is,

$$P \in K \iff |PF_1| + |PF_2| = 2a \qquad (16)$$

Foci   The fixed points F_1 and F_2 are called the **foci** of the ellipse. For convenience we denote the distance between the foci by $2c$; it follows that $2a > 2c$ so that $a > c$.

The definition of an ellipse provides the following construction of that curve. Place pins at the foci F_1 and F_2, and place a loop of string $F_1PF_2F_1$ of length $2c + 2a$ about the pins. Then $|PF_1| + |PF_2| = 2a$, since $|F_1F_2| = 2c$. If a pencil is placed in the loop and moved so as to keep the string tight, the point of the pencil being kept in the plane determined by its original position and the foci, the point of the pencil will describe an ellipse, for the sum $|PF_1| + |PF_2|$ is equal to $2a$ for any position of P.

Focal axis   The line through the foci of an ellipse is called its **focal axis.** The points V_1 and
Vertices V_2 in which an ellipse intersects its focal axis are called **vertices** of the ellipse.
Major axis   The segment V_1V_2 is called the **major axis** of the ellipse, and the midpoint of
Center V_1V_2 (which is also the midpoint of F_1F_2) is called the **center** of the ellipse.

To find an equation of an ellipse, we introduce a coordinate system in the plane by selecting the x axis to be the focal axis of the ellipse and the origin to be the center of the ellipse. Then the foci are the points $F_1(c, 0)$ and $F_2(-c, 0)$, as indicated in Fig. 4.15.

Let the ellipse be designated by K and let $P(x, y)$ be a point in the plane. Then by (16) we know that

$$P(x, y) \in K \iff |PF_1| + |PF_2| = 2a$$

Since

$$|PF_1| = \sqrt{(x - c)^2 + y^2} \qquad \text{and} \qquad |PF_2| = \sqrt{(x + c)^2 + y^2}$$

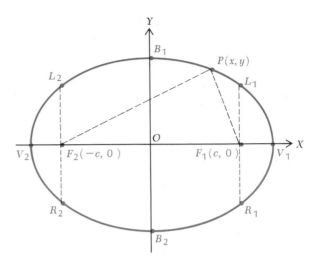

FIGURE 4.15

we have

$$P(x, y) \in K \iff \sqrt{(x-c)^2 + y^2} + \sqrt{(x+c)^2 + y^2} = 2a \qquad (17)$$

The reader may check that each of the following equations is equivalent to the equation appearing in (17).

$$\sqrt{(x-c)^2 + y^2} = 2a - \sqrt{(x+c)^2 + y^2}$$
$$(x-c)^2 + y^2 = 4a^2 - 4a\sqrt{(x+c)^2 + y^2} + (x+c)^2 + y^2$$
$$a\sqrt{(x+c)^2 + y^2} = a^2 + cx$$
$$a^2(x+c)^2 + a^2y^2 = a^4 + 2a^2cx + c^2x^2$$
$$(a^2 - c^2)x^2 + a^2y^2 = a^2(a^2 - c^2)$$
$$\frac{x^2}{a^2} + \frac{y^2}{a^2 - c^2} = 1$$

Therefore,

$$P(x, y) \in K \iff \frac{x^2}{a^2} + \frac{y^2}{a^2 - c^2} = 1 \qquad (18)$$

Since $a > c$, we know that $a^2 - c^2 > 0$. We may denote this positive number by b^2, and write (18) as

$$P(x, y) \in K \iff \frac{x^2}{a^2} + \frac{y^2}{b^2} = 1$$

where $b^2 = a^2 - c^2$. Hence we have the following theorem.

THEOREM   *The ellipse whose foci are $F_1(c, 0)$ and $F_2(-c, 0)$, and for which*
4.10   *$2a$ is the sum of the distances between any point on the ellipse and the two foci, is the graph of*

$$\frac{x^2}{a^2} + \frac{y^2}{b^2} = 1 \tag{19}$$

where b is the positive number defined by

$$b^2 = a^2 - c^2 \tag{20}$$

The x intercepts of the ellipse whose equation is (19) are found by setting $y = 0$ in (19) and solving the resulting equation for x; these intercepts are a and $-a$. Therefore, the coordinates of V_1 and V_2 are $(a, 0)$ and $(-a, 0)$, respectively, and the length of the major axis is $2a$. The segment B_1B_2 cut off by the ellipse on the

Minor axis   line through the center and perpendicular to the major axis is called the **minor axis** of the ellipse. The y intercepts of the ellipse that is the graph of (19) are b and $-b$, so the coordinates of B_1 and B_2 are $(0, b)$ and $(0, -b)$, respectively. The length of the minor axis is $2b$.

The graph of (19) is symmetric with respect to the x axis, with respect to the y axis, and with respect to the origin. Verify this statement.

If we solve (19) for y, we obtain

$$y = \pm \frac{b}{a} \sqrt{a^2 - x^2} \tag{21}$$

Hence, if y is to have only real values, x must be restricted to the interval $[-a; a]$. Similarly, if we solve (19) for x in terms of y, we obtain

$$x = \pm \frac{a}{b} \sqrt{b^2 - y^2}$$

and from this we see that if x is to have only real values, y must be restricted to the interval $[-b; b]$. In other words, if $R = \{(x, y) \mid b^2x^2 + a^2y^2 = a^2b^2\}$, then

$$\text{Domain of } R = [-a; a] \quad\quad \text{Range of } R = [-b; b]$$

The segment cut off by the ellipse from the line through a focus and perpen-
Latus rectum   dicular to the focal axis is called a **latus rectum** of the ellipse (the plural of *latus rectum* is *latera recta*). To find the length of the latus rectum R_1L_1 (Fig. 4.15), we replace x by c in (21), obtaining

$$y = \pm \frac{b}{a} \sqrt{a^2 - c^2} \quad\quad \text{or} \quad\quad y = \pm \frac{b^2}{a}$$

by use of (20). The coordinates of R_1 are $(c, -b^2/a)$ and those of L_1 are $(c, b^2/a)$. Hence $|R_1L_1| = 2b^2/a$. Similarly, it can be shown that $|R_2L_2| = 2b^2/a$.

In graphing an ellipse it is customary to graph the points V_1, V_2, B_1, B_2, R_1, L_1, R_2, and L_2 and draw a smooth curve through these points (Fig. 4.15).

Proceeding as we did to establish Theorem 4.10, we can prove the following theorem for an ellipse with foci on the y axis.

THEOREM 4.11 *The ellipse whose foci are $F_1(0, c)$ and $F_2(0, -c)$, and for which $2a$ is the sum of the distances between any point on the ellipse and the two foci, is the graph of*

$$\frac{x^2}{b^2} + \frac{y^2}{a^2} = 1 \tag{22}$$

where b is the positive number defined by

$$b^2 = a^2 - c^2 \tag{23}$$

For the ellipse which is the graph of (22) the lengths of the major axis, the minor axis, and a latus rectum have the same values as for the ellipse which is the graph of (19), namely, $2a$, $2b$, and $2b^2/a$, respectively.

It should be kept in mind that in Eqs. (19) and (22) the number a is greater than the number b. Suppose that we are given an equation which is equivalent to

$$\frac{x^2}{A} + \frac{y^2}{B} = 1$$

where A and B are both positive. If $A \neq B$, the graph of this equation is an ellipse with center at the origin. If $A > B$, the equation is of the form (19) and the foci are on the x axis. If $A < B$, the equation is of the form (22) and the foci are on the y axis. If $A = B$, the graph of the equation is a circle with equation $x^2 + y^2 = A$.

◆ EXAMPLE 1

Graph the equation $16x^2 + 25y^2 = 400$. Give the domain and the range of the relation $R = \{(x, y) \mid 16x^2 + 25y^2 = 400\}$.

Solution

Dividing both sides of the given equation by 400, we obtain the equivalent equation

$$\frac{x^2}{25} + \frac{y^2}{16} = 1$$

Since $25 > 16$, this equation is of the form (19) with $a^2 = 25$ and $b^2 = 16$. Hence

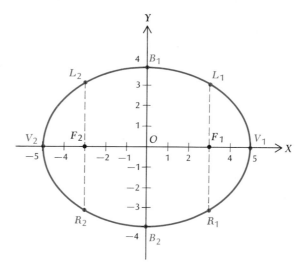

FIGURE 4.16

the graph of the given equation is an ellipse, with center at the origin and with foci on the x axis. For this ellipse $a = 5$ and $b = 4$; further, $c^2 = a^2 - b^2 = 25 - 16 = 9$, so $c = 3$. The vertices are $V_1(5, 0)$ and $V_2(-5, 0)$; the end points of the minor axis are $B_1(0, 4)$ and $B_2(0, -4)$; the foci are $F_1(3, 0)$ and $F_2(-3, 0)$. In addition,

$$|R_1L_1| = |R_2L_2| = \frac{2b^2}{a} = \frac{2(16)}{5} = \frac{32}{5}$$

So the end points of the latera recta are $R_1(3, -\frac{16}{5})$, $L_1(3, \frac{16}{5})$, $R_2(-3, -\frac{16}{5})$, and $L_2(-3, \frac{16}{5})$. The graph is shown in Fig. 4.16.

It should be clear that

$$\text{Domain of } R = [-5; 5] \qquad \text{Range of } R = [-4; 4]$$

Theorems 4.12 and 4.13 below may be established by appropriate translations in a manner similar to that in which Theorem 4.4 was proved.

THEOREM   *The ellipse whose center is at (h, k), for which the distance*
4.12   *from the center to a focus is c, and whose major axis is hori-*
zontal and of length 2a is the graph of

$$\frac{(x - h)^2}{a^2} + \frac{(y - k)^2}{b^2} = 1 \tag{24}$$

where $b = \sqrt{a^2 - c^2}$.

THEOREM 4.13 *The ellipse whose center is at* (h, k)*, for which the distance from the center to a focus is* c*, and whose major axis is vertical and of length* $2a$ *is the graph of*

$$\frac{(x-h)^2}{b^2} + \frac{(y-k)^2}{a^2} = 1 \qquad (25)$$

where $b = \sqrt{a^2 - c^2}$.

For the ellipse in Theorem 4.12 and that in Theorem 4.13 the length of a latus rectum is $2b^2/a$.

◆• EXAMPLE 2

Find an equation of the ellipse with center at $C(-1, 2)$, with one vertex at $V_1(-1, 5)$, and with one focus at $F_1(-1, 2 + \sqrt{5})$.

Solution

From the given data $c = |CF_1| = \sqrt{5}$, $a = |CV_1| = 3$. Using $b^2 = a^2 - c^2$, we find $b^2 = 9 - 5 = 4$, so $b = 2$. Since the major axis is vertical, we use Theorem 4.13 to

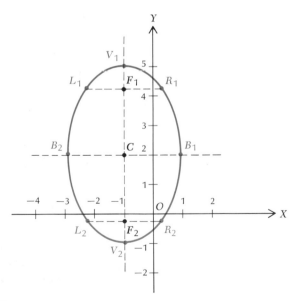

FIGURE 4.17

find that the ellipse is the graph of

$$\frac{(x+1)^2}{4} + \frac{(y-2)^2}{9} = 1$$

The other vertex is $V_2(-1, -1)$, and the other focus is $F_2(-1, 2 - \sqrt{5})$. The end points of the minor axis are $B_1(1, 2)$ and $B_2(-3, 2)$. The length of a latus rectum is $2b^2/a$, which in this case is $\frac{8}{3}$. Consequently, the end points of the latera recta are $R_1(\frac{1}{3}, 2 + \sqrt{5})$, $L_1(-\frac{7}{3}, 2 + \sqrt{5})$, $R_2(\frac{1}{3}, 2 - \sqrt{5})$, and $L_2(-\frac{7}{3}, 2 - \sqrt{5})$. The graph is shown in Fig. 4.17.

THEOREM 4.14   *Let*

$$Ax^2 + Cy^2 + Dx + Ey + F = 0$$

where $A \cdot C > 0^*$ and $A \neq C$, be an equation which can be written in the equivalent form

$$A\left(x + \frac{D}{2A}\right)^2 + C\left(y + \frac{E}{2C}\right)^2 = M \qquad (26)$$

where
$$M - \frac{D^2}{4A} + \frac{E^2}{4C} - F$$

(i)   *If $M = 0$, then the graph of the equation is the single point $(-D/2A, -E/2C)$.*

(ii)   *If $M > 0$, then (26) may be written as*

$$\frac{(x + D/2A)^2}{M/A} + \frac{(y + E/2C)^2}{M/C} = 1 \qquad (27)$$

which is an equation of an ellipse with its center at $(-D/2A, -E/2C)$. The major axis is horizontal or vertical, according as M/A or M/C is the larger.

(iii)   *If $M < 0$, then the graph is the null set.*

The proof of Theorem 4.14 is similar to the proof of Theorem 2.6 in Sec. 2.9 and is left for the student.

◆   EXAMPLE 3

Determine whether the graph of each of the following equations is an ellipse, a point, or the null set. If the graph is an ellipse, give the center, the foci, the

---

* The condition $A \cdot C > 0$ means that both A and C are positive numbers or both are negative numbers; we assume without loss of generality that they are both positive.

vertices, the end points of the minor axis, the length of the major axis, the length of the minor axis, the length of a latus rectum, and the coordinates of the end points of the latera recta, and construct the graph.

a. $25x^2 + 9y^2 + 150x - 36y + 36 = 0$

b. $9x^2 + 4y^2 - 36x - 8y + 76 = 0$

c. $x^2 + 4y^2 - 2x - 8y + 5 = 0$

Solution

a. The given equation is equivalent to

$$25(x^2 + 6x) + 9(y^2 - 4y) = -36$$

or

$$25(x^2 + 6x + 9) + 9(y^2 - 4y + 4) = 225 + 36 - 36$$

or

$$25(x + 3)^2 + 9(y - 2)^2 = 225$$

or

$$\frac{(x + 3)^2}{9} + \frac{(y - 2)^2}{25} = 1$$

Since $25 > 9$, this equation is of the form

$$\frac{(x - h)^2}{b^2} + \frac{(y - k)^2}{a^2} = 1$$

in which $a^2 = 25$ and $b^2 = 9$. Hence the graph of the given equation is an ellipse

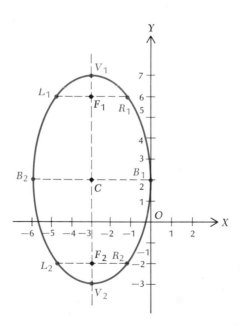

FIGURE 4.18

with center at $C(-3, 2)$ and with major axis vertical. Here $a = 5$, $b = 3$, and $c = \sqrt{a^2 - b^2} = \sqrt{16} = 4$. The vertices are $V_1(-3, 7)$ and $V_2(-3, -3)$, the end points of the minor axis are $B_1(0, 2)$ and $B_2(-6, 2)$, and the foci are $F_1(-3, 6)$ and $F_2(-3, -2)$. The length of a latus rectum $|RL|$ is given by $|RL| = 2b^2/a = 2(9)/5 = \frac{18}{5}$. So the end points of the latera recta (Fig. 4.18) are $R_1(-\frac{6}{5}, 6)$, $L_1(-\frac{24}{5}, 6)$, $R_2(-\frac{6}{5}, -2)$, $L_2(-\frac{24}{5}, -2)$.

b. By writing the given equation in the equivalent form

$$9(x - 2)^2 + 4(y - 1)^2 = -36$$

we see that the graph is the null set.

c. By writing the given equation in the equivalent form

$$(x - 1)^2 + 4(y - 1)^2 = 0$$

we see that the graph is the point $(1, 1)$.

EXERCISES

In each of Exercises 1–6 an equation of an ellipse is specified. For this ellipse give the center, vertices, foci, end points of the minor axis, length of a latus rectum, and end points of the latera recta. Graph the ellipse. Give the domain and the range of the relation determined by the given equation.

1. $25x^2 + 16y^2 - 400$

2. $x^2 + 2y^2 - 2$

3. $25x^2 + 4y^2 - 100$

4. $9x^2 + 25y^2 = 225$

5. $3x^2 + 4y^2 = 12$

6. $36x^2 + 27y^2 = 972$

In each of Exercises 7–13 find an equation of the ellipse with center at the origin which satisfies the given conditions. Graph this ellipse.

7. With length of major axis 10, length of minor axis 8, and foci on the y axis

8. With minor axis of length 10 and a vertex at $(6, 0)$

9. With a latus rectum of length $\frac{32}{7}$ and with one end of the minor axis at $(4, 0)$

10. With minor axis of length 12 and with a focus at $(8, 0)$

11. With major axis of length 16, foci on the x axis, and passing through the point $(4, 3)$

12. With a vertex at $(0, -7)$ and passing through the point $(-3, \frac{7}{2})$

13. Passes through the points $(-1, 4)$ and $(2, 3)$

14. Find an equation of the ellipse with center at $(-4, -2)$, with major axis horizontal and of length 10, and with minor axis of length 8.

15. Using the definition of an ellipse, find an equation of the ellipse with foci at (5, 0) and (−3, 0) for which $2a = 12$.

16. Find an equation of the ellipse with center at (−1, −2), major axis vertical and with length 6, and minor axis with length 4.

17. Find an equation of the circle whose diameter is the major axis of the graph of $9x^2 + 25y^2 = 225$ and with the center of the ellipse for its center. Graph the ellipse and the circle on the same coordinate system.

18. Find an equation of the ellipse whose center is (3, 2), with (7, 2) for one focus, and with (9, 2) for the corresponding vertex.

In each of Exercises 19–26 determine whether the graph of the given equation is an ellipse, a point, or the null set. If the graph is an ellipse, give the center, the foci, the vertices, the end points of the minor axis, the length of a latus rectum, and the end points of the latera recta, and construct the graph.

19. $25x^2 + 9y^2 - 50x + 36y - 164 = 0$

20. $4x^2 + 9y^2 - 8x + 18y + 12 = 0$ **21.** $x^2 + 2y^2 - 10x + 12y + 43 = 0$

22. $9x^2 + 25y^2 + 18x - 50y - 191 = 0$

23. $4x^2 + 3y^2 + 16x - 6y + 31 = 0$ **24.** $9x^2 + 8y^2 + 54x - 16y - 199 = 0$

25. $3x^2 + 8y^2 + 6x - 12y - 62 = 0$ **26.** $4x^2 + y^2 - 8x + 4y + 4 = 0$

27. Find an equation of the ellipse with foci at (−1, 3) and (−1, −5) and with major axis of length 10.

In each of Exercises 28–33 graph the given relation. Give the domain and the range of each relation.

28. $R = \{(x, y) \mid 25x^2 + 9y^2 = 225\}$ **29.** $R = \{(x, y) \mid 25x^2 + 9y^2 > 225\}$

30. $R = \{(x, y) \mid 25x^2 + 9y^2 < 225\}$

31. $R = \{(x, y) \mid 25x^2 + 9y^2 = 225 \text{ or } y = 3\}$

32. $R = \{(x, y) \mid 25x^2 + 9y^2 = 225 \text{ and } y = 3\}$

33. $R = \{(x, y) \mid 25x^2 + 9y^2 < 225 \text{ and } y > 3\}$

34. (a) Graph the equation $y = \frac{5}{3}\sqrt{9 - x^2}$. What is the domain and what is the range of the relation determined by this equation?

   (b) Graph the equation $y = -\frac{5}{3}\sqrt{9 - x^2}$. What is the domain and what is the range of the relation determined by this equation?

   (c) How are the graphs of the equations given in (a) and (b) related to the graph of $25x^2 + 9y^2 = 225$? Explain in terms of union of sets. What is the domain and what is the range of the relation determined by the equation $25x^2 + 9y^2 = 225$?

(*d*) How are the domains of the relations in (*a*) and (*b*) related to the domain of the relation in (*c*)?

(*e*) How are the ranges of the relations in (*a*) and (*b*) related to the range of the relation in (*c*)? Explain in terms of union of sets.

35. Find an equation of the set of points G which has the property that the sum of the distances of each point $P \in G$ from $(3, 6)$ and $(3, -2)$ is 12. Do this two ways: (*a*) by using the appropriate form of an equation of an ellipse; (*b*) directly from the definition of an ellipse.

36. Give a proof of Theorem 4.11 similar to that given in the text for Theorem 4.10.

37. Give a proof of Theorem 4.12 similar to that given in the text for Theorem 4.4.

38. Give a proof of Theorem 4.14 similar to that given in the text for Theorem 2.6 of Sec. 2.9.

39. Show that the length of the line segment joining a focus of the ellipse $b^2x^2 + a^2y^2 = a^2b^2$ to one end of the minor axis is a.

4.6 THE HYPERBOLA

Hyperbola

Let two points F_1 and F_2 and a number (which we denote by $2a$) be given such that $2a > 0$. A **hyperbola** is a set K of points in a plane with the property that a

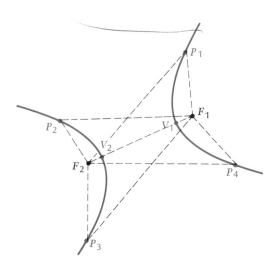

FIGURE 4.19

point P belongs to K if and only if the absolute value of the difference of the distances $|PF_1|$ and $|PF_2|$ between P and the fixed points F_1 and F_2 is equal to $2a$ (Fig. 4.19). That is,

$$P \in K \iff ||PF_1| - |PF_2|| = 2a \qquad (28)$$

Foci   The fixed points F_1 and F_2 are called the **foci** of the hyperbola. For convenience we denote the distance between the foci by $2c$; then it follows that $2a < 2c$, so that $a < c$.

Focal axis   The line through the foci of a hyperbola is called its **focal axis.** The points V_1
Vertices   and V_2 in which a hyperbola intersects its focal axis are called **vertices** of the
Transverse axis   hyperbola. The segment $V_1 V_2$ is the **transverse axis** of the hyperbola, and the
Center   midpoint of $V_1 V_2$ (which is also the midpoint of $F_1 F_2$) is called the **center** of the hyperbola.

To find an equation of a hyperbola, we introduce a coordinate system in the plane by choosing the x axis to be the focal axis of the hyperbola and the origin to be the center of the hyperbola. Then the foci are the points $F_1(c, 0)$ and $F_2(-c, 0)$ indicated in Fig. 4.20.

Let the hyperbola be designated by K and let $P(x, y)$ be a point in the plane. Then by (28) we know that

$$P(x, y) \in K \iff ||PF_1| - |PF_2|| = 2a$$

or

$$P(x, y) \in K \iff |PF_1| - |PF_2| = \pm 2a$$

Since

$$|PF_1| = \sqrt{(x - c)^2 + y^2} \qquad \text{and} \qquad |PF_2| = \sqrt{(x + c)^2 + y^2}$$

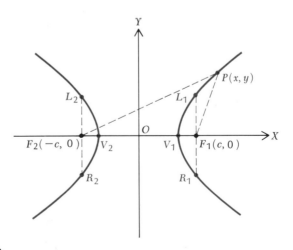

FIGURE 4.20

we have

$$P(x, y) \in K \iff \sqrt{(x-c)^2 + y^2} - \sqrt{(x+c)^2 + y^2} = \pm 2a \qquad (29)$$

Proceeding as for the ellipse, we may show that each of the following equations is equivalent to the equation appearing in (29):

$$(c^2 - a^2)x^2 - a^2 y^2 = a^2(c^2 - a^2)$$

$$\frac{x^2}{a^2} - \frac{y^2}{c^2 - a^2} = 1$$

Therefore,

$$P(x, y) \in K \iff \frac{x^2}{a^2} - \frac{y^2}{c^2 - a^2} = 1 \qquad (30)$$

Since $a < c$, we know that $c^2 - a^2 > 0$. We may denote this positive number by b^2 and write (30) as

$$P(x, y) \in K \iff \frac{x^2}{a^2} - \frac{y^2}{b^2} = 1$$

where $b^2 = c^2 - a^2$. Hence we have the following theorem.

THEOREM 4.15   *The hyperbola K whose foci are $F_1(c, 0)$ and $F_2(-c, 0)$, and for which $2a$ is the absolute value of the difference of the distances between any point on the hyperbola and the two foci, is the graph of*

$$\frac{x^2}{a^2} - \frac{y^2}{b^2} = 1 \qquad (31)$$

where b is the positive number defined by

$$b^2 = c^2 - a^2 \qquad (32)$$

The x intercepts of the hyperbola which is the graph of (31) are a and $-a$, so the coordinates of V_1 are $(a, 0)$ and the coordinates of V_2 are $(-a, 0)$, and the length of the transverse axis is $2a$. There are no y intercepts of the hyperbola since, if in Eq. (31) x is replaced by 0, the resulting equation in y has no roots in the set of real numbers.

The graph of (31) is symmetric with respect to the x axis, with respect to the y axis, and with respect to the origin. Verify this statement.

If we solve Eq. (31) for y, we obtain

$$y = \pm \frac{b}{a} \sqrt{x^2 - a^2} \qquad (33)$$

Hence, if y is to have only real values, x may not have values in the interval

$(-a; a)$; that is, x must be restricted to $(-\infty; -a] \cup [a; +\infty)$. This accounts for the hyperbola consisting of two disjoint branches, as shown in Fig. 4.20.

On the other hand, if we solve (31) for x we obtain

$$x = \pm \frac{a}{b} \sqrt{y^2 + b^2}$$

from which we see that there are real values of x for all real values of y.

From the results of the last two paragraphs it follows that if

$$R = \{(x, y) \mid b^2x^2 - a^2y^2 = a^2b^2\}$$

then

Domain of $R = (-\infty; -a] \cup [a; +\infty)$ Range of $R = (-\infty; +\infty)$

Latus rectum

The segment cut off by the hyperbola from the line through a focus and perpendicular to the focal axis is called a **latus rectum** of the hyperbola. The length of a latus rectum for the hyperbola is $2b^2/a$, as for the ellipse. Verify this statement.

Let G be the graph of a relation whose domain contains the interval $[a; +\infty)$ or the interval $(-\infty; -a]$ for some real number a, and let $P(x, y)$ be a point on G. If there is a line L which has the property that the distance d between $P(x, y)$ and L can be made arbitrarily close to zero for all values of x that are

Asymptote

sufficiently large (or sufficiently small), then the line L is called an *asymptote* of the graph G. It can be shown (although we shall not do so here) that the two lines which are the graphs of

$$y = \frac{b}{a} x \quad \text{and} \quad y = -\frac{b}{a} x \tag{34}$$

are asymptotes of the hyperbola which is the graph of

$$\frac{x^2}{a^2} - \frac{y^2}{b^2} = 1 \tag{35}$$

The asymptotes are represented by the dashed lines in Fig. 4.21.

In graphing a hyperbola with given equation, first graph the asymptotes, the vertices, and the end points of the latera recta. Then draw a smooth curve through the vertices and the end points of the latera recta, using the asymptotes as guide lines which the hyperbola never meets, but which the hyperbola approaches as its branches are extended indefinitely.

Let $P_1(x_1, y_1)$ be any point on the hyperbola which is the graph of (35), and let d_1 and d_2 denote the respective distances of $P_1(x_1, y_1)$ from the asymptotes whose equations are (34). Then, by Theorem 3.6,

$$d_1 = \frac{|bx_1 - ay_1|}{\sqrt{a^2 + b^2}} \quad \text{and} \quad d_2 = \frac{|bx_1 + ay_1|}{\sqrt{a^2 + b^2}}$$

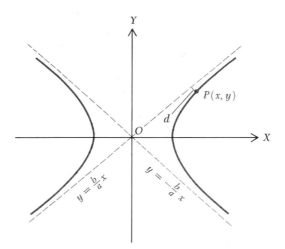

FIGURE 4.21

and consequently

$$d_1 \cdot d_2 = \frac{|bx_1 - ay_1|}{\sqrt{a^2 + b^2}} \cdot \frac{|bx_1 + ay_1|}{\sqrt{a^2 + b^2}} = \frac{|b^2 x_1{}^2 - a^2 y_1{}^2|}{a^2 + b^2} = \frac{a^2 b^2}{a^2 + b^2} \qquad (36)$$

We have proved that *the product of the distances of any point on a hyperbola from its asymptotes is constant.*

Proceeding as we did in establishing Theorem 4.15, we can prove the following result.

THEOREM 4.16   *The hyperbola whose foci are $F_1(0, c)$ and $F_2(0, -c)$, and for which $2a$ is the absolute value of the difference of the distances between any point on the hyperbola and the two foci, is the graph of*

$$\frac{y^2}{a^2} - \frac{x^2}{b^2} = 1 \qquad (37)$$

where b is the positive number defined by

$$b^2 = c^2 - a^2$$

The y intercepts of the hyperbola which is the graph of (37) are a and $-a$, so the vertices are $V_1(0, a)$ and $V_2(0, -a)$. There are no x intercepts. The length of the transverse axis and the length of a latus rectum have the same values as for the hyperbola which is the graph of (31), namely, $2a$ and $2b^2/a$, respectively.

The equations of the asymptotes of the hyperbola which is the graph of (37) are

$$y = \frac{a}{b}x \quad \text{and} \quad y = -\frac{a}{b}x$$

For a hyperbola we may have $a > b$, $a = b$, or $a < b$. Suppose we are given an equation which is equivalent to

$$\frac{x^2}{A} + \frac{y^2}{B} = 1$$

where $A \cdot B < 0$. The graph of this equation is a hyperbola with center at the origin. If A is positive and B is negative, the equation is of the form (31), and the foci are on the x axis. If A is negative and B is positive, the equation is of the form (37), and the foci are on the y axis.

A single equation for the asymptotes of the graph of

$$\frac{x^2}{A} + \frac{y^2}{B} = 1 \quad A \cdot B < 0$$

is

$$\frac{x^2}{A} + \frac{y^2}{B} = 0$$

Since A and B are of opposite signs, the latter equation factors into two factors of the first degree in x and y. Verify that the equation $x^2/a^2 - y^2/b^2 = 0$ is equivalent to the sentence

$$y = \frac{b}{a}x \quad \text{or} \quad y = -\frac{b}{a}x$$

and that the equation $y^2/a^2 - x^2/b^2 = 0$ is equivalent to the sentence

$$y = \frac{a}{b}x \quad \text{or} \quad y = -\frac{a}{b}x$$

That is,

$$\left\{ (x, y) \,\middle|\, \frac{x^2}{a^2} - \frac{y^2}{b^2} = 0 \right\} = \left\{ (x, y) \,\middle|\, y = \frac{b}{a}x \text{ or } y = -\frac{b}{a}x \right\}$$

and

$$\left\{ (x, y) \,\middle|\, \frac{y^2}{a^2} - \frac{x^2}{b^2} = 0 \right\} = \left\{ (x, y) \,\middle|\, y = \frac{a}{b}x \text{ or } y = -\frac{a}{b}x \right\}$$

▶ EXAMPLE

Graph the equation $16x^2 - 9y^2 - 144 = 0$. Give the domain and range of the relation $R = \{(x, y) \mid 16x^2 - 9y^2 - 144 = 0\}$.

Solution

The given equation is equivalent to

$$\frac{x^2}{9} - \frac{y^2}{16} = 1$$

which is of the form

$$\frac{x^2}{a^2} - \frac{y^2}{b^2} = 1$$

with $a^2 = 9$ and $b^2 = 16$. Hence, the graph of the given equation is a hyperbola with center at the origin and foci on the x axis. For this hyperbola $a = 3$, $b = 4$; since $c^2 = a^2 + b^2 = 9 + 16 = 25$, then $c = 5$. The vertices are $V_1(3, 0)$ and $V_2(-3, 0)$; the foci are $F_1(5, 0)$ and $F_2(-5, 0)$. The length of a latus rectum is equal to $2b^2/a = \frac{32}{3}$, and the end points of the latera recta (Fig. 4.22) are $R_1(5, -\frac{16}{3})$, $L_1(5, \frac{16}{3})$, $R_2(-5, -\frac{16}{3})$, $L_2(-5, \frac{16}{3})$. The asymptotes have the equation

$$\frac{x^2}{9} - \frac{y^2}{16} = 0$$

or the equations

$$y = \tfrac{4}{3}x \qquad \text{and} \qquad y = -\tfrac{4}{3}x$$

and are indicated by the dashed lines in Fig. 4.22.
   For the specified relation R,

$$\text{Domain of } R = (-\infty; -3] \cup [3; +\infty) \qquad \text{Range of } R = (-\infty; +\infty)$$

   Theorems 4.17 to 4.19 correspond to Theorems 4.12 to 4.14 for the ellipse, and may be proved by similar procedures.

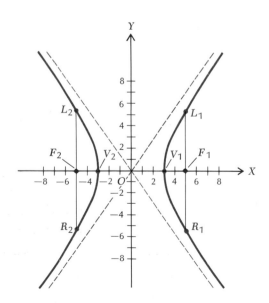

FIGURE 4.22

THEOREM 4.17 *The hyperbola with center at (h, k), for which the distance from the center to either focus is c, and whose transverse axis is parallel to the x axis and of length 2a, is the graph of*

$$\frac{(x-h)^2}{a^2} - \frac{(y-k)^2}{b^2} = 1 \qquad (38)$$

where $b = \sqrt{c^2 - a^2}$.

The asymptotes of the hyperbola which is the graph of (38) are the lines which are the graph of

$$\frac{(x-h)^2}{a^2} - \frac{(y-k)^2}{b^2} = 0$$

that is, the lines which are the graphs of

$$y - k = \frac{b}{a}(x-h) \qquad \text{and} \qquad y - k = -\frac{b}{a}(x-h)$$

respectively.

THEOREM 4.18 *The hyperbola with center at (h, k), for which the distance from the center to either focus is c, and whose transverse axis is parallel to the y axis and of length 2a, is the graph of*

$$\frac{(y-k)^2}{a^2} - \frac{(x-h)^2}{b^2} = 1 \qquad (39)$$

where $b = \sqrt{c^2 - a^2}$.

The asymptotes of the hyperbola which is the graph of (39) are the lines which are the graph of

$$\frac{(y-k)^2}{a^2} - \frac{(x-h)^2}{b^2} = 0$$

that is, the lines which are the graphs of

$$y - k = \frac{a}{b}(x-h) \qquad \text{and} \qquad y - k = -\frac{a}{b}(x-h)$$

respectively.

THEOREM 4.19 *Let*

$$Ax^2 + Cy^2 + Dx + Ey + F = 0$$

where $A \cdot C < 0$, be an equation which can be written in the *equivalent form*

$$A\left(x+\frac{D}{2A}\right)^2 + C\left(y+\frac{E}{2C}\right)^2 = M$$

where
$$M = \frac{D^2}{4A} + \frac{E^2}{4C} - F$$

(i) If $M = 0$, then the graph is made up of two intersecting straight lines.

(ii) If $M \neq 0$, then the graph is a hyperbola with center at $(-D/2A, -E/2C)$. The transverse axis is horizontal or vertical, according as M/A or M/C is positive.

4.7 THE RECTANGULAR HYPERBOLA

Rectangular hyperbola

If the two asymptotes of a hyperbola are perpendicular, the hyperbola is called a **rectangular hyperbola.** Therefore, a hyperbola with Eq. (35) is a rectangular hyperbola if and only if

$$\left(\frac{b}{a}\right)\cdot\left(-\frac{b}{a}\right) = -1 \qquad \text{or} \qquad b^2 = a^2$$

that is, if and only if $a = b$ (since $a > 0$ and $b > 0$). Consequently, an equation of a rectangular hyperbola with center at the origin and transverse axis of length $2a$ along the x axis is

$$x^2 - y^2 = a^2$$

For the rectangular hyperbola which is the graph of this equation, we have $c = \sqrt{a^2 + a^2} = a\sqrt{2}$, and so the foci are $F_1(a\sqrt{2}, 0)$ and $F_2(-a\sqrt{2}, 0)$. In this case formula (36) becomes

$$d_1 \cdot d_2 = \tfrac{1}{2}a^2 \qquad\qquad\qquad \text{(40)}$$

Suppose that a rectangular hyperbola is placed on a coordinate plane in such a way that the coordinate axes are the asymptotes of the hyperbola (Figs. 4.23 and 4.24). Then, if $P(x, y)$ is a point on the hyperbola, the distances d_1 and d_2 between the point and the two asymptotes are $|x|$ and $|y|$, respectively. If the hyperbola lies in the first and third quadrants, then $d_1 \cdot d_2 = |x|\,|y| = xy$, and from (40) we see that the hyperbola is the graph of

$$xy = \tfrac{1}{2}a^2$$

Such a hyperbola is shown in Fig. 4.23. If the hyperbola lies in the second and fourth quadrants, then $d_1 \cdot d_2 = |x|\,|y| = -xy$, and from (40) we see that the

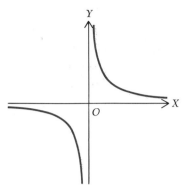

FIGURE 4.23 Graph of $xy = \frac{1}{2}a^2$.

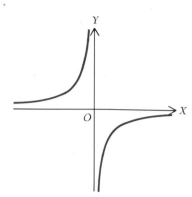

FIGURE 4.24 Graph of $xy = -\frac{1}{2}a^2$.

hyperbola is the graph of

$$xy = -\tfrac{1}{2}a^2$$

Such a hyperbola is shown in Fig. 4.24. Note that a represents the distance between the center of the hyperbola and a vertex of the hyperbola.

The student is asked to show that the equation

$$axy + bx + cy + d = 0 \tag{41}$$

is transformed into

$$a^2x'y' = bc - ad$$

by the translation defined by

$$x = x' - \frac{c}{a} \qquad y = y' - \frac{b}{a}$$

Therefore (41) is an equation of a rectangular hyperbola (see Exercises 42 and 43).

EXERCISES

In each of Exercises 1–6 for the hyperbola whose equation is specified, give the center, the vertices, the foci, the length of a latus rectum, the end points of the latera recta, and equations of the asymptotes. Graph the hyperbola. Give the domain and range of the relation determined by the given equation.

1. $3x^2 - 4y^2 = 48$ **2.** $9x^2 - 16y^2 = 144$ **3.** $4y^2 - 5x^2 = 20$

4. $9y^2 - 4x^2 = 36$ **5.** $4x^2 - 9y^2 = 36$ **6.** $x^2 - y^2 = 36$

In each of Exercises 7–14 find an equation of the hyperbola with center at the origin which satisfies the given conditions, and graph this hyperbola.

7. With transverse axis horizontal and of length 6 and passing through the point (5, 3)

8. With transverse axis of length 12 and with (8, 0) for a focus

9. With latus rectum of length 20 and with one vertex at (4, 0)

10. With $y = \pm\frac{5}{12}x$ as equations of the asymptotes and with one focus at (13, 0)

11. Passing through the points $(3, -2)$ and $(7, 6)$ and with transverse axis horizontal

12. With (0, 4) for one vertex and passing through the point (2, 8)

13. With (4, 0) for vertex and with $(-5, 0)$ for a focus

14. With $(\frac{5}{2}, 0)$ for a vertex and with $(-5, 0)$ for a focus

15. Find an equation of the hyperbola with center at $(-1, 3)$, transverse axis horizontal and of length 8, and distance between the foci equal to $2\sqrt{41}$.

16. Find an equation of the hyperbola with transverse axis of length 6 and foci at $(-2, -4)$ and $(-2, 6)$.

17. Using the definition of a hyperbola, find an equation of the hyperbola with foci at (6, 0) and $(-6, 0)$ for which $2a = 8$.

18. Prove that for the graph of $b^2x^2 - a^2y^2 = a^2b^2$, the distance from a focus to an asymptote has the value b.

In each of Exercises 19–26 determine whether the graph of the given equation is a hyperbola or a pair of intersecting straight lines, and construct the graph. If the graph is a hyperbola give the equations of its asymptotes, and construct the graph of the asymptotes in connection with the graph of the hyperbola.

19. $5x^2 - 4y^2 - 20x - 24y + 4 = 0$ **20.** $4x^2 - 9y^2 - 16x + 18y - 29 = 0$

21. $3y^2 + 6y - x^2 + 2x + 11 = 0$ **22.** $9x^2 - 16y^2 - 54x + 64y - 127 = 0$

23. $4y^2 - x^2 + 2x - 1 = 0$ **24.** $x^2 - y^2 - 12x + 16y - 36 = 0$

25. $9x^2 - 4y^2 - 18x - 24y - 27 = 0$ **26.** $9x^2 - 16y^2 - 18x + 96y - 279 = 0$

27. Prove Theorem 4.16.   **28.** Prove Theorem 4.17.

29. Prove Theorem 4.18.   **30.** Prove Theorem 4.19.

31. Show that an equation of a rectangular hyperbola with center at the origin and transverse axis of length $2a$ along the y axis is $y^2 - x^2 = a^2$.

32. Using the definition of a hyperbola, show that an equation of the hyperbola with foci $F_1(a, a)$ and $F_2(-a, -a)$ for which

$$|PF_1| - |PF_2| = \pm 2a$$

for any point $P(x, y)$ on the hyperbola is $xy = \frac{1}{2}a^2$. What are the coordinates of the vertices of this hyperbola?

33. As in Exercise 32, show that an equation of the hyperbola with foci $F_1(-a, a)$ and $F_2(a, -a)$ for which $|PF_1| - |PF_2| = \pm 2a$ is $xy = -\frac{1}{2}a^2$. What are the coordinates of the vertices of this hyperbola?

34. Show that any line parallel to an asymptote of a hyperbola meets the hyperbola at only one point.

35. Find an equation of the rectangular hyperbola that lies in the first and third quadrants, that has the coordinate axes for asymptotes, and that passes through (a) the point $(3, 4)$, (b) the point $(-7, -5)$. *Hint:* The equation has the form $xy = k$.

36. Find an equation of the rectangular hyperbola that lies in the first and third quadrants, that has the coordinate axes for asymptotes, and that passes through (a) the point $(-5, 6)$, (b) the point $(8, -3)$.

In each of Exercises 37–38 graph the given relation. Give the domain and the range of each relation.

37. $R = \{(x, y) \mid 4x^2 + 9y^2 = 180 \text{ or } xy = 12\}$

38. $R = \{(x, y) \mid 4x^2 + 9y^2 = 180 \text{ and } xy = 12\}$

39. Prove the theorem: An equation of the rectangular hyperbola with center at (h, k), with transverse axis of length $2a$, and with asymptotes parallel to the coordinate axes is

$$(x - h)(y - k) = \tfrac{1}{2}a^2$$

if the focal axis has inclination 45 degrees and is

$$(x - h)(y - k) = -\tfrac{1}{2}a^2$$

if the focal axis has inclination 135 degrees. *Hint:* Use equations $xy = \frac{1}{2}a^2$, $xy = -\frac{1}{2}a^2$, and the appropriate translations.

40. Find an equation of the hyperbola with the graphs of $x = 4$ and $y = 3$ for asymptotes which passes through the point $(6, 7)$. What is the length of the transverse axis? Find the vertices.

41. Boyle's law states that at a constant temperature the pressure p and the volume v of a gas satisfy the equation $pv = c$, for some fixed real number c. A certain gas under a pressure of 20 pounds per square inch has a volume of 300 cubic inches. Find c from the given data, and for that value of c graph the relation $R = \{(p, v) \mid pv = c\}$.

In each of Exercises 42 and 43 translate the coordinate axes so as to remove the first-degree terms to obtain an equation of the form $x'y' = k$. Graph the hyperbola, and in connection with this graph show both sets of coordinate axes.

42. $xy - x - 4y - 2 = 0$ **43.** $xy + 2x - 3y - 10 = 0$

4.8 PARAMETRIC REPRESENTATIONS OF THE PARABOLA, THE ELLIPSE, AND THE HYPERBOLA

In the case of the circle (and the line) we have seen that it is possible to determine two functions F and G with the property that the pair of equations

$$
\begin{aligned}
x &= F(t) \\
y &= G(t)
\end{aligned} \qquad t \in U \tag{42}
$$

represents the given circle (or the given line). The pair of equations (42) is called a parametric representation of the circle (or line). In this section we shall see that it is possible to find parametric representations for each of the three curves studied in this chapter.

The parabola

$$
K:\ y^2 = kx \tag{43}
$$

has several parametric representations. Two such representations are

$$
\begin{aligned}
x &= \frac{1}{k}\, t^2 \\
y &= t
\end{aligned} \qquad t \in Re \tag{44}
$$

and

$$
\begin{aligned}
x &= t^2 \\
y &= \sqrt{k}\, t
\end{aligned} \qquad t \in Re \tag{45}
$$

It is clear from substitution of (44) in (43) that for each real number t, the pair (x, y) obtained from (44) will satisfy the equation in (43); conversely, for every ordered pair (x, y) that satisfies (43), there will be a real number t for which (44) will hold. In a similar way we see that (45) is also a parametric representation of (43).

♦ EXAMPLE 1

Show that the pair of equations

$$
\begin{aligned}
x &= 4t^2 \\
y &= t
\end{aligned} \qquad t \in Re
$$

is a parametric representation of a parabola by eliminating t from the pair of equations to produce an equation in x and y.

Solution

Substituting t in place of y in the first of the two equations, we get

$$
x = 4y^2 \qquad \text{or} \qquad y^2 = \tfrac{1}{4}x
$$

which is an equation of the parabola with vertex $V(0, 0)$ and focus $F(\frac{1}{16}, 0)$.

♦ EXAMPLE 2

Eliminate t from the pair of equations

$$
\begin{aligned}
x &= 3t - 1 \\
y &= 2t^2 + 1
\end{aligned} \qquad t \in Re
$$

and thus obtain an equation in x and y. Identify and describe the curve that is the graph of this equation, and hence determine the curve for which the given pair of equations is a parametric representation.

Solution

From the first of the given equations we find

$$
t = \frac{x + 1}{3}
$$

Substituting $(x + 1)/3$ for t in the second equation, we get

$$
y = 2 \left(\frac{x + 1}{3} \right)^2 + 1
$$

which is equivalent to

$$
9y = 2x^2 + 4x + 11
$$

We recognize this as an equation of a parabola with axis parallel to the y axis. The vertex of the parabola is $V(-1, 1)$; the parabola opens upward with focus $F(-1, \frac{17}{8})$.

For a and b any positive real numbers, let us consider the pair of equations

$$
\begin{aligned}
x &= a \cos t \\
y &= b \cos t
\end{aligned} \qquad t \in U \tag{46}
$$

We see that, for any values of t, x and y as given by (46) have the property that

$$
\left(\frac{x}{a} \right)^2 + \left(\frac{y}{b} \right)^2 = \cos^2 t + \sin^2 t
$$

so that, for any $t \in U$, the ordered pair (x, y) given by (46) satisfies

$$
\frac{x^2}{a^2} + \frac{y^2}{b^2} = 1 \tag{47}
$$

Thus any pair (x, y) obtained from (46) will be the coordinates of a point on the ellipse with center $C(0, 0)$, vertices $(a, 0)$ and $(-a, 0)$, and ends of the minor axis $(0, b)$ and $(0, -b)$. Therefore, (46) will be a parametric representation of this ellipse provided it is possible to choose the universe U so that, corresponding to any ordered pair (x, y) that satisfies (47), there will be a value of t in U for which (46) will hold. That a proper choice for the universe U of the variable t can be made may be seen by considering a geometric interpretation of the parameter t, as was done in the case of the parametric representation

$$x = r \cos t \qquad y = r \sin t$$

of a circle (see Sec. 2.8). To obtain such a geometric interpretation, we construct two concentric circles with their common center at the origin $O(0, 0)$ and with radii a and b, respectively, where $a > b$ (see Fig. 4.25). Draw a line through O; designate the intersection of this line with the larger circle by A and its intersection with the smaller circle by B. Let $P(x, y)$ be the point with the same x coordinate as A and the same y coordinate as B. Also let M and N be the respective projections on the x axis of A and B.

Let t be the smallest positive angle formed by OA and OX, with OX as initial side; then, from the definitions of sine and cosine it follows that the coordinates of A are $(a \cos t, a \sin t)$, and the coordinates of B are $(b \cos t, b \sin t)$. Therefore, the coordinates of the point P are $(a \cos t, b \sin t)$, and P lies on the ellipse whose

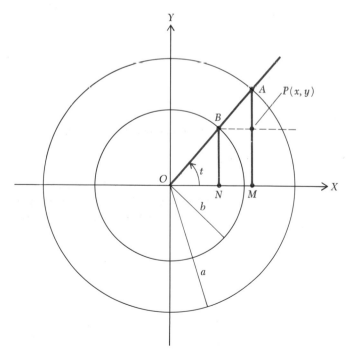

FIGURE 4.25

equation is given by (47). Also, given any point $P(x, y)$ on the ellipse, there will be a value of t between 0 and 2π which can be used in (46) to give the coordinates (x, y) of this point P.

Using the geometric interpretation of t given above, we see that, if $U \in [0; 2\pi]$, then (46) is a parametric representation of the ellipse whose equation is (47). If U is an interval of length less that 2π, Eqs. (46) will represent only a *part* of the ellipse. To illustrate, when $t = 0$, the point P has coordinates $(a, 0)$; when $t = \frac{1}{2}\pi$, the point P has coordinates $(0, b)$; so, for $t \in [0; \frac{1}{2}\pi]$, Eqs. (46) represent the portion of the ellipse K: $x^2/a^2 + y^2/b^2 = 1$ that lies in the first quadrant.

For a and b any *positive* real numbers, the parametric equations

$$x = a \sec t \qquad y = b \tan t \tag{48}$$

can be written in the form

$$\frac{x}{a} = \sec t \qquad \frac{y}{b} = \tan t$$

It follows that (recalling that $\sec^2 t = 1 + \tan^2 t$) for any value of t other than an odd multiple of $\frac{1}{2}\pi$, the pair (x, y) given by (48) will satisfy

$$\frac{x^2}{a^2} - \frac{y^2}{b^2} = 1 \tag{49}$$

Thus, every point on the graph of (48) will be a point on the hyperbola that is the graph of (49). By considerations similar to those used above in connection with the ellipse, it can be shown that for every ordered pair (x, y) that satisfies (49) there is a value of t which can be used in (48) to give this ordered pair (x, y). Therefore (48) is a parametric representation of the hyperbola K: $x^2/a^2 - y^2/b^2 = 1$, provided the universe of the parameter t is suitably chosen.

▶ EXAMPLE 3

When $t \in (0; \frac{1}{2}\pi)$, what portion of the hyperbola do the parametric equations (48) represent?

Solution

As t varies from 0 toward $\frac{1}{2}\pi$, sec t takes on all values greater than 1; hence x as given by (48) takes on all real values greater than 1. As t varies from 0 toward $\frac{1}{2}\pi$, tan t takes on all positive values; hence y as given by (48) takes on all positive values. Therefore, when $t \in (0; \frac{1}{2}\pi)$, Eqs. (48) represent the portion of the hyperbola K: $x^2/a^2 - y^2/b^2 = 1$ that lies in the first quadrant.

The student should verify that if $t \in (\frac{1}{2}\pi; \frac{3}{2}\pi)$, Eqs. (48) represent the portion of the hyperbola that lies in the second and third quadrants.

Any set of parametric equations

$$x = F(t)$$
$$y = G(t) \qquad t \in U \qquad (50)$$

determines a relation

$$R = \{(x, y) \mid x = F(t), y = G(t), t \in U\}$$

We follow the convention that, unless specifically stated to the contrary, the universe U of the parameter t in (50) will be taken to be the set of all real numbers with the property that for every value of t in U, Eqs. (50) give real values for x and y. To illustrate, for the equations

$$x = t$$
$$y^2 = 4t \qquad t \in U$$

we shall choose U to be the set of all nonnegative real numbers.

EXERCISES

In each of Exercises 1–10 the given parametric equations determine a relation of the form $R = \{(x, y) \mid x = F(t), y = G(t)\}$. Eliminate t from the equations $x = F(t)$ and $y = G(t)$ to obtain an equation in x and y that determines the relation R. Graph R.

1. $x = t$; $y^2 = 2t$
2. $x = 2t + 1$; $y = t^2 - 4$

3. $x = 2t + 3$; $y = \frac{1}{2}t^2 - 4$
4. $x = 3 \sec t$; $y = 6 \tan t$

5. $x = 3 + 4 \cos t$; $y = 3 \sin t$
6. $x = 3 + 5 \sin t$; $y = 6 - 4 \cos t$

7. $x = \cos 2t$; $y = \sin t$
8. $x = \cos \frac{1}{2}t$, $y = 1 + \cos t$

9. $x = 2t$; $y = 6/t$
10. $x = 4/t$; $y = t^2 + 2$

5 | CONIC SECTIONS, ROTATIONS, AND INVARIANTS

5.1 CONIC SECTIONS

All the curves that have been studied in Chaps. 2 to 4 (circle, line, parabola, ellipse, and hyperbola) belong to a class of curves known as *conic sections*. The ancient Greeks studied these curves by noticing that each one can be produced by cutting a *cone* (defined as in the next paragraph) by a plane; that is, each is a plane section of a cone.

Right circular cone

Vertex of a cone

Conic section

A cone may be defined as follows. Let there be given a line L, a point P on L, and an angle α. The surface composed of all lines through P which make an angle α with L is called a **double-napped right circular cone** (Fig. 5.1). The line L is the axis and the point P is the **vertex** of the cone. Each of the lines through P which make up the cone is called an **element** of the cone. A **conic section** is the set of points forming the intersection of a plane and a double-napped right circular cone.

If the plane intersecting the cone is perpendicular to the axis of the cone, the intersection is a circle (Fig. 5.2); if the plane passes through the vertex of the cone, the intersection is a point.

If the plane is not perpendicular to the axis of the cone and if it cuts every

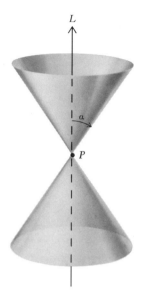

FIGURE 5.1

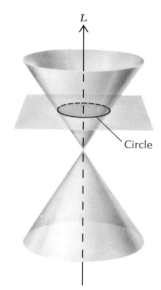

FIGURE 5.2

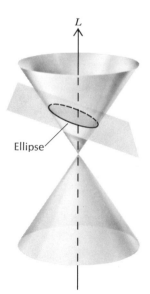

FIGURE 5.3

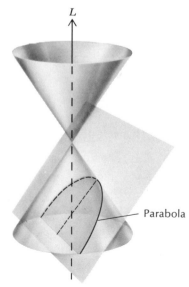

FIGURE 5.4

element of the cone on one side of the vertex, the intersection is an ellipse (Fig. 5.3).

If the plane is parallel to one element of the cone and cuts every other element, the intersection is a parabola (Fig. 5.4).

If the plane cuts both nappes of the cone and does not pass through the vertex, the intersection is a hyperbola (Fig. 5.5).

If the plane intersecting the cone passes through the vertex, the intersection consists of a point, two intersecting lines (Fig. 5.6), or a single line (Fig. 5.7).

We do not give proofs of the above statements, since they would involve solid geometry. The circle, parabola, ellipse, and hyperbola were first obtained by the ancient Greeks in the manner described above; they established many properties of these curves by methods of solid geometry.

Our study of conic sections in the preceding chapters is conveniently summarized in the following theorem.

THEOREM 5.1   *If the graph of*

$$Ax^2 + Cy^2 + Dx + Ey + F = 0 \qquad (1)$$

consists of at least one point, then that graph is either a conic section or two parallel lines.

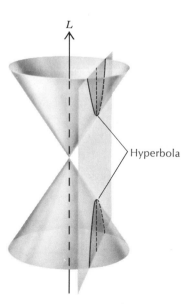

FIGURE 5.5

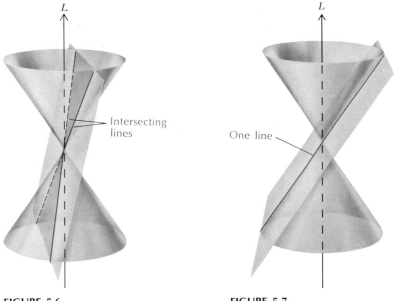

FIGURE 5.6   **FIGURE 5.7**

Proof

   (i)   If $A = C = 0$, the graph is a line (by Theorem 3.4 in Sec. 3.2).
   (ii) If $A = C \neq 0$, the graph of (1) is a circle, a point, or the null set (by Theorem 2.6 in Sec. 2.9).
   (iii) If one (and only one) of A and C is zero, the graph is a parabola, two parallel lines, one line, or the null set (by Theorems 4.5 to 4.8 in Sec. 4.4).
   (iv) If $A \cdot C > 0$, the graph is either an ellipse, a circle (if $A = C$), a point, or the null set (by Theorem 4.14 in Sec. 4.5).
   (v)   If $A \cdot C < 0$, the graph is either a hyperbola or a pair of intersecting lines (by Theorem 4.19 in Sec. 4.6).

General equation of the second degree

The *general equation of the second degree* is

$$Ax^2 + Bxy + Cy^2 + Dx + Ey + F = 0 \qquad (2)$$

In the equations of the conic sections we have considered up to now there has been no xy term (except for the rectangular hyperbola). This has been true because for the parabola, ellipse, and the hyperbola the axis has been parallel to, or coincident with, a coordinate axis. In Sec. 5.2 we shall consider the general equation (2) with $B \neq 0$ and show that it is always possible to choose a new coordinate system so that the graph of (2) will, in the new coordinate system, be the graph of

$$A'x'^2 + C'y'^2 + D'x' + E'y' + F' = 0$$

where at least one of the coefficients A' and C' is not zero.

We list a few of the applications of conic sections. The path of a projectile, neglecting air resistance, is a parabola. The cable of a suspension bridge whose load is uniformly distributed along the bridge hangs in the shape of a parabola. Suppose that a parabola is revolved about its axis to generate a parabolic mirror. If a source of light is placed at the focus of the parabola, each ray of light is reflected as a ray parallel to the axis of the parabola. Conversely, rays of light coming in parallel to the axis will be reflected through the focus. Thus, a parabolic mirror can be used in automobile headlights and spotlights. Arches of bridges sometimes have parabolic form. The orbits in which the planets revolve about the sun are ellipses with one focus at the sun. Masonry bridges frequently have arches in the form of semiellipses. Springs like those in automobiles are often semielliptic in shape. Elliptic gears are used in some machines where a slow, powerful stroke is needed in only part of each revolution.

EXERCISES

In each of Exercises 1–5 find an equation of the set of points which satisfy the given condition. Identify this set as a particular one of the conic sections.

1. Each point of the set is equidistant from the points $(-1, 5)$ and $(3, 7)$.

2. Each point of the set is at a distance of 3 from the point $(2, 1)$.

3. Each point of the set is equidistant from the point $(4, -3)$ and the line whose equation is $y - 5 = 0$.

4. For each point of the set the absolute value of the difference of its distances from $(3, 0)$ and $(-3, 0)$ is equal to 5.

5. For each point of the set the sum of its distances from the points $(4, 0)$ and $(-4, 0)$ is equal to 10.

In each part of Exercises 6 and 7 graph the given relation. Give the domain and the range of each relation.

6. (a) $R_1 = \{(x, y) \mid 4x^2 + y^2 = 100\}$
(b) $R_2 = \{(x, y) \mid y = 2x - 2\}$
(c) $R_3 = \{(x, y) \mid 4x^2 + y^2 = 100 \text{ or } y = 2x - 2\}$

7. (a) $R_1 = \{(x, y) \mid y = x^2 - 2x - 3\}$
(b) $R_2 = \{(x, y) \mid y > x^2 - 2x - 3\}$
(c) $R_3 = \{(x, y) \mid y > x^2 - 2x - 3 \text{ and } y \leqslant 0\}$

8. A cable of a suspension bridge hangs in the form of a parabola, the supporting towers of the cables being 800 feet apart, as indicated in Fig. 5.8. The

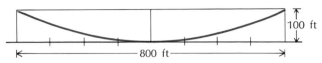

100 ft

800 ft

FIGURE 5.8

cable passes over supporting towers at a height of 100 feet above the roadway, and the lowest point of the cable is on the level with the roadway. Find the lengths of vertical supporting rods from the cable to the roadway at intervals of 100 feet from the center of the bridge to a supporting tower.

9. A cable of a suspension bridge hangs in the form of a parabola, the supporting towers of the cable being 1,000 feet apart. The cable passes over supporting towers at a height of 215 feet above the roadway, and the lowest point of the cable is 15 feet above the roadway. Find the lengths of vertical supporting rods from the cable to the roadway at intervals of 50 feet from the center of the bridge to a supporting tower.

5.2 ROTATION OF COORDINATE AXES

As stated in Sec. 5.1, the general equation of the second degree in x and y is

$$Ax^2 + Bxy + Cy^2 + Dx + Ey + F = 0 \tag{3}$$

If $B = 0$, (3) has the form

$$Ax^2 + Cy^2 + Dx + Ey + F = 0 \tag{4}$$

We have seen, by making use of translation of coordinate axes (Sec. 4.4), that if the graph of (4) consists of at least one point, then that graph is a conic section or two parallel lines. In this section we show that we may introduce a new set of coordinate axes in a coordinate plane in such a way that a set of points which is the graph of (3) will be the graph of an equation of the form (4) with respect to the new set of axes. The way in which this new set of rectangular coordinate axes is introduced in the coordinate plane is called *rotation of axes*.

Consider two rectangular coordinate systems with the same origin O, as indicated in Fig. 5.9, with the angle *from OX to OX'* denoted by θ. Let P be any point in the plane, except the origin, and let α be the angle *from OX' to OP*. Let P have coordinates (x_1, y_1) with respect to the XOY system, and coordinates (x_1', y_1') with respect to the $X'OY'$ system. Then

$$\frac{x_1}{OP} = \cos(\theta + \alpha)$$

or

$$\frac{x_1}{OP} = \cos\theta \cos\alpha - \sin\theta \sin\alpha \tag{5}$$

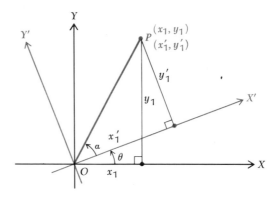

FIGURE 5.9

Since

$$\sin \alpha = \frac{y_1'}{OP} \quad \text{and} \quad \cos \alpha = \frac{x_1'}{OP}$$

we may write (5) as

$$\frac{x_1}{OP} = \frac{x_1'}{OP} \cos \theta - \frac{y_1'}{OP} \sin \theta$$

or

$$x_1 = x_1' \cos \theta - y_1' \sin \theta$$

In a similar manner we can show that

$$y_1 = x_1' \sin \theta + y_1' \cos \theta$$

Therefore, if the coordinate system $X'OY'$ is obtained from the system XOY by a rotation of axes, *with θ being the angle from OX to OX'*, and if a point has coordinates (x, y) in the XOY system and (x', y') in the $X'OY'$ system, then

Rotation formulas

$$\begin{aligned} x &= x' \cos \theta - y' \sin \theta \\ y &= x' \sin \theta + y' \cos \theta \end{aligned} \tag{6}$$

Angle of rotation

Equations (6) are called the *formulas for a rotation of axes through an angle* θ, and θ is called the *angle of rotation.*

◆ EXAMPLE 1

Let G be the graph of

$$5x^2 + 4xy + 2y^2 = 1 \tag{7}$$

Rotate the coordinate system through an acute angle θ for which $\tan \theta = \frac{1}{2}$, and find an equation of G with respect to the new coordinate system.

Solution

From Fig. 5.10 we see that $\sin \theta = 1/\sqrt{5}$, $\cos \theta = 2/\sqrt{5}$. Substituting these values

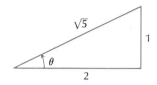

FIGURE 5.10

in (6), we obtain

$$x = \frac{2x' - y'}{\sqrt{5}} \qquad y = \frac{x' + 2y'}{\sqrt{5}} \tag{8}$$

as formulas that will effect the specified rotation. Under the transformation (8) the given equation (7) becomes

$$5\left(\frac{2x' - y'}{\sqrt{5}}\right)^2 + 4\left(\frac{2x' - y'}{\sqrt{5}}\right) \cdot \left(\frac{x' + 2y'}{\sqrt{5}}\right) + 2\left(\frac{x' + 2y'}{\sqrt{5}}\right)^2 = 1$$

or, on simplification,

$$6x'^2 + y'^2 = 1 \tag{9}$$

This is an equation of G with respect to the $X'OY'$ coordinate system. We write (9) in the form

$$\frac{x'^2}{(1/\sqrt{6})^2} + \frac{y'^2}{1^2} = 1 \tag{10}$$

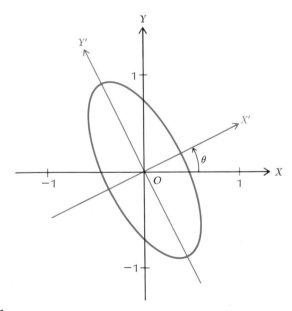

FIGURE 5.11

which we recognize as the equation of an ellipse with the major axis along the y' axis and for which $b = 1/\sqrt{6}$ and $a = 1$. The ellipse which is the graph of (10) is shown in Fig. 5.11 with the two sets of coordinate axes.

What we accomplished in Example 1 for the graph of a particular equation (7) may be done in the general situation, as shown by the following theorem.

THEOREM 5.2   *Let G be the graph, with respect to the XOY coordinate system, of a general equation of the second degree.*

$$Ax^2 + Bxy + Cy^2 + Dx + Ey + F = 0 \qquad (11)$$

with $B \neq 0$. Let $X'OY'$ designate a new coordinate system obtained by a rotation of axes through an angle θ. If θ is chosen so that

$$\tan 2\theta = \frac{B}{A - C} \qquad whenever\, A \neq C \qquad (12)$$

and $\theta = 45\ degrees$ *whenever $A = C$*

then G is the graph, with respect to the $X'OY'$ system, of

$$A'x'^2 + C'y'^2 + D'x' + E'y' + F' = 0 \qquad (13)$$

Proof

If we rotate the axes through an angle θ by means of the formulas (6), the reader should verify that Eq. (11) is transformed into

$$A'x'^2 + B'x'y' + C'y'^2 + D'x' + E'y' + F' = 0 \qquad (14)$$

where
$$A' = A \cos^2 \theta + B \sin \theta \cos \theta + C \sin^2 \theta$$
$$B' = B \cos 2\theta - (A - C) \sin 2\theta$$
$$C' = A \sin^2 \theta - B \sin \theta \cos \theta + C \cos^2 \theta$$
$$D' = D \cos \theta + E \sin \theta$$
$$E' = E \cos \theta - D \sin \theta$$
$$F' = F$$

Equation (14) will have the form (13) if and only if $B' = 0$, that is, if and only if

$$B \cos 2\theta - (A - C) \sin 2\theta = 0 \qquad (15)$$

If $A \neq C$, the condition (15) may be written

$$\tan 2\theta = \frac{B}{A - C} \qquad (16)$$

Although an infinite number of angles satisfy the condition (16), it will always be satisfied by some value of 2θ between 0 and 180 degrees, and therefore by some value of θ between 0 and 90 degrees, and it is customary to choose this value for θ.

If $A = C$, condition (15) becomes $\cos 2\theta = 0$, and for this condition it is sufficient to choose $2\theta = 90$ degrees and $\theta = 45$ degrees.

Therefore, the theorem is proved.

Theorem 5.3 follows from Theorems 5.1 and 5.2.

THEOREM 5.3   *If the graph of*

$$Ax^2 + Bxy + Cy^2 + Dx + Ey + F = 0$$

consists of at least one point, then that graph is either a conic section or two parallel lines.

▶ EXAMPLE 2

Determine the positive acute angle θ through which the coordinate axes must be rotated in order to transform the equation

$$9x^2 - 24xy + 16y^2 - 40x - 30y + 100 = 0 \qquad (17)$$

into an equation in x' and y' which has no $x'y'$ term. Then by the appropriate translation transform this equation in x' and y' into one of the type forms for a conic section. Graph this conic section, and on this graph show the three sets of coordinate axes.

Solution

For the given equation $A = 9$, $B = -24$, $C = 16$, and

$$\tan 2\theta = \frac{B}{A - C} = \frac{-24}{9 - 16} = \frac{24}{7}$$

We find $\sin \theta$ and $\cos \theta$ as follows:

$$\sin \theta = \sqrt{\frac{1 - \cos 2\theta}{2}} = \sqrt{\frac{1 - \frac{7}{25}}{2}} = \frac{3}{5}$$

and

$$\cos \theta = \sqrt{\frac{1 + \cos 2\theta}{2}} = \sqrt{\frac{1 + \frac{7}{25}}{2}} = \frac{4}{5}$$

So the formulas for the rotation are

$$x = \frac{4x' - 3y'}{5} \qquad y = \frac{3x' + 4y'}{5} \qquad (18)$$

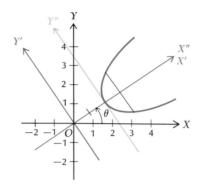

FIGURE 5.12

Using this transformation in (17), performing the operations, and collecting terms, we obtain

$$(144 - 288 + 144)x'^2 + (168 + 216 - 384)x'y' + (81 + 288 + 256)y'^2$$
$$- 25(32 + 18)x' + 25(24 - 24)y' + 2{,}500 = 0$$

which simplifies to $y'^2 - 2x' + 4 = 0$, or

$$y'^2 = 2(x' - 2) \tag{19}$$

We introduce a third set of coordinate axes by means of the translation $x'' = x' - 2$, $y'' = y'$, and transform (19) into

$$y''^2 = 2x'' \tag{20}$$

We recognize (20) as an equation of the form $y^2 = 4px$, and therefore the equation of a parabola. The graph of this parabola is shown in Fig. 5.12 with the three sets of coordinate axes.

EXERCISES

Simplify each of the following equations by the appropriate rotation and translation of axes. Graph the curve whose equation is given, and show all sets of coordinate axes used.

1. $x^2 - 3xy + y^2 = 8$

2. $5x^2 + 4xy + 2y^2 - 24x - 12y + 29 = 0$

3. $4x^2 - 3xy = 18$

4. $7x^2 - 48xy - 7y^2 + 70x + 10y + 100 = 0$

5. $xy = 4$ **6.** $8x^2 + 4xy + 5y^2 = 36$

7. $16x^2 - 24xy + 9y^2 - 85x - 30y + 175 = 0$

8. $17x^2 - 312xy + 108y^2 + 900 = 0$

9. $13x^2 - 10xy + 13y^2 = 72$ **10.** $9x^2 + 24xy + 16y^2 - 5y - 25 = 0$

11. $5x^2 + 6xy + 5y^2 - 32x - 32y + 32 = 0$

12. $36x^2 - 24xy + 29y^2 - 360x - 30y + 945 = 0$

13. $x^2 + 24xy - 6y^2 + 52x + 24y - 283 = 0$

14. $24xy - 7y^2 + 72x - 162y - 423 = 0$

5.3 CONDITION FOR $Ax^2 + Bxy + Cy^2 + Dx + Ey + F$ TO BE THE PRODUCT OF LINEAR FACTORS

We have seen that for certain values of the coefficients, the graph of $Ax^2 + Bxy + Cy^2 + Dx + Ey + F = 0$ will be two lines (either distinct or coincident). In this section we shall discuss a method for determining when this will happen without having to perform a rotation and a translation of axes in order to simplify the given equation.

It is clear that if the equation

$$Ax^2 + Bxy + Cy^2 + Dx + Ey + F = 0 \qquad (21)$$

is equivalent to an equation of the form

$$(a_1x + b_1y + c_1)(a_2x + b_2y + c_2) = 0 \qquad (22)$$

where $a_1, a_2, b_1, b_2, c_1,$ and c_2 are real, a_1 and b_1 are not both zero, and a_2 and b_2 are not both zero, then the graph of (21) will be two lines (possibly coincident). Therefore, to determine when the graph of (21) will be two lines, we seek a condition or conditions under which the left side of Eq. (21) can be written as the product of two first-degree factors in x and y.

Let us assume that $A \neq 0$ and then solve Eq. (21) for x in terms of y. We find that (21) can be written as

$$Ax^2 + (By + D)x + Cy^2 + Ey + F = 0$$

and so $$x = \frac{-(By + D) \pm \sqrt{(By + D)^2 - 4A(Cy^2 + Ey + F)}}{2A} \qquad (23)$$

If the expression under the radical sign in (23) is a perfect square, say the square of $\alpha y + \beta$, we shall have found the condition we were seeking, for then the left side of (21) can be written in factored form as

$$A\left(x - \frac{-(By + D) + (\alpha y + \beta)}{2A}\right)\left(x - \frac{-(By + D) - (\alpha y + \beta)}{2A}\right)$$

and hence as the product of two first-degree factors in x and y.

The expression under the radical sign in (23) can be written as

$$(B^2 - 4AC)y^2 + (2BD - 4AE)y + D^2 - 4AF$$

as the student should verify, and this quadratic expression in y will be a perfect square if and only if

$$(2BD - 4AE)^2 - 4(B^2 - 4AC)(D^2 - 4AF) = 0 \qquad (24)$$

By expanding the products in (24) and collecting like terms we find that (24) can be written in the form

$$4ACF + BDE - AE^2 - B^2F - CD^2 = 0 \qquad (25)$$

The student should verify that (25) can be written in determinant form as

$$\begin{vmatrix} 2A & B & D \\ B & 2C & E \\ D & E & 2F \end{vmatrix} = 0 \qquad (26)$$

We shall denote the determinant appearing in (26) by the symbol Δ. We have shown that, if $A \neq 0$, then Eq. (21) is equivalent to an equation of the form (22) whenever

$$\Delta = \begin{vmatrix} 2A & B & D \\ B & 2C & E \\ D & E & 2F \end{vmatrix} = 0$$

Now if $A = 0$ and $C \neq 0$, we can solve Eq. (21) for y in terms of x. Then, proceeding as we did above, we can show that, if $A = 0$ and $C \neq 0$, Eq. (21) can be written in the form (22) whenever $\Delta = 0$.

If $A = 0$, $C = 0$, and $B \neq 0$, then (21) takes the form $Bxy + Dx + Ey + F = 0$. In Exercise 9 the student is asked to show that this equation is equivalent to an equation of the form (22) provided that $\Delta = 0$.

If $A = 0$, $B = 0$, and $C = 0$, then (21) reduces to a linear equation whose graph is a line, and it is clear that in this case $\Delta = 0$.

Therefore, whenever $\Delta = 0$, the general second-degree equation (21) is equivalent to an equation of the form (22). If $\Delta = 0$, we have

$$\begin{aligned} \{(x, y) \mid Ax^2 &+ Bxy + Cy^2 + Dx + Ey + F = 0\} \\ &= \{(x, y) \mid (a_1x + b_1y + c_1)(a_2x + b_2y + c_2) = 0\} \\ &= \{(x, y) \mid a_1x + b_1y + c_1 = 0\} \cup \{(x, y) \mid a_2x + b_2y + c_2 = 0\} \end{aligned}$$

If all the numbers a_1, a_2, b_1, b_2, c_1, c_2 are real with a_1 and b_1 not both zero and a_2 and b_2 not both zero, the graph of (21) consists of two lines (intersecting, parallel, or coincident). If some of these numbers are not real (i.e., complex with nonzero imaginary part) the graph of (21), where the universe of the variables is Re, will be a single point (see Exercise 7) or will be the empty set (see Exercise 8).

The results described in this section are summarized in Theorem 5.4.

THEOREM 5.4 *For the left side of the general second-degree equation*

$$Ax^2 + Bxy + Cy^2 + Dx + Ey + F = 0 \qquad (21)$$

to be the product of two linear factors, it is necessary and sufficient that $\Delta = 0$. Whenever $\Delta = 0$ the graph (in the two-dimensional coordinate plane) consists of two lines, a point, or the empty set.

When we wish to determine the graph of a given equation of the form (21) with $B \neq 0$, it is usually better to compute the value of the determinant Δ before we undertake the computations involved in rotating the coordinate system. For, if Δ happens to be zero, we know from Theorem 5.4 that the left side of the equation can be factored into linear factors, and these factors can be found either by trial and error or by use of the quadratic formula. This procedure materially shortens the work of determining the graph whenever $\Delta = 0$.

◆ EXAMPLE

Use Theorem 5.4 to show that the graph G of

$$2x^2 + xy - 6y^2 + 4x + y + 2 = 0$$

consists of a pair of straight lines, and construct G.

Solution

Here

$$\Delta = \begin{vmatrix} 2A & B & D \\ B & 2C & E \\ D & E & 2F \end{vmatrix} = \begin{vmatrix} 4 & 1 & 4 \\ 1 & -12 & 1 \\ 4 & 1 & 4 \end{vmatrix} = 0$$

Since $\Delta = 0$, Theorem 5.4 assures us that the left side of the given equation can be factored into linear factors, and we find the factored form of the equation to be

$$(x + 2y + 1)(2x - 3y + 2) = 0$$

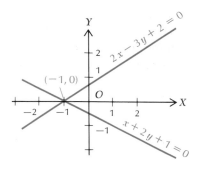

FIGURE 5.13

G is the graph of

$$\{(x, y) \mid (x + 2y + 1)(2x - 3y + 2) = 0\}$$
$$= \{(x, y) \mid x + 2y + 1 = 0\} \cup \{(x, y) \mid 2x - 3y + 2 = 0\}$$

and is shown in Fig. 5.13. The point of intersection of the lines L_1: $x + 2y + 1 = 0$ and L_2: $2x - 3y + 2 = 0$ is $(-1, 0)$.

EXERCISES

In each of Exercises 1–8 compute the value of the determinant Δ for the given equation. If $\Delta = 0$, write the equation in its factored form (22), describe its graph, and construct the graph (unless the graph is the empty set).

1. $3x^2 - 4xy - 4y^2 + 16x + 16y - 12 = 0$

2. $9x^2 - 12xy + 4y^2 + 12x - 8y + 4 = 0$

3. $5x^2 + 4xy + 2y^2 = 1$ (See Example 1 of Sec. 5.2.)

4. $xy = 4$ **5.** $6x^2 + xy - 2y^2 - 8x - 3y + 2 = 0$

6. $x^2 + 2xy + y^2 + 2x + 2y + 1 = 0$ **7.** $x^2 + 3xy + 3y^2 - x + 1 = 0$

8. $x^2 + 2xy + y^2 + 2x + 2y + 6 = 0$

9. If $A = C = 0$ in Eq. (21), the equation becomes

$$Bxy + Dx + Ey + F = 0 \qquad B \neq 0$$

Show that this equation can be written in the form (22) if and only if $\Delta = 0$.

5.4 INVARIANTS

There are certain expressions involving the coefficients in the general equation of the second degree in two variables whose values remain unchanged when the variables are transformed by either a translation or a rotation of the coordinate axes. In any exhaustive and detailed analysis of the general equation of the second degree and the conic sections which are the graphs of this equation, a study of these "invariant" expressions needs to be included. However, this material is not essential to a basic understanding and use of the elements of analytic geometry.

If the coordinate axes are subjected to either a translation or a rotation, the general equation of the second degree in x and y,

$$Ax^2 + Bxy + Cy^2 + Dx + Ey + F = 0 \tag{27}$$

is transformed into the equation

$$A'x'^2 + B'x'y' + C'y'^2 + D'x' + E'y' + F' = 0 \tag{28}$$

For the translation defined by

$$x = x' + h \qquad y = y' + k$$

the student should show that

$$A' = A \tag{29}$$
$$B' = B \tag{30}$$
$$C' = C \tag{31}$$
$$D' = 2Ah + Bk + D \tag{32}$$
$$E' = 2Ck + Bh + E \tag{33}$$
$$F' = Ah^2 + Bhk + Ck^2 + Dh + Ek + F \tag{34}$$

For the rotation through an angle θ, defined by

$$x = x' \cos \theta - y' \sin \theta \qquad y = x' \sin \theta + y' \cos \theta$$

the student was asked in Sec. 5.2 to verify that

$$A' = A \cos^2 \theta + B \sin \theta \cos \theta + C \sin^2 \theta \tag{35}$$
$$B' = B \cos 2\theta - (A - C) \sin 2\theta \tag{36}$$
$$C' = A \sin^2 \theta - B \sin \theta \cos \theta + C \cos^2 \theta \tag{37}$$
$$D' = D \cos \theta + E \sin \theta \tag{38}$$
$$E' = E \cos \theta - D \sin \theta \tag{39}$$
$$F' = F \tag{40}$$

There are some expressions involving the coefficients A, B, C, D, E, and F whose values are unchanged when A is replaced by A', B by B', C by C', etc.

For example, under *translation* of axes it is clear from (29) to (31) that

$$A + B = A' + B' \qquad 2A - C = 2A' - C'$$

Also, under *rotation* we find by adding (35) and (37) that

$$A' + C' = A(\cos^2 \theta + \sin^2 \theta) + C(\sin^2 \theta + \cos^2 \theta)$$

so that

$$A + C = A' + C'$$

Any expression in the coefficients A, B, C, D, E, and F which has the property that its value is unchanged when A is replaced by A', B by B', etc., where the values of A', B', C', D', E', and F' are given by Eqs. (29) to (34), is said to be **invariant under translation** of axes. An expression whose value is unchanged when A is replaced by A', B by B', etc., where the values of A', B', C', D', E', and F' are given by Eqs. (35) to (40), is said to be **invariant under rotation** of axes.

Invariant under translation

Invariant under rotation

We have noted that $A + B$ and $2A - C$ are invariant under translation and that $A + C$ is invariant under rotation.

There are some expressions that are invariant under *both* translation and rotation. Such expressions can frequently be used to advantage as an aid in identifying the nature of the graph of Eq. (27).

We shall be particularly interested in the three expressions $I_1 = A + C$,

$$I_2 = B^2 - 4AC, \text{ and } \Delta = \begin{vmatrix} 2A & B & D \\ B & 2C & E \\ D & E & 2F \end{vmatrix}$$

Each of these expressions is invariant under *both* translation and rotation of coordinate axes.

That I_1 is invariant under both translation and rotation follows immediately from Eqs. (29) and (31) and from Eqs. (35) and (37). A proof that I_2 is invariant under translation and rotation is given in Theorem 5.5.

Theorem 5.4 indicates that the property $\Delta = 0$ is invariant under both rotation and translation (since these transformations of axes do not alter the graph of the equation). A proof that Δ itself is invariant involves considerable algebraic computation which is more readily carried out by methods of matrix algebra not included in this book.

THEOREM 5.5 *The expression $I_2 = B^2 - 4AC$ is invariant under both translation and rotation of axes:*

$$B^2 - 4AC = B'^2 - 4A'C'$$

Proof

(i) For translation, the result is immediate from Eqs. (29) to (31).

(ii)   For rotation, we use Eqs. (35) to (37) to obtain

$$B'^2 - 4A'C' = [B \cos 2\theta - (A - C) \sin 2\theta]^2$$
$$- 4(A \cos^2 \theta + B \sin \theta \cos \theta$$
$$+ C \sin^2 \theta)(A \sin^2 \theta - B \sin \theta \cos \theta + C \cos^2 \theta)$$
$$= (B^2 - 4AC) \cos^4 \theta + (B^2 - 4AC) \sin^4 \theta + 2(B^2 - 4AC) \sin^2 \theta \cos^2 \theta$$
$$= (B^2 - 4AC)(\cos^2 \theta + \sin^2 \theta)^2$$
$$= B^2 - 4AC$$

The student should verify the steps in this computation.

We shall now discuss ways in which the three invariants I_1, I_2, and Δ can be used to determine the nature of the graph of Eq. (27). We shall assume that at least one of the coefficients A, B, C is not zero; otherwise Eq. (27) would become a linear equation $Dx + Ey + F = 0$.

Let us suppose that the invariant I_1 has the value zero; that is, suppose

$$A + C = 0 \tag{41}$$

There are two ways in which this can occur:

   (i) $A = C = 0$
   (ii) $A = -C \neq 0$

CASE (i)   For this case we have $B \neq 0$, and Eq. (27) has the form

$$Bxy + Dx + Ey + F = 0 \tag{42}$$

By means of a *translation* of axes, (42) can be transformed into

$$B'x'y' + F' = 0 \tag{43}$$

As we have seen in Chap. 4, the graph of (43) is a rectangular hyperbola in case $F' \neq 0$; when $F' = 0$, the graph of (43) is two intersecting lines (the x' and y' axes).

CASE (ii)   For this case we can choose a value of the angle θ, so that a *rotation* of axes through angle θ will transform Eq. (27) into an equation of the form (see Theorem 5.2)

$$A'x'^2 + C'y'^2 + D'x' + E'y' + F' = 0 \tag{44}$$

Since $A + C$ is invariant under rotation of axes, we have, in (44), $A' + C' = 0$. By a *translation* of axes, Eq. (44) can be transformed into

$$A''x''^2 + C''y''^2 + F'' = 0 \tag{45}$$

Again, since $A' + C'$ is invariant under translation, we have, in (45), $A'' + C'' = 0$, so that (45) can be written as

$$A''x''^2 - A''y''^2 + F'' = 0 \tag{46}$$

If $F'' \neq 0$, the graph of this equation is a rectangular hyperbola; if $F'' = 0$, the graph of this equation is two intersecting lines $(x'' - y'' = 0, \; x'' + y'' = 0)$.

We have now shown that if $A + C = 0$ in Eq. (27), then the graph of the equation is either a rectangular hyperbola or two perpendicular intersecting lines. We note that in Eq. (43) $\Delta \neq 0$ when $F' \neq 0$ and $\Delta = 0$ when $F' = 0$; also, in Eq. (46) $\Delta \neq 0$ when $F'' \neq 0$ and $\Delta = 0$ when $F'' = 0$. We have proved Theorem 5.6.

THEOREM 5.6   *If, in Eq.* (27), $A + C = 0$, *then the graph of* (27) *is a rectangular hyperbola in case* $\Delta \neq 0$ *and is two perpendicular lines in case* $\Delta = 0$.

The invariant $I_2 = B^2 - 4AC$ is particularly useful in determining the nature of the graph of the general second-degree equation (27). Recall that Theorem 5.2 says that a value of the angle θ can always be selected so that, after a rotation of axes, $B' = 0$ in Eq. (28) and

$$A'x'^2 + C'y'^2 + D'x' + E'y' + F' = 0$$

The proof of Theorem 5.1 indicates that the nature of the graph of this equation largely depends on $A' \cdot C'$ being positive, negative, or zero. Since $B' = 0$,

$$B^2 - 4AC = -4A'C'$$

Hence, the nature of the graph of (27) largely depends on $B^2 - 4AC$ being positive, negative, or zero.

Using the conclusions and details of the proof of Theorem 5.1, together with analyses similar to those used in the proof of Theorem 5.6, and recalling that Δ is invariant under translation and rotation, we can obtain the results listed in Theorem 5.7.

THEOREM 5.7   *The graph of*

$$Ax^2 + Bxy + Cy^2 + Dx + Ey + F = 0$$

is:

(i)   *An ellipse, or a circle, or* $\emptyset$, *in case* $B^2 - 4AC < 0$ *and* $\Delta \neq 0$

(ii)   *A point, in case* $B^2 - 4AC < 0$ *and* $\Delta = 0$

(iii) *A parabola, in case* $B^2 - 4AC = 0$ *and* $\Delta \neq 0$

(iv)   *Two parallel lines, or one line, or* $\emptyset$, *in case* $B^2 - 4AC = 0$ *and* $\Delta = 0$

(v)   *A hyperbola, in case* $B^2 - 4AC > 0$ *and* $\Delta \neq 0$

(vi)   *Two intersecting lines, in case* $B^2 - 4AC > 0$ *and* $\Delta = 0$

▶ EXAMPLE 1

Use Theorem 5.6 to determine the nature of the graph of

$$K: x^2 - 2xy - y^2 + 2x - y + 2 = 0$$

Solution

Clearly, $A + C = 1 + (-1) = 0$. The student should show that $\Delta = -18$. Thus, by Theorem 5.6, K is a rectangular hyperbola. In Exercise 13 the student is asked to graph K.

  Observe that ellipses (or circles) and empty sets (sometimes called "imaginary ellipses") are both included in part (i) of Theorem 5.7 for the case $B^2 - 4AC < 0$ and $\Delta \neq 0$. To determine whether the graph is a nonempty set in this case we may be able, on occasion, to use some simple computation; otherwise a transformation of coordinates will be needed for this determination. The following two examples illustrate the use of Theorem 5.7(i).

▶ EXAMPLE 2

Determine the nature of the graph of

$$5x^2 + 4xy + 2y^2 = 1 \tag{47}$$

Solution

For the given equation we have $A = 5$, $B = 4$, $C = 2$, $D = E = 0$, $F = -1$ so that

$$B^2 - 4AC = 16 - 40 = -24 < 0$$

and
$$\Delta = \begin{vmatrix} 10 & 4 & 0 \\ 4 & 4 & 0 \\ 0 & 0 & -2 \end{vmatrix} \neq 0$$

Therefore, by Theorem 5.7(i), the graph of (47) is an ellipse or the empty set. The graph is not $\emptyset$, as can be seen by observing that the ordered pair $(0, \sqrt{2})$ satisfies Eq. (47). Hence the graph of (47) is an ellipse (see Example 1 in Sec. 5.2).

▶ EXAMPLE 3

Determine the nature of the graph of

$$5x^2 + 4xy + 2y^2 + 1 = 0 \tag{48}$$

Solution

Corresponding coefficients in (47) and (48) are the same, except for F. Therefore, for (48),

$$B^2 - 4AC = -24 < 0 \qquad \text{and} \qquad \Delta \neq 0$$

and the graph of (48) is an ellipse or the empty set. Considerations of the type used in Example 1 are not conclusive in this situation. A rotation of the coordinate axes through the angle θ determined in Example 1 of Sec. 5.2 leads to the equation

$$6x'^2 + y'^2 = -1$$

and the graph of this equation is clearly the empty set (since no ordered pair of real numbers satisfies the equation).

Parts (ii), (iii), (v), and (vi) of Theorem 5.7 give unequivocal identifications of the nature of the graph of a second-degree equation in two variables.

♦ EXAMPLE 4

Determine the nature of the graph of

$$9x^2 - 24xy + 16y^2 - 40x - 30y + 100 = 0 \qquad (49)$$

Solution

For Eq. (49), $B^2 - 4AC = (-24)^2 - 4(9)(16) = 0$ and

$$\Delta = \begin{vmatrix} 18 & -24 & -40 \\ -24 & 32 & -30 \\ -40 & -30 & 200 \end{vmatrix} \neq 0$$

From Theorem 5.7(iii) we know that the graph of Eq. (49) is a parabola (see Example 2 in Sec. 5.2).

In Example 1 of this section we saw that the graph of $x^2 - 2xy - y^2 + 2x - y + 2 = 0$ is a rectangular hyperbola. The information that the graph is a hyperbola could be obtained by noticing that

$$B^2 - 4AC = (-2)^2 - 4(1)(-1) = 8 > 0$$

and

$$\Delta = -18 \neq 0$$

and then using Theorem 5.7(v).

♦ EXAMPLE 5

Determine the nature of the graph of

$$2x^2 + xy - 6y^2 + 4x + y + 2 = 0 \qquad (50)$$

Solution

For Eq. (50) we have
$$B^2 - 4AC = 1 - 4(2)(-6) > 0$$

As we saw in the Example in Sec. 5.3,
$$\Delta = 0$$

From Theorem 5.7(vi) we know that the graph of (50) consists of two intersecting lines (see the Example in Sec. 5.3).

EXERCISES

1–4. For the equation in each of Exercises 1, 3, 5, and 7, respectively, of Sec. 5.2, determine the value of $B^2 - 4AC$ and Δ. Then use Theorem 5.7 to identify the graph. Compare your conclusions with results previously obtained for these exercises.

For the equation in each of Exercises 5–12 find the value of $B^2 - 4AC$ and Δ; then use Theorem 5.7 to identify the graph of the equation.

5. $13x^2 - 10xy + 13y^2 = 72$

6. $x^2 + 2\sqrt{3}xy + 3y^2 + 24y - 24\sqrt{3}x = 0$

7. $9x^2 + 24xy + 16y^2 - 5y - 25 = 0$

8. $4x^2 + 24xy + 11y^2 + 72x + 16y - 156 = 0$

9. $9x^2 - 12xy + 4y^2 + 12x - 8y + 4 = 0$

10. $x^2 + 2xy + 10y^2 - 2x - 2y + 1 = 0$

11. $52x^2 - 72xy + 73y^2 + 400x - 950y + 2{,}725 = 0$

12. $9x^2 - 6xy + y^2 - 3x + y - 2 = 0$

13. We have already noted in Example 1 that $K: x^2 - 2xy - y^2 + 2x - y + 2 = 0$ is a rectangular hyperbola. Simplify the equation of K by the appropriate rotation and translation. Graph K, and on this graph show all sets of coordinate axes used.

14. Show that the distance between the points $P_1(x_1, y_1)$ and $P_2(x_2, y_2)$ (see Sec. 2.2) is invariant under translation and rotation.

15. Show that the tangent of the angles between two lines L_1 with slope m_1 and L_2 with slope m_2 is invariant under translation and rotation.

16. Show that the transformation $x = kx'$, $y = ky'$ leaves invariant the tangent of the angle between two lines, but does not leave invariant the distance between two points.

6 | POLAR COORDINATES

6.1 THE POLAR COORDINATE SYSTEM

Up to this point we have been graphing relations and equations in rectangular coordinate systems. In Sec. 1.7 we introduced the two-dimensional *rectangular coordinate system*, and in Chaps. 2 to 5 we studied the geometrical interpretation of relations and equations based on the correspondence between points in a rectangular coordinate system and ordered pairs of real numbers. Each ordered pair of real numbers can be made to correspond to a point in other kinds of coordinate systems. The basic requirement for any two-dimensional coordinate system is a procedure whereby to each ordered pair of real numbers there is associated one and only one point. We now describe the *polar coordinate system;* it and the rectangular coordinate system are the two most commonly used two-dimensional coordinate systems.

Polar origin
Polar axis
Polar coordinate system

Let O be a fixed point called the **origin** and let OM be a fixed ray extending from O which we shall call the **polar axis** (Fig. 6.1). The origin and polar axis so constructed form a two-dimensional **polar coordinate system.** In the polar coordinate system determined by the origin O and polar axis OM, the point corresponding to an ordered pair of real numbers (a, b) is the point P with the

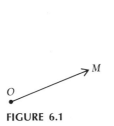

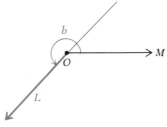

FIGURE 6.1   **FIGURE 6.2**

following properties:

(i)   *P* lies on the line *L* through *O* which makes a *directed* angle of radian measure *b* with the polar axis.

(ii) *P* lies on *L* at a directed distance *a* from *O*.

If *b* is positive, the angle is measured counterclockwise from the polar axis to *L*; if *b* is negative, the angle is measured clockwise from the polar axis to *L*. The positive direction on *L* is the direction from *O* along the terminal side of the angle with radian measure *b* (Fig. 6.2). To indicate that a point *P* corresponds to an ordered pair of real numbers (a, b) in a polar coordinate system, we write $P[a, b]$; that is, we shall use square brackets in the designation $P[a, b]$ of a point in a polar coordinate system in contrast to the use of parentheses in the designation $P(a, b)$ of a point in a rectangular coordinate system.

The points $P_1[3, \frac{1}{6}\pi]$, $P_2[3, 2]$, $P_3[\frac{5}{2}, \frac{5}{4}\pi]$, and $P_4[2, -\frac{1}{4}\pi]$ are shown in Figs. 6.3 to 6.6, respectively. Observe that in plotting a point $P[a, b]$ in a polar coordinate system it is usually convenient first to determine the directed line *L* which makes an angle of radian measure *b* with the polar axis and then to measure a directed distance *a* from *O* on the directed line *L*.

It is customary to use the letters *r* and *θ* to designate the entries of an ordered pair that is to be graphed in a polar coordinate system. If $P[r, \theta]$ is the point corresponding to the ordered pair (r, θ) in a polar coordinate system, the numbers

Polar coordinates   *r* and *θ* are called the *polar coordinates* of *P*. The line segment of directed length *r*, which we shall designate simply as the "directed distance *r*," is called the

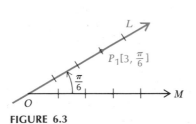

FIGURE 6.3   **FIGURE 6.4**

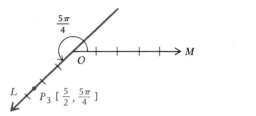

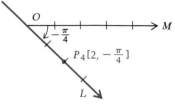

FIGURE 6.5   FIGURE 6.6

Radius vector

Vectorial angle

radius vector of $P[r, \theta]$. The directed angle whose radian measure is θ, which we shall designate simply as "the directed angle θ," is called the **vectorial angle** of $P[r, \theta]$. For the point $P_2[3, 2]$, shown in Fig. 6.4, the radius vector is 3, the vectorial angle is 2 (radians), and the polar coordinates are 3 and 2.

As we have indicated, to an ordered pair of polar coordinates (r, θ) there corresponds one and only one point $P[r, \theta]$ in a polar coordinate system. However, in a given polar coordinate system, a given point P has an unlimited number of pairs of polar coordinates. (This is in contrast to the fact that, in a given rectangular coordinate system, a given point has only one pair of rectangular coordinates.) To illustrate, the point $P_1[3, \frac{1}{6}\pi]$ of Fig. 6.3 with polar coordinates 3 and $\frac{1}{6}\pi$ is the graph, in polar coordinates, of the following pairs:

$$(3, \tfrac{1}{6}\pi + 2\pi), \qquad (3, \tfrac{1}{6}\pi - 2\pi), \qquad (-3, \tfrac{1}{6}\pi + \pi), \qquad (-3, \tfrac{1}{6}\pi - \pi)$$

We indicate this fact by writing

$$P[3, \tfrac{1}{6}\pi] = P[3, \tfrac{1}{6}\pi + 2\pi] = P[3, \tfrac{1}{6}\pi - 2\pi] = P[-3, \tfrac{1}{6}\pi + \pi] = P[-3, \tfrac{1}{6}\pi - \pi]$$

In general,

$$P[r, \theta] = P[r, \theta + 2n\pi] = P[-r, \theta + (2n+1)\pi]$$

where n is any integer.

We note that the origin O of a polar coordinate system can be represented as $O[0, \theta]$, where θ is *any* real number.

The plotting of points in a polar coordinate system is facilitated by the use of polar coordinate paper on which are drawn equally spaced circles with centers at the origin and equally spaced lines through the origin (Fig. 6.7). The points $P_1[2, \frac{1}{3}\pi]$, $P_2[3, 2]$, $P_3[-4, \frac{1}{4}\pi]$, and $P_4[3, \frac{7}{4}\pi]$ are shown in Fig. 6.7, where successive circles have radii that differ by $\frac{1}{2}$ unit.

For a point $P[r, \theta]$ in a polar coordinate system we have considered θ as a real number which specifies the radian measure of an angle. It is possible to consider θ as a number of degrees, specifying of course the degree measure of an angle. When θ is to be interpreted as a number of degrees it will be specifically indicated; otherwise θ will represent radian measure. In this connection we recall

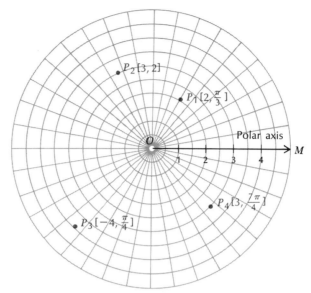

FIGURE 6.7

the following:

$$1 \text{ degree} = \frac{1}{360} \text{ revolution}$$

so

$$1 \text{ revolution} = 360 \text{ degrees} \qquad (1)$$

Also

$$1 \text{ radian} = \frac{1}{2\pi} \text{ revolution}$$

so

$$1 \text{ revolution} = 2\pi \text{ radians} \qquad (2)$$

From (1) and (2) we have

$$2\pi \text{ radians} = 360 \text{ degrees}$$
$$\pi \text{ radians} = 180 \text{ degrees}$$

Therefore,

$$1 \text{ radian} = \frac{180}{\pi} \text{ degrees}$$

$$1 \text{ degree} = \frac{\pi}{180} \text{ radian}$$

From these observations it follows that $\frac{1}{3}\pi$ radians $= 60$ degrees, $\frac{1}{4}\pi$ radian $=$ 45 degrees, $\frac{7}{4}\pi$ radians $= 315$ degrees, and the points P_1, P_3, and P_4 of Fig. 6.7 are the points

$$P_1[2, 60°], \qquad P_3[-4, 45°], \qquad P_4[3, 315°]$$

respectively.

EXERCISES

In each of Exercises 1 and 2 plot on a polar coordinate system the given points.

1. $P[4, 30°]; P[3, 120°]; P[-2, 45°]; P[-5, 135°]$

2. $P[-1, 10°]; P[-3, 150°]; P[4, 240°]; P[3, 300°]$

Express each of the following in radians.

3. 12 degrees   **4.** -10 degrees   **5.** 40 degrees   **6.** 18 degrees

Express each of the following in degrees.

7. $\frac{3}{5}\pi$ radians   **8.** $\frac{1}{8}\pi$ radian   **9.** $-\frac{3}{2}\pi$ radians   **10.** $\frac{9}{2}\pi$ radians

In each of Exercises 11 and 12 plot on a polar coordinate system the given points.

11. $P[3, \frac{1}{3}\pi]; P[-1, \frac{5}{6}\pi]; P[2, \pi]; P[6, -\pi]$

12. $P[-1, -\pi]; P[3, \frac{3}{2}\pi]; P[4, \frac{11}{12}\pi]; P[\frac{5}{2}, \frac{7}{6}\pi]$

13. Give three other pairs of polar coordinates for each of the points of Exercise 11.

14. Give three other pairs of polar coordinates for each of the points of Exercise 12.

15. Plot on a polar coordinate system the points $[4, 0], [4, \frac{1}{6}\pi], [4, \frac{1}{4}\pi], [4, \frac{1}{3}\pi], [4, \frac{1}{2}\pi], [4, \frac{3}{4}\pi], [4, \pi], [4, \frac{3}{2}\pi], [4, \frac{7}{4}\pi], [4, 2\pi]$, and join them with a smooth curve. What does this curve appear to be?

16. Plot on a polar coordinate system the points $[1, \frac{1}{6}\pi], [2, \frac{1}{6}\pi], [3, \frac{1}{6}\pi], [4, \frac{1}{6}\pi], [-1, \frac{1}{6}\pi], [-2, \frac{1}{6}\pi], [-3, \frac{1}{6}\pi], [-4, \frac{1}{6}\pi]$, and join them with a smooth curve. What does this curve appear to be?

6.2 GRAPHS OF EQUATIONS IN POLAR COORDINATES

The **graph in a polar coordinate system** of a relation R is the set of points G with the two properties that:

   (i)   If $(r, \theta) \in R$, then $P[r, \theta] \in G$.

   (ii) If $P \in G$, then *at least one* pair of polar coordinates of P belongs to R.

Graph in polar coordinates

If $S_{r\theta}$ is a sentence in the variables r and θ, the **graph in polar coordinates of the sentence** $S_{r\theta}$ is the graph in polar coordinates of the relation $R = \{(r, \theta) \mid S_{r\theta}\}$.

To illustrate, the graph of the sentence "$r = 5$" is the graph (in polar coordinates) of the relation $R_1 = \{(r, \theta) \mid r = 5\}$. The graph of R_1 is the circle with center at the origin and radius 5 (Fig. 6.8). The graph of the sentence "$\theta = 1$" is the

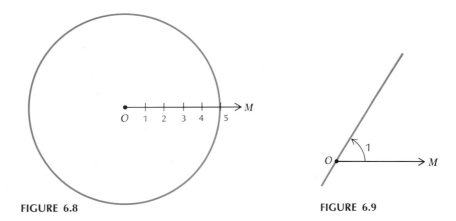

FIGURE 6.8   **FIGURE 6.9**

graph of the relation $R_2 = \{(r, \theta) \mid \theta = 1\}$. The graph of R_2 is the line through the origin that makes an angle of 1 radian with the polar axis (Fig. 6.9).

It should be clear that the graph (in polar coordinates) of any equation of the form

$$r = k \tag{3}$$

where k is a real nonzero number, is a circle with center at the origin and radius $|k|$. Further, any circle with center at the origin is the graph (in polar coordinates) of an equation of the form (3).

It should also be clear that the graph (in polar coordinates) of any equation of the form

$$\theta = k \tag{4}$$

where k is a real number, is a line through the origin. Also, any line through the origin is the graph (in polar coordinates) of an equation of the form (4).

To illustrate, the line which contains the polar axis is the graph of the equation $\theta = 0$, and also of the equations $\theta = \pi$, $\theta = 2\pi$, $\theta = -\pi$, etc. The circle with center at the origin and radius 6 is the graph of $r = 6$ and also of $r = -6$.

To construct the graph of a sentence $S_{r\theta}$ in polar coordinates, we may determine several ordered pairs belonging to the relation $\{(r, \theta) \mid S_{r\theta}\}$ and plot these pairs on a polar coordinate system. We may also make use of any properties of symmetry, as we explain in the next section. The following example illustrates some common procedures.

◆ EXAMPLE

Construct the graph G of the equation $r = 2(1 - \cos \theta)$.

Solution

Before determining several ordered pairs that satisfy the equation, let us make some general observations.

Since $-1 \leqslant \cos \theta \leqslant 1$, it follows that $0 \leqslant 1 - \cos \theta \leqslant 2$ and that $0 \leqslant r \leqslant 4$. We note that $r = 0$ when $\theta = 0$ and when $\theta = 2\pi$; $r = 4$ when $\theta = \pi$.

Since $\cos (-\theta) = \cos \theta$, it follows that if the point $P_1[r_1, \theta_1]$ lies on the graph G of $r = 2(1 - \cos \theta)$, then the point $P_2[r_1, -\theta_1]$ also lies on G. Thus G is symmetric with respect to the line containing the polar axis.

These observations may be used either as an aid in constructing the graph G or as a check on the graph constructed by other means. In this example we shall use them in the latter way.

Representative ordered pairs belonging to the relation

$$R = \{(r, \theta) \mid r = 2(1 - \cos \theta)\}$$

may be found by letting θ be the so-called *special angles* $0, \frac{1}{6}\pi, \frac{1}{4}\pi, \frac{1}{3}\pi, \frac{1}{2}\pi, \frac{2}{3}\pi,$ $\frac{3}{4}\pi, \frac{5}{6}\pi,$ and π, whose trigonometric ratios we should know without use of a trigonometric table. Substituting these values of θ in the equation $r = 2(1 - \cos \theta)$, we determine corresponding values of r and construct the following table (in which the values of $\cos \theta$ and r are given to two decimal places).

θ	0	$\frac{1}{6}\pi$	$\frac{1}{4}\pi$	$\frac{1}{3}\pi$	$\frac{1}{2}\pi$	$\frac{2}{3}\pi$	$\frac{3}{4}\pi$	$\frac{5}{6}\pi$	π
$\cos \theta$	1.00	0.87	0.71	0.50	0.00	-0.50	-0.71	-0.87	-1.00
r	0.00	0.26	0.58	1.00	2.00	3.00	3.42	3.74	4.00

θ	$\frac{7}{6}\pi$	$\frac{5}{4}\pi$	$\frac{4}{3}\pi$	$\frac{3}{2}\pi$	$\frac{5}{3}\pi$	$\frac{7}{4}\pi$	$\frac{11}{6}\pi$	2π
$\cos \theta$	-0.87	-0.71	-0.50	0.00	0.50	0.71	0.87	1.00
r	3.74	3.42	3.00	2.00	1.00	0.58	0.26	0.00

Graphing the ordered pairs (r, θ) given in the table and joining them with a curve (smooth, except at O), we obtain the graph shown in Fig. 6.10. We observe that this graph has the properties listed at the beginning of this solution. The graph is symmetric about the line containing the polar axis; as θ approaches 0, the point on the graph approaches the origin, and as θ approaches 2π, the point on the graph approaches the origin. Since $\cos \theta$ has period 2π [because $\cos (\theta + 2n\pi) = \cos \theta$], no additional points on the graph G will be obtained

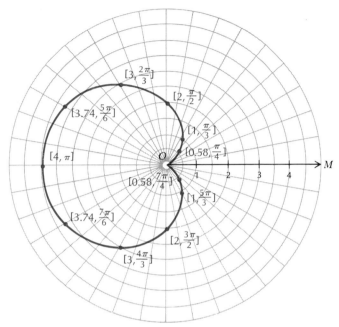

FIGURE 6.10

by assigning values to θ that are outside the interval $[0; 2\pi]$, and the graph shown in Fig. 6.10 is the graph G of the equation $r = 2(1 - \cos \theta)$.

A curve which is the graph of one of the equations

$$r = a(1 + \cos \theta) \qquad r = a(1 - \cos \theta)$$
$$r = a(1 + \sin \theta) \qquad r = a(1 - \sin \theta)$$

Cardioid   is called a *cardioid*. In the Example above we constructed the cardioid with equation $r = a(1 - \cos \theta)$, where $a = 2$.

6.3 SYMMETRY IN POLAR COORDINATES

In the Example of Sec. 6.2 we observed that G: $r = 2(1 - \cos \theta)$ was symmetric with respect to the line containing the polar axis. This observation was based on the fact that whenever a point $P_1[r, \theta]$ belonged to G then the point $P_2[r, -\theta]$ also belonged to G; that is,

$$P_1[r, \theta] \in G \quad \Rightarrow \quad P_2[r, -\theta] \in G$$

In considering various types of symmetry in polar coordinates we find it convenient to superimpose a rectangular coordinate system on the polar coordinate system with the x axis containing the polar axis and the y axis as the line which is the graph of $\theta = \frac{1}{2}\pi$ (Fig. 6.11). This superposition will also be used in the next section when we discuss the conversion from polar coordinates to rectangular coordinates, and vice versa.

From an examination of an appropriate figure, such as Fig. 6.11, we see that if point P_1 is to be symmetric to $P[r, \theta]$ relative to the x axis (the line containing the polar axis), then the polar coordinates of P_1 must be either $[r, -\theta + 2n\pi]$, or $[-r, \pi - \theta + 2n\pi] = [-r, -\theta + (2n+1)\pi]$, for some integer n. Thus we are led to the following test for symmetry concerning $G: E(r, \theta) = 0$, the graph of the equation $E(r, \theta) = 0$:

(i) $G: E(r, \theta) = 0$ *is symmetric with respect to the x axis provided that*

$$P[r, \theta] \in G \quad \Rightarrow \quad P_1[r, -\theta + 2n\pi] \in G$$

or
$$P[r, \theta] \in G \quad \Rightarrow \quad P_1[-r, -\theta + (2n+1)\pi] \in G$$

for some integer n.

Consequently such symmetry exists provided that the equation $E(r, \theta) = 0$ remains unchanged if θ is replaced by $-\theta + 2n\pi$ or if r is replaced by $-r$ and θ by $-\theta + (2n+1)\pi$ for some integer n.

From an examination of an appropriate figure, such as Fig. 6.12, we see that if

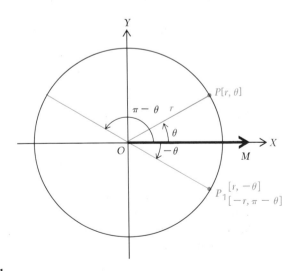

FIGURE 6.11

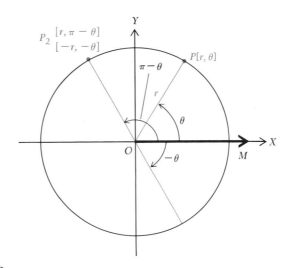

FIGURE 6.12

point P_2 is to be symmetric to $P[r, \theta]$ relative to the y axis (which is the graph of $\theta = \frac{1}{2}\pi$), then the polar coordinates of P_2 must be either $[r, \pi - \theta + 2n\pi] = [r, -\theta + (2n+1)\pi]$, or $[-r, -\theta + 2n\pi]$, for some integer n. Therefore,

(ii) $G: E(r, \theta) = 0$ *is symmetric with respect to the* y *axis provided that*

$$P[r, \theta] \in G \implies P_2[r, -\theta + (2n+1)\pi] \in G$$

or $\qquad P[r, \theta] \in G \implies P_2[-r, -\theta + 2n\pi] \in G$

for some integer n.

Consequently such symmetry exists provided that the equation $E(r, \theta) = 0$ remains unchanged if θ is replaced by $-\theta + (2n+1)\pi$ or if r is replaced by $-r$ and θ by $-\theta + 2n\pi$ for some integer n.

Figure 6.13 illustrates that if point P_3 is to be symmetric to $P[r, \theta]$ relative to the origin O, then the polar coordinates of P_3 must be either $[r, \pi + \theta + 2n\pi] = [r, \theta + (2n+1)\pi]$, or $[-r, \theta + 2n\pi]$, for some integer n. Therefore,

(iii) $G: E(r, \theta) = 0$ *is symmetric with respect to the origin* O *provided that*

$$P[r, \theta] \in G \implies P_3[r, \theta + (2n+1)\pi] \in G$$

or $\qquad P[r, \theta] \in G \implies P_3[-r, \theta + 2n\pi] \in G$

for some integer n.

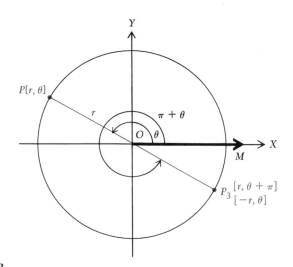

FIGURE 6.13

Consequently such symmetry exists provided that the equation $E(r, \theta) = 0$ remains unchanged if θ is replaced by $\theta + (2n + 1)\pi$ or if r is replaced by $-r$ and θ by $\theta + 2n\pi$ for some integer n.

Tests for symmetry   We shall refer to (i) to (iii) above as *tests for symmetry in polar coordinates.* In using these tests we begin with $n = 0$. If this gives no information, we proceed with $n = \pm 1$, $n = \pm 2$, etc.

Recall that if a graph G is symmetric with respect to both the x axis and the y axis, then G is symmetric with respect to the origin (Theorem 4.3). Also recall Exercise 21 in Sec. 4.2.

Determinations of symmetry in polar coordinates are more complicated than such determinations in rectangular coordinates because a point has an unlimited number of pairs of polar coordinates.

In working with symmetry in polar coordinates, the following trigonometric identities should be kept in mind:

$$\begin{array}{ll} \sin(-\theta) = -\sin\theta & \cos(-\theta) = \cos\theta \\ \sin(\pi - \theta) = \sin\theta & \cos(\pi - \theta) = -\cos\theta \\ \sin(\theta + \pi) = -\sin\theta & \cos(\theta + \pi) = -\cos\theta \end{array}$$

◆ EXAMPLE 1

Construct the graph G of the equation $r = 6 \sin 2\theta$.

Solution

Since $-1 \leqslant \sin 2\theta \leqslant 1$, we have $-6 \leqslant r \leqslant 6$ for the graph G. We note that $r = 6$

when $\sin 2\theta = 1$, and $r = -6$ when $\sin 2\theta = -1$. Thus, for $0 \leq \theta < 2\pi$, we have $r = 6$ when $\theta = \frac{1}{4}\pi$ or $\frac{5}{4}\pi$, and $r = -6$ when $\theta = \frac{3}{4}\pi$ or $\frac{7}{4}\pi$. Also, for points on G,

$$r = 0 \iff \sin 2\theta = 0 \iff 2\theta = n\pi \iff \theta = \frac{n\pi}{2}$$

where n is any integer. So $0, \frac{1}{2}\pi, \pi, \frac{3}{2}\pi$ are "directions in which G passes through the origin."

Let us use test (i) for symmetry with $n = 0$. If we replace θ by $-\theta$ in $r = 6 \sin 2\theta$, we get

$$r = 6 \sin 2(-\theta) = 6 \sin(-2\theta) = -6 \sin 2\theta$$

which is not equivalent to the given equation. But, if we replace r by $-r$ and θ by $\pi - \theta$ in $r = 6 \sin 2\theta$, we get

$$-r = 6 \sin 2(\pi - \theta) = 6 \sin(2\pi - 2\theta) = 6 \sin(-2\theta) = -6 \sin 2\theta$$

So $\qquad r = 6 \sin 2\theta$

Hence G is symmetric with respect to the x axis.

Next we use test (ii) with $n = 0$. If we replace θ by $\pi - \theta$ in $r = 6 \sin 2\theta$, we get

$$r = 6 \sin 2(\pi - \theta) = 6 \sin(2\pi - 2\theta) = 6 \sin(-2\theta) = -6 \sin 2\theta$$

which is not equivalent to the given equation. However, if we replace r by $-r$ and θ by $-\theta$ in $r = 6 \sin 2\theta$, we get

$$-r = 6 \sin 2(-\theta) = 6 \sin(-2\theta) = -6 \sin 2\theta$$

So $\qquad r = 6 \sin 2\theta$

Therefore G is symmetric with respect to the y axis.

Since G is symmetric with respect to both the x axis and the y axis, it is also symmetric with respect to the origin O.

Since we are concerned here with $\sin 2\theta$, it is convenient to assign to θ values so that 2θ will be a special angle. In this manner for $0 \leq \theta \leq \frac{1}{2}\pi$ with $0 \leq 2\theta \leq \pi$

TABLE 6.1

θ	0	$\frac{1}{12}\pi$	$\frac{1}{8}\pi$	$\frac{1}{6}\pi$	$\frac{1}{4}\pi$	$\frac{1}{3}\pi$	$\frac{3}{8}\pi$	$\frac{5}{12}\pi$	$\frac{1}{2}\pi$
2θ	0	$\frac{1}{6}\pi$	$\frac{1}{4}\pi$	$\frac{1}{3}\pi$	$\frac{1}{2}\pi$	$\frac{2}{3}\pi$	$\frac{3}{4}\pi$	$\frac{5}{6}\pi$	π
$\sin 2\theta$	0	$\frac{1}{2}$	$\frac{1}{2}\sqrt{2}$	$\frac{1}{2}\sqrt{3}$	1	$\frac{1}{2}\sqrt{3}$	$\frac{1}{2}\sqrt{2}$	$\frac{1}{2}$	0
r	0	3	$3\sqrt{2}$	$3\sqrt{3}$	6	$3\sqrt{3}$	$3\sqrt{2}$	3	0
Point	O	P_1	P_2	P_3	P_4	P_5	P_6	P_7	O

and sin $2\theta \geqslant 0$, we construct Table 6.1. The first and fourth rows of this table give coordinates of the origin O and the points $P_1, \ldots, P_7$; the latter are located in the first quadrant, as indicated in Fig. 6.14. By joining these points and the origin, we get the portion of G lying in the first quadrant.

Since G is symmetric with respect to both the x axis and the y axis, we could complete the graph of G simply by using these established symmetries. Such procedure is customary, and the student is urged to use it whenever possible. However, it is instructive to construct G for $\frac{1}{2}\pi \leqslant \theta \leqslant \pi$ directly, as we did for $0 \leqslant \theta \leqslant \frac{1}{2}\pi$.

Extending Table 6.1 for $\frac{1}{2}\pi \leqslant \theta \leqslant \pi$ with $\pi \leqslant 2\theta \leqslant 2\pi$ and sin $2\theta \leqslant 0$, we obtain Table 6.2. The first and fourth rows of Table 6.2 give coordinates of the origin O and the points $P_8, \ldots, P_{14}$. Observe that for each of the latter points θ is a *second*-quadrant angle and r has a *negative* value. Therefore these points are located in the *fourth* quadrant, as indicated in Fig. 6.14.

Using the fact that G is symmetric with respect to the origin, we can construct that portion of G which is located in the third quadrant (for which $\pi < \theta < \frac{3}{2}\pi$) and which is symmetric to the portion of G we have constructed in the first quadrant. Similarly, we can construct that portion of G which is located in the second quadrant (for which $\frac{3}{2}\pi < \theta < 2\pi$) and which is symmetric to that portion of G constructed in the fourth quadrant.

Since sin 2θ is periodic with period 2π, no additional points on G are obtained

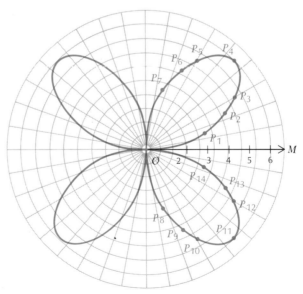

FIGURE 6.14

TABLE 6.2

θ	$\frac{1}{2}\pi$	$\frac{7}{12}\pi$	$\frac{5}{8}\pi$	$\frac{2}{3}\pi$	$\frac{3}{4}\pi$	$\frac{5}{6}\pi$	$\frac{7}{8}\pi$	$\frac{11}{12}\pi$	π
2θ	π	$\frac{7}{6}\pi$	$\frac{5}{4}\pi$	$\frac{4}{3}\pi$	$\frac{3}{2}\pi$	$\frac{5}{3}\pi$	$\frac{7}{4}\pi$	$\frac{11}{6}\pi$	2π
$\sin 2\theta$	0	$-\frac{1}{2}$	$-\frac{1}{2}\sqrt{2}$	$-\frac{1}{2}\sqrt{3}$	-1	$-\frac{1}{2}\sqrt{3}$	$-\frac{1}{2}\sqrt{2}$	$-\frac{1}{2}$	0
r	0	-3	$-3\sqrt{2}$	$-3\sqrt{3}$	-6	$-3\sqrt{3}$	$-3\sqrt{2}$	-3	0
Point	O	P_8	P_9	P_{10}	P_{11}	P_{12}	P_{13}	P_{14}	O

by assigning to θ a value outside the interval $[0; 2\pi]$.

The graph of either of the equations

$$r = a \sin n\theta \qquad r = a \cos n\theta$$

Roses where a is a real number and n is a positive integer, is called an *n-leaved rose* if n is an *odd* integer and a *2n-leaved rose* if n is an *even* integer. These roses have properties illustrated somewhat by Fig. 6.14. Each of the loops in a rose curve is called a leaf. In Example 1, for which $r = 6 \sin 2\theta$, $n = 2$, the graph is a 4-leaved rose.

♦ EXAMPLE 2

Construct the graph G of the equation $r = 4 \sin 3\theta$.

Solution

Since the value of $\sin 3\theta$ is between -1 and 1, r for points on G cannot be less than -4 nor greater than 4; $r = 4$ for $\theta = \frac{1}{6}\pi$ or $\theta = \frac{5}{6}\pi$; $r = -4$ for $\theta = \frac{1}{2}\pi$.
    For points on G,

$$r = 0 \iff \sin 3\theta = 0 \iff 3\theta = n\pi \iff \theta = \frac{n\pi}{3}$$

where n is any integer. So, 0, $\frac{1}{3}\pi$, $\frac{2}{3}\pi$, π, $\frac{4}{3}\pi$, and $\frac{5}{3}\pi$ are "directions in which G passes through the origin."
    G: $r = 4 \sin 3\theta$ is a 3-leaved rose. From the above observations, there is one leaf for $\theta \in [0; \frac{1}{3}\pi]$, with its stem (or greatest radius vector) along the line $\theta = \frac{1}{6}\pi$.
    Since we are concerned here with $\sin 3\theta$, we assign to θ values which will make 3θ a special angle. In this manner for $0 \leq \theta \leq \frac{1}{3}\pi$, with $0 \leq 3\theta \leq \pi$ and $\sin 3\theta \geq 0$, we construct Table 6.3. Locating the points $O, P_1, \ldots, P_7$ on a

polar coordinate system and drawing a smooth curve through them, we obtain the leaf in the first quadrant shown in Fig. 6.15.

TABLE 6.3

θ	0	$\frac{1}{18}\pi$	$\frac{1}{12}\pi$	$\frac{1}{9}\pi$	$\frac{1}{6}\pi$	$\frac{2}{9}\pi$	$\frac{1}{4}\pi$	$\frac{5}{18}\pi$	$\frac{1}{3}\pi$
3θ	0	$\frac{1}{6}\pi$	$\frac{1}{4}\pi$	$\frac{1}{3}\pi$	$\frac{1}{2}\pi$	$\frac{2}{3}\pi$	$\frac{3}{4}\pi$	$\frac{5}{6}\pi$	π
$\sin 3\theta$	0	$\frac{1}{2}$	$\frac{1}{2}\sqrt{2}$	$\frac{1}{2}\sqrt{3}$	1	$\frac{1}{2}\sqrt{3}$	$\frac{1}{2}\sqrt{2}$	$\frac{1}{2}$	0
r	0	2	$2\sqrt{2}$	$2\sqrt{3}$	4	$2\sqrt{3}$	$2\sqrt{2}$	2	0
Point	O	P_1	P_2	P_3	P_4	P_5	P_6	P_7	O

Let us try to use the second part of test (ii) for symmetry with $n = 0$. If we replace (r, θ) by $(-r, -\theta)$ in $r = 5 \sin 3\theta$, we get

$$-r = 5 \sin 3(-\theta) = 5 \sin (-3\theta) = -5 \sin 3\theta$$

which is equivalent to $r = 5 \sin 3\theta$. Therefore G is symmetric with respect to the y axis, and corresponding to the leaf of G which we have constructed in the first quadrant there is a leaf in the second quadrant, as shown in Fig. 6.15. For this leaf $\frac{2}{3}\pi \leq \theta \leq \pi$, with its stem along the line L: $\theta = \frac{5}{6}\pi$. Here $2\pi \leq 3\theta \leq 3\pi$, and $r \geq 0$.

The third leaf of G occurs when $\frac{1}{3}\pi \leq \theta \leq \frac{2}{3}\pi$, with $\pi \leq 3\theta \leq 2\pi$ and $r \leq 0$. The stem is along the line L: $\theta = \frac{1}{2}\pi$ with the end of this stem being the point $[-4, \frac{1}{2}\pi]$. This leaf may be constructed directly with the aid of an appropriate table. More easily, one can construct it by using its properties stated above and the fact that it has the same shape and size as the leaf we constructed in the first quadrant.

We have so far considered only values of θ for which $0 \leq \theta \leq \pi$. However, if we let θ take on values for which $\pi < \theta < 2\pi$, we find that we obtain again the points on the leaf in the first quadrant for $\pi < \theta < \frac{4}{3}\pi$; for $\frac{4}{3}\pi < \theta < \frac{5}{3}\pi$ we obtain the points on the leaf with stem along $\theta = \frac{1}{2}\pi$; for $\frac{5}{3}\pi < \theta < 2\pi$ we obtain the points on the leaf in the second quadrant. From these facts and the fact that $\sin 3\theta$ is periodic with period 2π we see that Fig. 6.15 shows the entire graph G.

▶ EXAMPLE 3

Construct the graph G of $r^2 = 9 \cos 2\theta$.

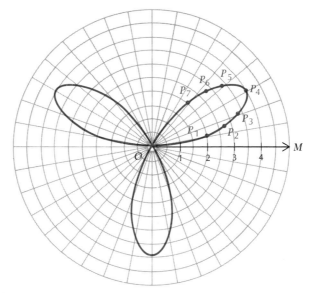

FIGURE 6.15

Solution

Here r attains its largest and smallest values when $\cos 2\theta = 1$, and, for $2\theta \in [0; 2\pi]$,

$$\cos 2\theta = 1 \quad \Rightarrow \quad 2\theta = 0 \text{ or } 2\pi \quad \Rightarrow \quad \theta = 0 \text{ or } \pi$$

So $r = \pm 3$ when $\theta = 0$ and when $\theta = \pi$.

Real values of r are obtained only when $\cos 2\theta \geqslant 0$; therefore, r is real when

$$-\tfrac{1}{2}\pi \leqslant 2\theta \leqslant \tfrac{1}{2}\pi \qquad \text{and} \qquad \tfrac{3}{2}\pi \leqslant 2\theta \leqslant \tfrac{5}{2}\pi$$

that is, when

$$-\tfrac{1}{4}\pi \leqslant \theta \leqslant \tfrac{1}{4}\pi \qquad \text{and} \qquad \tfrac{3}{4}\pi \leqslant \theta \leqslant \tfrac{5}{4}\pi$$

For points on G

$$r = 0 \quad \Longleftrightarrow \quad \cos 2\theta = 0$$

For $\theta = -\tfrac{1}{4}\pi, \tfrac{1}{4}\pi, \tfrac{3}{4}\pi, \tfrac{5}{4}\pi$,

$$\cos 2\theta = 0$$

Hence $-\tfrac{1}{4}\pi, \tfrac{1}{4}\pi, \tfrac{3}{4}\pi, \tfrac{5}{4}\pi$ are "directions in which G passes through the origin."

If we replace θ by $-\theta$ in $r^2 = 9 \cos 2\theta$, we get $r^2 = 9 \cos 2(-\theta) = 9 \cos 2\theta$, so G is symmetric with respect to the x axis. Also, if we replace r by $-r$ and θ by $-\theta$ in $r^2 = 9 \cos 2\theta$, we get $(-r)^2 = 9 \cos 2(-\theta)$ or $r^2 = 9 \cos 2\theta$, so G is also symmetric with respect to the y axis and hence with respect to the origin. Therefore, we can obtain the entire graph G by symmetry when we have constructed that portion of G lying in the first quadrant.

TABLE 6.4					
θ	0	$\frac{1}{12}\pi$	$\frac{1}{8}\pi$	$\frac{1}{6}\pi$	$\frac{1}{4}\pi$
2θ	0	$\frac{1}{6}\pi$	$\frac{1}{4}\pi$	$\frac{1}{3}\pi$	$\frac{1}{2}\pi$
$\cos 2\theta$	1	0.87	0.71	0.50	0
r^2	9	7.63	6.39	4.50	0
r	3	2.76	2.53	2.12	0
Point	P_1	P_2	P_3	P_4	O

We construct Table 6.4; the first and fifth rows of this table give the coordinates of the points P_1, P_2, P_3, P_4 and the origin. Plotting these points and joining them with a smooth curve, we get the portion of G for the first quadrant (Fig. 6.16).

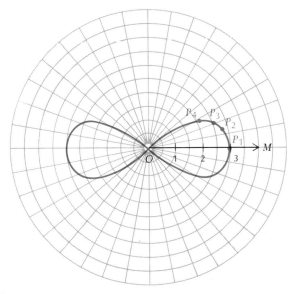

FIGURE 6.16

Using it and the observations which we made above regarding symmetry, we construct the other part of G, as shown in Fig. 6.16.

Lemniscate   The graph of $r^2 = 9 \cos 2\theta$, shown in Fig. 6.16, is called a *lemniscate*, as is the graph of any equation of the form $r^2 = a^2 \cos 2\theta$ or $r^2 = a^2 \sin 2\theta$.

EXERCISES

In each of Exercises 1–11 identify and construct the graph of the given equation.

1. $r = 3(1 + \cos \theta)$ **2.** $r = 4(1 - \sin \theta)$

3. $r = a(1 + \sin \theta), a > 0$ **4.** $r = 4 \cos 3\theta$

5. $r = a \cos 2\theta, a > 0$ **6.** $r = a \sin 4\theta, a > 0$

7. $r^2 = 4 \sin 2\theta$ **8.** $r = 3$

9. $r = -4$ **10.** $\theta = \frac{1}{3}\pi$ **11.** $\theta = -\frac{3}{4}\pi$

Let a and b be nonzero real numbers. The graph of each of the equations *Limaçon* $r = a + b \cos \theta$ and $r = a + b \sin \theta$ is called a *limacon*. If $a + b$ and $a - b$ have different signs (one positive and the other negative), the limaçon has an inner loop.

In each of Exercises 12–19 construct the graph of the given equation.

12. $r = 1 + 2 \cos \theta$ **13.** $r = -1 + 2 \cos \theta$

14. $r = -6 + 4 \cos \theta$ **15.** $r = 4 + 2 \sin \theta$

16. $r = 3 - \sin \theta$ **17.** $r = 3(1 - 2 \cos \theta)$

18. $r = 1 + 2 \sin \theta$ **19.** $r = -2 - 2 \sin \theta$

In each of Exercises 20–23 graph the indicated region of the plane.

20. $\{(r, \theta) \mid 0 \leq r \leq 2, 0 \leq \theta \leq \frac{1}{3}\pi\}$ **21.** $\{(r, \theta) \mid 1 \leq r \leq 3, \frac{1}{6}\pi \leq \theta \leq \frac{1}{3}\pi\}$

22. $\{(r, \theta) \mid 2 \leq r \leq 4, 0 \leq \theta \leq \pi\}$ **23.** $\{(r, \theta) \mid 0 \leq r \leq 3, \theta = 1\}$

24. Construct the graph of $r = a \sin^3 \frac{1}{3}\theta$.

6.4 CONVERSION OF COORDINATES

Let us superimpose a rectangular coordinate system on a polar coordinate system in such a way that the origins of the two systems coincide and the polar axis lies along the positive x axis, as we did in Sec. 6.3. Any point P in the plane has polar coordinates r and θ and rectangular coordinates x and y, and we write

$$P(x, y) = P[r, \theta]$$

We expect that there is a relationship between the rectangular coordinates x, y and the polar coordinates r, θ. It is the purpose of this section to find and use this relationship.

If $r > 0$ so that P is on the terminal side of θ and $r = |OP|$ (Fig. 6.17), then

$$\cos \theta = \frac{x}{|OP|} = \frac{x}{r} \qquad \sin \theta = \frac{y}{|OP|} = \frac{y}{r}$$

and
$$x = r \cos \theta \qquad y = r \sin \theta$$

If $r < 0$, then P is on the terminal side of $\theta + \pi$ (that is, on the extension of the terminal side of θ) and $r = -|OP|$ (Fig. 6.18). Let P_1 be the point that is symmetric to $P(x, y)$ with respect to the origin, so that the rectangular coordinates of P_1 are $(-x, -y)$ and the polar coordinates of P_1 are $[-r, \theta]$. Then $|OP_1| = |OP| = -r$ (note that $-r > 0$) and

$$\cos \theta = \frac{-x}{|OP_1|} = \frac{-x}{-r} = \frac{x}{r} \qquad \sin \theta = \frac{-y}{|OP_1|} = \frac{-y}{-r} = \frac{y}{r}$$

so that

$$x = r \cos \theta \qquad y = r \sin \theta$$

Therefore, $P(x, y) = P[r, \theta]$ if and only if

Conversion formulas

$$x = r \cos \theta \qquad y = r \sin \theta \tag{5}$$

When a rectangular coordinate system and a polar coordinate system are superimposed as described in the first paragraph of this section, formulas (5) enable us to find the rectangular coordinates of a point when its polar coordinates are known. We call the formulas (5) the *conversion formulas*. In the remainder

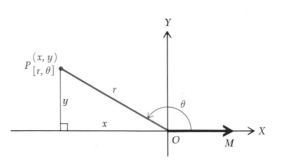

FIGURE 6.17

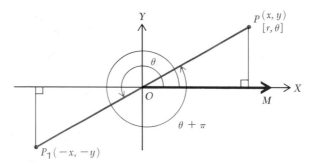

FIGURE 6.18

of this book whenever we consider both rectangular and polar coordinates of a point we shall assume that the two coordinate systems are superimposed as described above.

◆ EXAMPLE 1

Find the rectangular coordinates of the point $P[4, \frac{2}{3}\pi]$.

Solution

We wish to determine values for x and y so that $P(x, y) = P[4, \frac{2}{3}\pi]$. Using the conversion formulas (5), with $r = 4$ and $\theta = \frac{2}{3}\pi$, we get

$$x = 4 \cos \tfrac{2}{3}\pi = 4 \cos (\pi - \tfrac{1}{3}\pi) = -4 \cos \tfrac{1}{3}\pi = -2$$
$$y = 4 \sin \tfrac{2}{3}\pi = 4 \sin (\pi - \tfrac{1}{3}\pi) = 4 \sin \tfrac{1}{3}\pi = 2\sqrt{3}$$

◆ EXAMPLE 2

Find two sets of polar coordinates r and θ of the point $P(-1, -1)$.

Solution

Here $x = -1$, $y = -1$, and by using the conversion formulas we get

$$-1 = r \cos \theta \qquad \text{and} \qquad -1 = r \sin \theta$$

Squaring both sides of these equalities and adding the results, we get $2 = r^2$. So $r = \pm\sqrt{2}$. Also, using the equalities above, we obtain $\tan \theta = 1$. Observe that $P(-1, -1)$ is in the third quadrant, so that $P(-1, -1) = P[\sqrt{2}, \frac{5}{4}\pi] = P[-\sqrt{2}, \frac{1}{4}\pi]$.

If we square both sides of the conversion formulas $x = r \cos \theta$, $y = r \sin \theta$ and add the results, we obtain

$$x^2 + y^2 = r^2 \qquad r = \pm\sqrt{x^2 + y^2} \tag{6}$$

If $r \neq 0$,

$$\cos \theta = \frac{x}{r} = \frac{x}{\pm\sqrt{x^2 + y^2}} \qquad \sin \theta = \frac{y}{\pm\sqrt{x^2 + y^2}} \tag{7}$$

If $x \neq 0$,

$$\tan \theta = \frac{y}{x} \tag{8}$$

If $x = 0$ and $y \neq 0$, then $\tan \theta$ is not defined, but $\theta = (2n + 1)\frac{1}{2}\pi$, where n is an integer. If $x = 0$ and $y = 0$, then $\tan \theta$ is undefined; but we know that $P(0, 0)$ is the origin O, which has the polar coordinates $[0, \theta]$, where θ is any number.

The equalities (5) enable us to transform an equation in rectangular coordinates x and y to an equation in polar coordinates, and equalities (6) to (8) may be helpful in transforming an equation in polar coordinates to an equation in rectangular coordinates.

◆ EXAMPLE 3

Find an equation in polar coordinates of the curve C for which $x^2 + y^2 - 2ay = 0$ is an equation in rectangular coordinates. Graph C.

Solution

By use of equalities (5) the given equation is transformed into

$$r^2 - 2ar \sin \theta = 0 \qquad \text{or} \qquad r(r - 2a \sin \theta) = 0$$

Thus, C is the graph of the relation

$$R = \{(r, \theta) \mid r = 0\} \cup \{(r, \theta) \mid r = 2a \sin \theta\}$$

Since the coordinates of the point $O(0, 0)$ satisfy the equation $r = 2a \sin \theta$, the graph of $r = 0$ is included in the graph of $r = 2a \sin \theta$. Therefore, we may write

$$R = \{(r, \theta) \mid r = 2a \sin \theta\}$$

and $r = 2a \sin \theta$ is an equation of C. As we know from Sec. 2.9, C: $x^2 + y^2 - 2ay = 0$ is a circle with radius a and center at the point $P_1(0, a) = P_1[a, \frac{1}{2}\pi]$. The graph of C appears in Fig. 6.19.

◆ EXAMPLE 4

Find an equation in rectangular coordinates of the curve C for which $r = 2a \cos \theta$ is an equation in polar coordinates. Graph C.

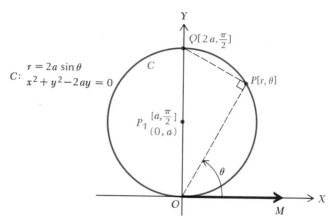

FIGURE 6.19

Solution

In order to make use of equalities (5) and (6), it is convenient here to multiply each side of $r = 2a \cos \theta$ by r to obtain

$$r^2 = 2ar \cos \theta$$

The graph of $r^2 = 2ar \cos \theta$ is the graph of the relation

$$R = \{(r, \theta) \mid r = 0\} \cup \{(r, \theta) \mid r = 2a \cos \theta\}$$

Since the coordinates of the point $O[0, \frac{1}{2}\pi]$ satisfy the equation $r = 2a \cos \theta$, the graph of $r = 0$ is included in the graph of $r = 2a \cos \theta$. Therefore, the graph of R (and hence the graph of $r^2 = 2ar \cos \theta$) is the same as the graph of $r = 2a \cos \theta$.
   Using $x^2 + y^2 = r^2$ from (6) and $x = r \cos \theta$ from (5), we transform $r^2 = 2ar \cos \theta$ into

$$x^2 + y^2 = 2ax$$

which is an equation of C in rectangular coordinates. The graph of C is shown in Fig. 6.20, and it is a circle with radius a and center at the point $P_1[a, 0] = P_1(a, 0)$.

▶ EXAMPLE 5

Find an equation in rectangular coordinates of the curve C for which

$$r = \frac{8}{2 - \cos \theta} \tag{9}$$

is an equation in polar coordinates.

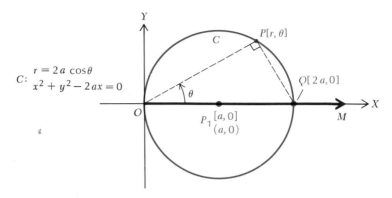

FIGURE 6.20

Solution

Multiplying each side of (9) by $2 - \cos\theta$, we obtain $2r - r\cos\theta = 8$ or

$$2r = r\cos\theta + 8$$

By using $x = r\cos\theta$ from the conversion formulas (5), this last equation can be written as

$$2r = x + 8$$

or, on squaring both sides,

$$4r^2 = x^2 + 16x + 64$$

Now using $x^2 + y^2 = r^2$ from (6), we get

$$4(x^2 + y^2) - x^2 + 16x + 64$$
$$3x^2 + 4y^2 - 16x - 64 = 0 \tag{10}$$

Using the methods discussed in Chap. 4, we find that Eq. (10) can be written in the form

$$\frac{(x - \frac{8}{3})^2}{\frac{256}{9}} + \frac{y^2}{\frac{64}{3}} = 1$$

which is an equation of an ellipse with center at $(\frac{8}{3}, 0)$, one vertex at $(8, 0)$, and one focus at $(0, 0)$, as shown in Fig. 6.21.

Our work to this point has shown that every point on the graph of (9) is on the ellipse which is the graph of (10). However, in arriving at Eq. (10) we squared both sides of the given equation, and this procedure sometimes produces an equation that is not equivalent to the given equation. Therefore, we must now determine whether every point on the ellipse that is the graph of (10) is also on the graph of (9). Using the conversion formulas (5), we see that (10) can be written in the form

$$3r^2 \cos^2 \theta + 4r^2 \sin^2 \theta - 16r \cos \theta - 64 = 0$$

This equation is equivalent to each of the following equations:

$$3r^2 \cos^2 \theta + 4r^2(1 - \cos^2 \theta) - 16r \cos \theta - 64 = 0$$
$$4r^2 - r^2 \cos^2 \theta - 16r \cos \theta - 64 = 0$$
$$4r^2 - (r \cos \theta + 8)^2 = 0$$
$$(2r - r \cos \theta - 8)(2r + r \cos \theta + 8) = 0$$

That is, the ellipse [which is the graph of (10)] is the graph, in polar coordinates, of the relation

$$R = \{(r, \theta) \mid 2r - r \cos \theta - 8 = 0\} \cup \{(r, \theta) \mid 2r + r \cos \theta + 8 = 0\}$$
$$= \left\{(r, \theta) \mid r = \frac{8}{2 - \cos \theta}\right\} \cup \left\{(r, \theta) \mid r = \frac{-8}{2 + \cos \theta}\right\}$$
$$= R_1 \cup R_2$$

where

$$R_1 = \left\{(r, \theta) \mid r = \frac{8}{2 - \cos \theta}\right\} \qquad R_2 = \left\{(r, \theta) \mid r = \frac{-8}{2 + \cos \theta}\right\}$$

We recall that $P[r, \theta] = P[-r, \theta + \pi]$ and observe that if we replace r by $-r$ and θ by $\theta + \pi$ in the equation $r = 8/(2 - \cos \theta)$ we obtain

$$-r = \frac{8}{2 - \cos (\theta + \pi)}$$

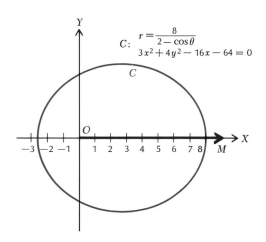

FIGURE 6.21

which is equivalent to

$$r = \frac{-8}{2 + \cos \theta}$$

This result shows that the graph of the relation R_1 is the same as the graph of the relation R_2. Hence, if a point is on the ellipse with Eq. (10), that point is on the graph of $r = 8/(2 - \cos \theta)$.

We have now shown that $3x^2 + 4y^2 - 16x - 64 = 0$ is an equation in rectangular coordinates of the curve for which $r = 8/(2 - \cos \theta)$ is an equation in polar coordinates.

Our consideration of the relations R_1 and R_2 in Example 5 illustrates the fact that *two different equations in polar coordinates may have the same graph.* This situation arises from the fact that a point has many different pairs of polar coordinates.

EXERCISES

Find the rectangular coordinates of each of the points in Exercises 1 and 2.

1. $[-3, \frac{1}{2}\pi]$, $[3\sqrt{2}, \frac{3}{4}\pi]$, $[-3, \pi]$, $[4, \frac{2}{3}\pi]$

2. $[5\sqrt{2}, \frac{1}{4}\pi]$, $[-6, \frac{2}{3}\pi]$, $[8, \pi]$, $[\sqrt{8}, -\frac{3}{4}\pi]$

Find two pairs of polar coordinates for each of the points whose rectangular coordinates are given in Exercises 3 and 4.

3. $(-6\sqrt{3}, -6)$, $(-3, 0)$, $(4 - 4)$, $(3, 3)$

4. $(3\sqrt{3}, -3)$, $(-5, 5)$, $(-2\sqrt{3}, -6)$, $(0, -3)$

In each of Exercises 5–10 an equation of a curve is given in rectangular coordinates. Find an equation of this curve in polar coordinates. Graph the curve in either rectangular or polar coordinates.

5. $x = 4$ **6.** $y = -3$ **7.** $x^2 + y^2 = 16$

8. $x^2 + y^2 = 6x + 8y$ **9.** $x^2 + 4y^2 = 4$ **10.** $(x^2 + y^2)^2 = x^2 - y^2$

In each of Exercises 11–16 an equation of a curve is given in polar coordinates. Find an equation of this curve in rectangular coordinates. Graph the curve in either rectangular or polar coordinates.

11. $r = 7$ **12.** $r = 6 \sin \theta$

13. $r = 9 \tan^2 \theta \sec \theta$ **14.** $r^2 = 25 \sin 2\theta$

15. $r(2 \cos \theta + 3 \sin \theta) = 5$ **16.** $r = 2/(1 + \cos \theta)$

17. Show that the graphs of $r = 4/(1 + \sin \theta)$ and $r = -4/(1 - \sin \theta)$ are the same. Find an equation of this graph in rectangular coordinates. Construct this graph on either a rectangular or a polar coordinate system.

6.5 EQUATIONS OF LINES AND CIRCLES IN POLAR COORDINATES

Recall from Sec. 3.2 that every line L in the rectangular coordinate plane has an equation of the form

$$Ax + By + C = 0 \tag{11}$$

where A, B, and C are real numbers. With the use of the conversion formulas (5), Eq. (11) can be written in polar coordinates as

$$r(A \cos \theta + B \sin \theta) + C = 0 \tag{12}$$

If a line L is perpendicular to the x axis, it has a rectangular equation of the form

$$x = a$$

which, since $x = r \cos \theta$ from the conversion formulas, can be written in polar coordinates as

$$r \cos \theta = a \tag{13}$$

Equation (13) can also be obtained by examining Fig. 6.22 and observing that, for any point $P[r, \theta]$ on line L, $\cos \theta = a/r$, or $r \cos \theta = a$.

If a line L is perpendicular to the y axis, it has a rectangular equation of the form

$$y = b$$

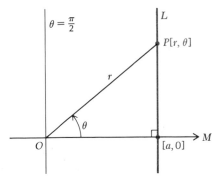

FIGURE 6.22

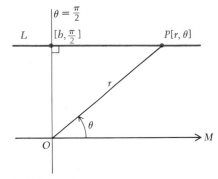

FIGURE 6.23

which, since $y = r \sin \theta$, can be written in polar coordinates as

$$r \sin \theta = b \tag{14}$$

Equation (14) of a line perpendicular to the y axis can also be obtained by examining Fig. 6.23 and observing that, for any point on line L, $\sin \theta = b/r$, or $r \sin \theta = b$.

Recall that a line through the origin has an equation in polar coordinates of the form

$$\theta = k$$

Consider the circle with center at the point $P_1[r_1, \theta_1]$ and with radius a (Fig. 6.24). Let $P[r, \theta]$ be any point on the circle. By applying the law of cosines to the triangle P_1OP we obtain

$$r^2 + r_1{}^2 - 2r_1 r \cos(\theta - \theta_1) = a^2 \tag{15}$$

as an equation, in polar coordinates, of the circle. The general equation (15) of a circle in polar coordinates is not used very often. However, several special cases of Eq. (15) are useful.

If the circle C passes through the origin (Fig. 6.25), then, in (15), $r_1 = a$ and the equation becomes

$$r^2 - 2ar \cos(\theta - \theta_1) = 0$$
or
$$r[r - 2a \cos(\theta - \theta_1)] = 0$$

Thus, the circle C with center at $P_1[a, \theta_1]$ and radius a is the graph of the relation

$$R = \{(r, \theta) \mid r = 0\} \cup \{(r, \theta) \mid r = 2a \cos(\theta - \theta_1)\}$$

Observe that the coordinates of the point $[0, \theta_1 + \tfrac{1}{2}\pi]$ satisfy the equation $r = 2a \cos(\theta - \theta_1)$; hence the graph of $\{(r, \theta) \mid r = 0\}$ is included in the graph of $\{(r, \theta) \mid r = 2a \cos(\theta - \theta_1)\}$. Hence

$$r = 2a \cos(\theta - \theta_1) \tag{16}$$

as an equation, in polar coordinates, of such a circle. Note that if $a > 0$ the center the origin. Equation (16) may also be obtained directly from Fig. 6.25, by using the fact that a triangle inscribed in a circle with one side coincident with a diameter is a right triangle.

If a circle C has center at $P_1[a, 0]$ and passes through the origin, as in Fig. 6.26, then $\theta_1 = 0$ in Eq. (16), and we have

$$r = 2a \cos \theta \tag{17}$$

as an equation, in polar coordinates, of such a circle. Note that if $a > 0$ the center is on the polar axis, while if $a < 0$, the center is on the polar axis extended.

If a circle C has center at $P_1[a, \tfrac{1}{2}\pi]$ and passes through the origin, as in Fig.

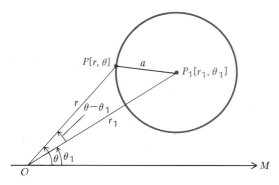

FIGURE 6.24   **FIGURE 6.25**

6.27, then $\theta_1 = \frac{1}{2}\pi$ in Eq. (16), and we have

$$r = 2a \cos\left(\theta - \tfrac{1}{2}\pi\right)$$

or, equivalently,

$$r = 2a \sin\theta \tag{18}$$

as an equation, in polar coordinates, of such a circle.

Equation (17) may be obtained directly from Fig. 6.26, and Eq. (18) may be obtained directly from Fig. 6.27, again by using the fact that a triangle inscribed in a circle with one side coincident with a diameter is a right triangle.

Recall that a circle with center at the origin and radius a has

$$r = a$$

for an equation in polar coordinates.

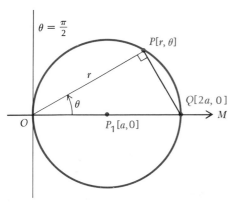

FIGURE 6.26

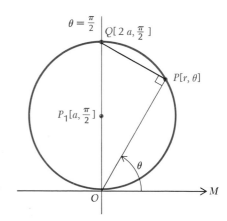

FIGURE 6.27

EXERCISES

Write an equation in polar coordinates of the line specified in each of Exercises 1–4.

    1. Perpendicular to the polar axis and passing through $P[6, 0]$
    2. The horizontal line through the point $[-3, \frac{1}{2}\pi]$
    3. Parallel to the polar axis and 2 units below it
    4. The vertical line through the point $[4, -\pi]$

Write an equation in polar coordinates of the circle specified in each of Exercises 5–8.

    5. With center at $[-6, 0]$ and radius 6
    6. With center at the origin and radius 7
    7. With center at $[4, 0]$ and radius 4
    8. With center at $[6, \frac{1}{4}\pi]$ and radius 6

In each of Exercises 9–12 give the polar coordinates of the center and the radius of the circle with the given equation.

    9. $r = 7 \cos \theta$ **10.** $r = -5 \sin \theta$

    11. $r = 6 \sin \theta$ **12.** $r = -4 \cos \theta$

    13. Construct the graph of the equation in Exercise 9.
    14. Construct the graph of the equation in Exercise 10.
    15. Construct the graph of the equation in Exercise 11.
    16. Construct the graph of the equation in Exercise 12.

In each of Exercises 17–24 graph the given equation. Partially check your work by finding four points whose coordinates satisfy the given equation, and plot these points on the coordinate system.

    17. $r \sin \theta = 7$ **18.** $r \cos \theta = 2$ **19.** $r \sin \theta = -5$

    20. $r \cos \theta = -3$ **21.** $r = 6 \cos \theta$ **22.** $r = 3 \sin \theta$

    23. $r = 4 \cos (\theta - \frac{1}{4}\pi)$ **24.** $r = 6 \cos (\theta - \frac{2}{3}\pi)$

    25. By use of the conversion formulas, transform the equation

$$x^2 + y^2 - ax - by = 0$$

to an equation in polar coordinates, and thereby show that the circle which passes through the origin, the point $[a, 0]$, and the point $[b, \frac{1}{2}\pi]$ has

$$r = a \cos \theta + b \sin \theta$$

for an equation.

26. Verify that Eq. (16) can be obtained directly from Fig. 6.25, using the fact that a triangle inscribed in a circle with one side coincident with a diameter is a right triangle.

27. Verify that Eq. (17) can be obtained directly from Fig. 6.26, and that Eq. (18) can be obtained directly from Fig. 6.27 (using the fact mentioned in Exercise 26).

6.6 THE PARABOLA, ELLIPSE, AND HYPERBOLA IN POLAR COORDINATES

Let us consider a set K of points in a plane with the property that a point P belongs to K if and only if the distance between P and a fixed point F is equal to a positive real number e times the distance between P and a fixed line D. In this section we obtain equations, in polar coordinates, for such a set K of points. If the real number e is equal to 1, then the set K is a parabola according to the definition given in Sec. 4.1. We shall see that if $e < 1$, the set K is an ellipse, and if $e > 1$, the set K is a hyperbola. Thus, it will be seen that the set K described in the first sentence of this section is a *conic section*. The fixed point F is called the **focus**,
Focus the fixed line D is called the **directrix**, and the positive number e is called the
Directrix
Eccentricity **eccentricity** of the conic section. We shall derive equations in polar coordinates of the conic section K when the focus is located at the origin O of a polar coordinate system and the directrix is either parallel to or perpendicular to the line containing the polar axis.

Let the focus F of the conic section K be at the origin O, and let the directrix D be perpendicular to the line containing the polar axis at the point $Q[p, \pi]$, where $p > 0$. Thus $F = O$ and D has equation $r \cos \theta = -p$ (see Fig. 6.28). Now let

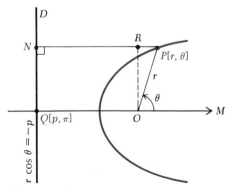

FIGURE 6.28 $r = ep/(1 - e \cos \theta)$.

$P[r, \theta]$ be a point *not* on the directrix D, and denote by N the projection on D of the point $P[r, \theta]$. Then

$$P \in K \quad \Longleftrightarrow \quad |OP| = e|PN|$$

If the point P is located as shown in Fig. 6.28, we see that

$$|OP| = r \qquad |PN| = |PR| + |RN| = r \cos \theta + p$$

By drawing suitable figures, the student should convince himself that, no matter what the position of P relative to O and D,

$$|OP| = |r| \qquad |PN| = |r \cos \theta + p|$$

Therefore,

$$P \in K \quad \Longleftrightarrow \quad |r| = e \, |r \cos \theta + p|$$
$$\Longleftrightarrow \quad r = e(r \cos \theta + p) \text{ or } r = -e(r \cos \theta + p)$$

Then, solving for r, we get

$$P \in K \quad \Longleftrightarrow \quad r = \frac{ep}{1 - e \cos \theta} \text{ or } r = \frac{-ep}{1 + e \cos \theta}$$

and K is the graph of the relation

$$R = \left\{ (r, \theta) \mid r = \frac{ep}{1 - e \cos \theta} \right\} \cup \left\{ (r, \theta) \mid r = \frac{-ep}{1 + e \cos \theta} \right\}$$

If the coordinates of the point $P_1[r_1, \theta_1]$ satisfy the equation $r = ep/(1 - e \cos \theta)$, then

$$r_1 = \frac{ep}{1 - e \cos \theta_1}$$

$$-r_1 = \frac{-ep}{1 - e \cos \theta_1}$$

$$-r_1 = \frac{-ep}{1 + e \cos (\theta_1 + \pi)} \tag{19}$$

which says that the ordered pair $[-r_1, \theta_1 + \pi]$ does satisfy the equation $r = -ep/(1 + e \cos \theta)$. But $[-r_1, \theta_1 + \pi]$ are also coordinates of P_1, so that if P_1 lies on the graph of $r = ep/(1 - e \cos \theta)$, it also lies on the graph of $r = -ep/(1 + e \cos \theta)$. Conversely, if P_1 lies on the graph of $r = -ep/(1 + e \cos \theta)$, it also lies on the graph of $r = ep/(1 - e \cos \theta)$. Thus, the conic section with focus at the origin O and directrix with equation $r \cos \theta = -p$ $(p > 0)$ is the graph, in polar coordinates, of *either* of the equations

$$r = \frac{ep}{1 - e \cos \theta} \tag{20}$$

$$r = \frac{-ep}{1 + e \cos \theta} \tag{21}$$

If the directrix of the conic section K is perpendicular to the polar axis at the point $Q[p, 0]$ where $p > 0$, as in Fig. 6.29, the student should show (by reasoning similar to that in the preceding paragraph) that K is the graph, in polar coordinates, of *either* of the equations

$$r = \frac{ep}{1 + e \cos \theta} \tag{22}$$

$$r = \frac{-ep}{1 - e \cos \theta} \tag{23}$$

Let K be a conic section with focus at the origin O and directrix parallel to the polar axis through the point $Q[p, \frac{1}{2}\pi]$ with $p > 0$ (see Fig. 6.30). By reasoning similar to that above, it can be shown that K is the graph, in polar coordinates, of *either* of the equations

$$r = \frac{ep}{1 + e \sin \theta} \tag{24}$$

$$r = \frac{-ep}{1 - e \sin \theta} \tag{25}$$

If the conic section has directrix parallel to the polar axis through the point $Q[-p, \frac{1}{2}\pi]$ with $p > 0$ (see Fig. 6.31), it is the graph, in polar coordinates, of *either* of the equations

$$r = \frac{ep}{1 - e \sin \theta} \tag{26}$$

$$r = \frac{-ep}{1 + e \sin \theta} \tag{27}$$

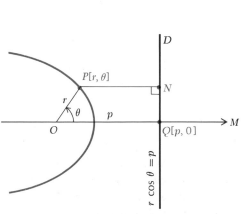

FIGURE 6.29 $r = ep/(1 + e \cos \theta)$.

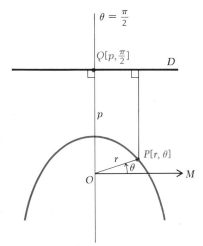

FIGURE 6.30 $r = ep/(1 + e \sin \theta)$.

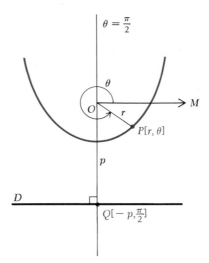

FIGURE 6.31 $r = ep/(1 - e \sin \theta)$.

Let us consider the equation

$$r = \frac{ep}{1 - e \cos \theta} \tag{20}$$

which is an equation in polar coordinates of the conic section with focus and directrix as shown in Fig. 6.28. By using the formulas (6) and (7) we can write Eq. (20) in rectangular coordinates as follows:

$$\pm\sqrt{x^2 + y^2} = \frac{ep}{1 - ex/\pm\sqrt{x^2 + y^2}}$$
$$\pm\sqrt{x^2 + y^2} = e(x + p)$$
$$x^2 + y^2 = e^2(x^2 + 2px + p^2)$$
$$(1 - e^2)x^2 + y^2 - 2pe^2x - p^2e^2 = 0 \tag{28}$$

The graph of (28) in rectangular coordinates is the same set of points as the graph of (20) in polar coordinates. From the results established in Chap. 4 we know that

(i)   If $e = 1$, the graph of (28), and hence of (20), is a parabola.
(ii)   If $e < 1$, the graph of (28), and hence of (20), is an ellipse.
(iii) If $e > 1$, the graph of (28), and hence of (20), is a hyperbola.

It can be shown that the same results hold for Eqs. (21) to (27). When we are given an equation of one of the forms in this section, we can first determine the type of conic section from the value of e. Next we can determine the points in which the graph intersects the line with equation $\theta = 0$ and the line with equation $\theta = \frac{1}{2}\pi$. These *intercept points* P_1, P_2, P_3, P_4 may be obtained by setting $\theta = 0$,

$\frac{1}{2}\pi$, π, $\frac{3}{2}\pi$ in the equation provided $e < 1$ or $e > 1$. If $e = 1$ there will be only three intercept points. By using the intercept points and a few additional points, together with the knowledge of the type of conic section, the graph of a given equation of one of the types (20) to (27) can be constructed.

♦   EXAMPLE 1

Identify and construct the graph of the equation

$$r = \frac{8}{2 - \cos\theta}$$

Solution

The equations of conic sections which we have considered in this section are either of the form

$$r = \frac{k}{1 \pm b\cos\theta}$$

or of the form

$$r = \frac{k}{1 \pm b\sin\theta}$$

To put the given equation in one of these forms, we divide both the numerator and the denominator of the fraction on the right by 2 to obtain

$$r = \frac{4}{1 - \frac{1}{2}\cos\theta} \qquad \text{or} \qquad r = \frac{\frac{1}{2}(8)}{1 - \frac{1}{2}\cos\theta}$$

This equation is of the form (20) with $e = \frac{1}{2}$ and $p = 8$, so the graph is an ellipse. The coordinates of the intercept points and four additional points are given in the table below, and the graph is shown in Fig. 6.21.

θ	0	$\frac{1}{3}\pi$	$\frac{1}{2}\pi$	$\frac{2}{3}\pi$	π	$\frac{4}{3}\pi$	$\frac{3}{2}\pi$	$\frac{5}{3}\pi$
$\cos\theta$	1	$\frac{1}{2}$	0	$-\frac{1}{2}$	-1	$-\frac{1}{2}$	0	$\frac{1}{2}$
r	8	$\frac{16}{3}$	4	$\frac{16}{5}$	$\frac{8}{3}$	$\frac{16}{5}$	4	$\frac{16}{3}$

♦   EXAMPLE 2

Identify and construct the graph of

$$r = \frac{8}{3 + 5\sin\theta}$$

Solution

Writing the given equation as

$$r = \frac{\frac{8}{3}}{1 + \frac{5}{3}\sin\theta} \qquad \text{or} \qquad r = \frac{\frac{5}{3}\left(\frac{8}{5}\right)}{1 + \frac{5}{3}\sin\theta}$$

and comparing this with (24), we see that $e = \frac{5}{3}$, and so the graph G is a hyperbola with $p = \frac{8}{5}$. The coordinates of the intercept points and four additional points are given in the table below.

θ	0	$\frac{1}{6}\pi$	$\frac{1}{2}\pi$	$\frac{5}{6}\pi$	π	$\frac{10}{9}\pi$	$\frac{3}{2}\pi$	$\frac{17}{9}\pi$
$\sin\theta$	0	$\frac{1}{2}$	1	$\frac{1}{2}$	0	-0.34	-1	-0.34
r	$\frac{8}{3}$	$\frac{16}{11}$	1	$\frac{16}{11}$	$\frac{8}{3}$	5.7	-4	5.7
Point	P_1	P_2	P_3	P_4	P_5	P_6	P_7	P_8

Points P_1, P_2, P_3, P_4, P_5, P_6, and P_8 determine the lower branch of the hyperbola shown in Fig. 6.32. $P_3[1, \frac{1}{2}\pi]$ is the vertex on this branch, and $P_7[-7, \frac{3}{2}\pi]$ is the

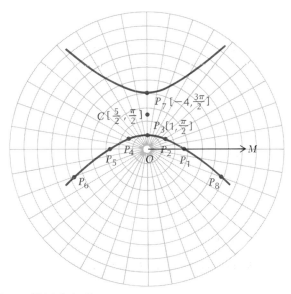

FIGURE 6.32 $r = \frac{8}{3}/(1 + \frac{5}{3}\sin\theta)$.

vertex on the other branch. Observe that

$$[r, \theta] \in G \quad \Rightarrow \quad [r, \pi - \theta] \in G$$

so G is symmetric with respect to the line L: $\theta = \frac{1}{2}\pi$. The center C is midway between the vertices, so we have $C[\frac{5}{2}, \frac{1}{2}\pi]$. From this information and the symmetry of the hyperbola, we can readily construct the upper branch of the hyperbola (Fig. 6.32).

EXERCISES

In each of Exercises 1–8 give the eccentricity of the conic section whose equation appears, and identify and construct the graph of this conic section.

1. $r = 6/(2 + \cos \theta)$ **2.** $r = 3/(1 - \cos \theta)$

3. $r = 9/(3 + \sin \theta)$ **4.** $r = 20/(4 - 3 \sin \theta)$

5. $r = 6/(1 - \cos \theta)$ **6.** $r = 5/(2 + 3 \sin \theta)$

7. $r = -4/(2 + \cos \theta)$ **8.** $r = -1/(3 - \sin \theta)$

Find an equation of the conic with a focus at the origin and with the given properties.

9. $e = 11$; vertex at $[3, \pi]$

10. $e = \frac{1}{2}$; directrix parallel to and 5 units to the left of the line for which $\theta = \frac{1}{2}\pi$

6.7 THE SPIRALS

We have seen that some curves, such as the cardioids and the roses, are studied more advantageously through the use of polar coordinates than through the use of rectangular coordinates. This is also true of those curves commonly called spirals.

Spiral   A **spiral** is a curve with the property that as a point moves along the curve in such a way that the polar angle of the point increases, then the radius vector either steadily increases or steadily decreases.

The following are the most frequently encountered spirals (here a is a real number):

The *spiral of Archimedes* with $r = a\theta$ for an equation.
The *reciprocal spiral* with $r\theta = a$ for an equation.
The *logarithmic spiral* with $r = e^{a\theta}$, or $\log_e r = a\theta$, for an equation. Here e

does not represent eccentricity; rather, it represents the irrational number whose value is approximately 2.718.

The *lituus* with $r^2\theta = a^2$ for an equation.

▶ EXAMPLE 1

Construct the graph G of the spiral of Archimedes with $r = 2\theta$ for an equation and $\theta \in [0; \tfrac{3}{2}\pi]$.

Solution

We construct the table below (with θ and r given to two decimal places), and with its aid we construct the graph G which is the heavily drawn curve in Fig. 6.33. The determination of the two decimal approximations for the values of θ is facilitated by use of an appropriate reference table.

θ	0	$\tfrac{1}{6}\pi$	$\tfrac{1}{3}\pi$	$\tfrac{1}{2}\pi$	$\tfrac{2}{3}\pi$	$\tfrac{5}{6}\pi$	π	$\tfrac{7}{6}\pi$
θ	0	0.52	1.05	1.57	2.09	2.62	3.14	3.67
r	0	1.04	2.10	3.14	4.18	5.24	6.28	7.34

θ	$\tfrac{4}{3}\pi$	$\tfrac{3}{2}\pi$	$\tfrac{5}{3}\pi$	$\tfrac{11}{6}\pi$	2π	$\tfrac{13}{6}\pi$	$\tfrac{7}{3}\pi$	$\tfrac{5}{2}\pi$
θ	4.19	4.71	5.24	5.76	6.28	6.81	7.33	7.85
r	8.38	9.42	10.48	11.52	12.56	13.62	14.66	15.70

If we replace (r, θ) by $(-r, -\theta)$ in the equation $r = 2\theta$, we get

$$-r = 2(-\theta)$$

or, equivalently,

$$r = 2\theta$$

Therefore, the graph of $r = 2\theta$ is symmetric with respect to the y axis. The dashed curve in Fig. 6.33 is the graph of $r = 2\theta$ for $\theta \in [-\tfrac{3}{2}\pi; 0]$.

In graphing a logarithmic spiral with $r = e^{a\theta}$ or $\log_e r = a\theta$ for an equation, it is frequently helpful to set $a = hk$, where h is selected so that $e^h = 10$. If this is done

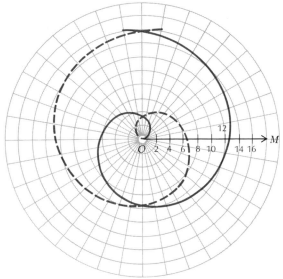

FIGURE 6.33 $r = 2\theta$.

we can write

$$r = e^{a\theta} = e^{hk\theta} = (e^h)^{k\theta} = 10^{k\theta}$$

or
$$\log_{10} r = k\theta$$

In virtue of these equalities we call the graph of either

$$r = 10^{k\theta} \qquad \text{or} \qquad \log_{10} r = k\theta$$

a logarithmic spiral.

◆ EXAMPLE 2

Construct the graph G of the logarithmic spiral with $r = 10^{(0.1)\theta}$, or with $\log_{10} r = (0.1)\theta$ for an equation, and $\theta \in [2\pi; 3\pi]$.

Solution

We need to construct a table in which the assigned values of θ are given (in radians) to three decimal places. Then the values of r are determined by referring to a table of common logarithms (logarithms to the base 10). In this manner we construct the table on page 222, which gives approximate values of the coordinates for seven selected points on G. Plotting these points and joining them with a smooth curve, we get the curve shown in Fig. 6.34.

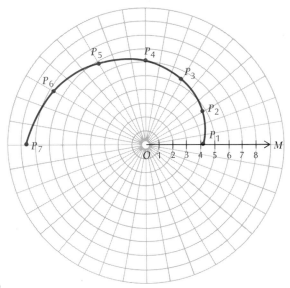

FIGURE 6.34

θ	2π	$\frac{13}{6}\pi$	$\frac{7}{3}\pi$	$\frac{5}{2}\pi$	$\frac{8}{3}\pi$	$\frac{17}{6}\pi$	3π
$(0.1)\theta$	0.628	0.681	0.733	0.785	0.837	0.889	0.942
r	4.2	4.8	5.4	6.1	6.9	7.8	8.8
Point	P_1	P_2	P_3	P_4	P_5	P_6	P_7

EXERCISES

1. Construct the graph of $r = 2\theta$ for $\theta \in [\frac{3}{2}\pi; 4\pi]$.

2. Construct the graph of $r = 2\theta$ for $\theta \in [-4; -\frac{3}{2}\pi]$.

3. For the equation $r = 10^{(0.1)\theta}$ complete the following table for $\theta \in [3\pi; 4\pi]$ as we did in the construction of the table of Example 2, and with the use of this table extend the graph of Fig. 6.34 for $\theta \in [3\pi; 4\pi]$.

θ	$\frac{19}{6}\pi$	$\frac{10}{3}\pi$	$\frac{7}{2}\pi$	$\frac{11}{3}\pi$	$\frac{23}{6}\pi$	4π
$(0.1)\theta$						
r						

4. Construct the graph of $r\theta = 1$ for $\theta \in [1; 10]$.

5. With the aid of the table below, construct the graph of $r = e^\theta$ for $\theta \in [0; 3]$.

θ	0	0.5	1	1.5	2	2.5	3
r	1	1.6	2.7	4.5	7.4	12.2	20.1

6. Construct the graph of $r = \frac{1}{2}\theta$ for $\theta \in [-10; 10]$.

7. Construct the graph of $r = -2\theta$ for $\theta \in [-\frac{3}{2}\pi; \frac{3}{2}\pi]$.

8. Construct the graph of $|r| = \theta$ for $\theta \in [0; 4\pi]$.

9. Construct the graph of $r = 2^\theta$ for $\theta \in [0; 4]$.

10. Construct the graph of $r = \theta$ for $\theta \in [-\frac{4}{3}\pi; \frac{4}{3}\pi]$.

11. Construct the graph of $(r-1)^2 = 4\theta$ for $\theta \in [0; \pi]$.

12. Construct the graph of $r^2\theta = 4$ for $\theta \in [1; 16]$.

6.8 POINTS OF INTERSECTION OF CURVES IN POLAR COORDINATES

Suppose that C_1 and C_2 are curves which are the graphs, in polar coordinates, of the equations $E_1(r, \theta) = 0$ and $E_2(r, \theta) = 0$, respectively. Let us consider how we may determine the points that are common to both C_1 and C_2.

Let $P_1[r_1, \theta_1]$ be a point in a polar coordinate system. If it is true that

$$E_1(r_1, \theta_1) = 0 \quad \text{and} \quad E_2(r_1, \theta_1) = 0 \tag{29}$$

then P_1 is a point common to both C_1 and C_2. However, the point P_1 also has polar coordinates $[r_1, \theta_1 + 2n\pi]$ and $[-r, \theta_1 + (2n+1)\pi]$ for any integer n. Therefore (29) is not the only condition under which $P_1[r_1, \theta_1]$ is a point of intersection of C_1 and C_2. For example, if it is true that

$$E_1(r_1, \theta_1) = 0 \quad \text{and} \quad E_2[-r_1, \theta_1 + (2n+1)\pi] = 0 \tag{30}$$

for some integer n, then P_1 is a point common to both C_1 and C_2. Also, if

$$E_1(r_1, \theta_1) = 0 \quad \text{and} \quad E_2(r_1, \theta_1 + 2n\pi) = 0 \tag{31}$$

for some integer n, then P_1 is a point of intersection of C_1 and C_2.

Origin as intersection point   Cases in which the origin is a point of intersection of C_1 and C_2 present a different situation because the origin O is represented in polar coordinates by a pair of the form $[0, \theta]$, where θ can have any value. Therefore, if

$$E_1(0, \theta_1) = 0 \quad \text{and} \quad E_2(0, \theta_2) = 0$$

for some values of θ_1 and θ_2, then the origin O is a point of intersection of C_1 and C_2 regardless of the values of θ_1 and θ_2.

◆ EXAMPLE 1

Determine the points of intersection of

$$C_1: \ r = 3 \sin \theta \qquad \text{and} \qquad C_2: \ r = 1 + \sin \theta$$

Identify C_1 and C_2, construct these curves on the same coordinate system, and indicate on your figure the points of intersection. Also indicate, by shading, the relation

$$R = \{(r, \theta) \mid P[r, \theta] \text{ is inside } C_1 \text{ and outside } C_2\}$$

Solution

First let us determine whether the origin O lies on both curves. O will lie on C_1 provided there is some number θ_1 for which $(0, \theta_1) \in \{(r, \theta) \mid r = 3 \sin \theta\}$, that is, for which $r = 3 \sin \theta_1 = 0$. Now,

$$0 = 3 \sin \theta_1 \ \Longleftrightarrow \ \sin \theta_1 = 0 \ \Longleftrightarrow \ \theta_1 = n\pi$$

for any integer n. Hence the curve C_1 passes through the origin.

The origin O will lie on C_2 provided there is some number θ_2 for which $(0, \theta_2) \in \{(r, \theta) \mid r = 1 + \sin \theta\}$, that is, for which $r = 1 + \sin \theta_2 = 0$. Here

$$0 = 1 + \sin \theta_2 \ \Longleftrightarrow \ \sin \theta_2 = -1 \ \Longleftrightarrow \ \theta_2 = \tfrac{3}{2}\pi + 2n\pi$$

for any integer n. Therefore C_2 passes through the origin and O is a point of intersection of C_1 and C_2. (Note that there is no pair of coordinates of the origin that satisfies *both* equations.)

Using (31) we see that if the pair of equations

$$\begin{aligned} r &= 3 \sin \theta \\ r &= 1 + \sin (\theta + 2n\pi) \end{aligned} \tag{32}$$

has a nonempty solution set, then this solution will give coordinates of points of intersection of C_1 and C_2. We can eliminate r in Eqs. (32) to obtain

$$3 \sin \theta = 1 + \sin (\theta + 2n\pi)$$

which can be written as

$$3 \sin \theta = 1 + \sin \theta$$

or as

$$2 \sin \theta = 1$$

Now $\qquad 2 \sin \theta = 1 \ \Longleftrightarrow \ \sin \theta = \tfrac{1}{2}$

$$\Longleftrightarrow \ \theta = \tfrac{1}{6}\pi + 2n\pi \ \text{ or } \ \theta = \tfrac{5}{6}\pi + 2k\pi$$

for any integers n and k. Substituting these values in the equation for C_1, we get

$$r = 3 \sin (\tfrac{1}{6}\pi + 2n\pi) = \tfrac{3}{2} \qquad \text{or} \qquad r = 3 \sin (\tfrac{5}{6}\pi + 2k\pi) = \tfrac{3}{2}$$

Therefore, $P_1[\frac{3}{2}, \frac{1}{6}\pi]$ and $P_2[\frac{3}{2}, \frac{5}{6}\pi]$ are both points of intersection of C_1 and C_2.

C_1 is the circle and C_2 is the cardioid shown in Fig. 6.35, and it appears from this figure that O, $P_1[\frac{3}{2}, \frac{1}{6}\pi]$, and $P_2[\frac{3}{2}, \frac{5}{6}\pi]$ are the only points of intersection of C_1 and C_2. To check this conjecture let us use (30) and determine the solution set of the pair of equations

$$r = 3 \sin \theta$$
$$-r = 1 + \sin [\theta + (2n + 1)\pi] \tag{33}$$

Eliminating r in (33), we obtain

$$-3 \sin \theta = 1 + \sin [\theta + (2n + 1)\pi]$$

which can be written as

$$-3 \sin \theta = 1 - \sin \theta$$

or as $\qquad\qquad -2 \sin \theta = 1$

Now $\qquad -2 \sin \theta = 1 \iff \sin \theta = -\frac{1}{2}$

$$\iff \theta = \tfrac{7}{6}\pi + 2n\pi \text{ or } \theta = \tfrac{11}{6}\pi + 2k\pi$$

for any integers n and k. Substituting these values in $r = 3 \sin \theta$, we get

$$r = 3 \sin (\tfrac{7}{6}\pi + 2n\pi) = -\tfrac{3}{2} \qquad \text{or} \qquad r = 3 \sin (\tfrac{11}{6}\pi) = -\tfrac{3}{2}$$

So $P_3[-\frac{3}{2}, \frac{7}{6}\pi]$ and $P_4[-\frac{3}{2}, \frac{11}{6}\pi]$ are points of intersection of C_1 and C_2. But P_3 is the same point as P_1, and P_4 is the same point as P_2. We conclude that O, P_1, and P_2 are the only points of intersection of C_1 and C_2.

The graph of the relation R is the shaded region in Fig. 6.35.

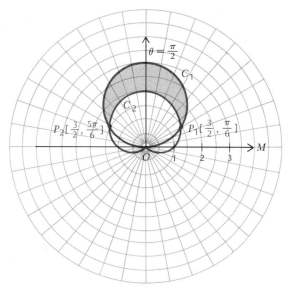

FIGURE 6.35

➤ EXAMPLE 2

Find the points of intersection of

$$C_1: \; r = 4(1 - \cos \theta) \quad \text{and} \quad C_2: \; r = \frac{2}{1 + \cos \theta}$$

Identify C_1 and C_2, graph them on the same polar coordinate system, and indicate the points of intersection. Also indicate, by shading, the graph of

$$R = \{(r, \theta) \mid P[r, \theta] \text{ is inside } C_1 \text{ and outside } C_2\}$$

Solution

In order for the origin to be on C_2 there would have to be a value of θ for which $0 = 2/(1 + \cos \theta)$. Since there is no such value of θ, the origin does not lie on C_2; hence the origin is not a point of intersection of C_1 and C_2.

Any ordered pair of polar coordinates that satisfy the pair of equations

$$r = 4(1 - \cos \theta)$$
$$r = \frac{2}{1 + \cos \theta} \tag{34}$$

will be coordinates of points of intersection of C_1 and C_2. Eliminating r in (34), we get

$$4(1 - \cos \theta) = \frac{2}{1 + \cos \theta}$$

which can be written as

$$4(1 - \cos^2 \theta) = 2$$

or as

$$\sin^2 \theta = \tfrac{1}{2}$$

Now $\sin^2 \theta = \tfrac{1}{2} \iff \sin \theta = \dfrac{1}{\sqrt{2}}$ or $\sin \theta = -\dfrac{1}{\sqrt{2}}$

$$\iff \theta = \tfrac{1}{4}\pi + 2n\pi \; \text{ or } \; \theta = \tfrac{7}{4}\pi + 2n\pi$$
$$\text{or } \; \theta = \tfrac{3}{4}\pi + 2n\pi \; \text{ or } \; \theta = \tfrac{5}{4}\pi + 2n\pi$$

Using these values of θ in turn in $r = 4(1 - \cos \theta)$, we find

$$P_1[4 - 2\sqrt{2}, \tfrac{1}{4}\pi], \quad P_2[4 - 2\sqrt{2}, \tfrac{7}{4}\pi],$$
$$P_3[4 + 2\sqrt{2}, \tfrac{3}{4}\pi], \quad P_4[4 + 2\sqrt{2}, \tfrac{5}{4}\pi]$$

to be points of intersection of C_1 and C_2. C_1 is the cardioid and C_2 is the parabola shown in Fig. 6.36. It appears from the figure that these are the only points of intersection of C_1 and C_2; this can be verified by proceeding as we did in Example 1. The graph of R is the shaded region in Fig. 6.36.

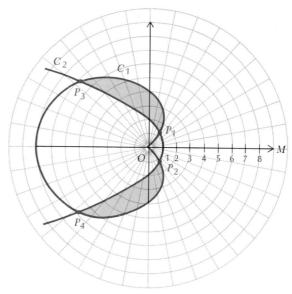

FIGURE 6.36

◆ EXAMPLE 3

Find the points of intersection of the limaçon C_1: $r = 2 \cos \theta - 1$ and the parabola C_2: $r = 1/(1 + \cos \theta)$.

Solution

Note that the origin is not on the parabola C_2 and so O is not a point of intersection of the two curves.

Any ordered pair that satisfies the pair of equations

$$r = 2 \cos \theta - 1$$
$$r = \frac{1}{1 + \cos \theta} \qquad (35)$$

will be coordinates of a point of intersection of C_1 and C_2. From (35) we obtain

$$2 \cos \theta - 1 = \frac{1}{1 + \cos \theta}$$

which can be written as

$$2 \cos^2 \theta + \cos \theta - 2 = 0$$

Now $2 \cos^2 \theta + \cos \theta - 2 = 0 \quad \Longleftrightarrow$

$$\cos \theta = \frac{-1 + \sqrt{17}}{2} \text{ or } \cos \theta = \frac{-1 - \sqrt{17}}{2}$$

We see that

$$\left\{ \theta \mid \cos \theta = \frac{-1 - \sqrt{17}}{2} \right\} = \emptyset$$

and, by use of the table in the Appendix,

$$\left\{ \theta \mid \cos \theta = \frac{-1 + \sqrt{17}}{2} \right\} = \{39° + n \cdot 360°, \ 321° + n \cdot 360°\}$$

Using the equation for C_1, we find that the points $P_1[0.554, 39°]$ and $P_2[0.554, 321°]$ are points of intersection of C_1 and C_2.

The graphs of C_1 and C_2 are shown in Fig. 6.37, and from this figure it appears that there are points of intersection other than P_1 and P_2. Using the facts summarized in (30), we know that any ordered pairs that satisfy the pair of equations

$$r = 2 \cos \theta - 1$$

$$-r = \frac{1}{1 + \cos \left[\theta + (2n + 1)\pi\right]} \tag{36}$$

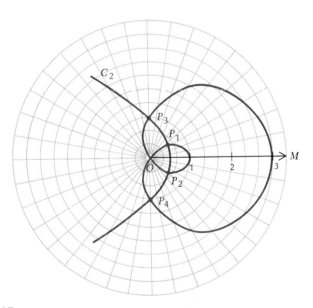

FIGURE 6.37

will be coordinates of points of intersection of C_1 and C_2. Eliminating r from the pair (36), we get

$$2 \cos \theta - 1 = -\frac{1}{1 + \cos [\theta + (2n + 1)\pi]}$$

which can be written as

$$(2 \cos \theta - 1)(1 - \cos \theta) = -1$$

or as $\qquad 2 \cos^2 \theta - 3 \cos \theta = 0 \qquad$ or $\qquad \cos \theta(2 \cos \theta - 3) = 0$

Now $\quad \cos \theta(2 \cos \theta - 3) = 0 \iff \quad \cos \theta = 0 \text{ or } \cos \theta = \frac{3}{2}$
$$\iff \quad \theta = 90° + n \cdot 360° \text{ or } \theta = 270° + n \cdot 360°$$

Using these values of θ in the equation for C_2, we find that $P_3[1, 90°]$ and $P_4[1, 270°]$ are points of intersection of C_1 and C_4, as shown in Fig. 6.37. In this connection note that the ordered pair $(1, 90°)$ does not satisfy the equation of the limaçon C_1, but the ordered pair $(-1, 270°)$ does satisfy the equation of C_1, and the point with coordinates $[-1, 270°]$ is the same point as $P_3[1, 90°]$.

EXERCISES

In each of Exercises 1 and 2 show that the origin is on the graph of the given equation.

    1. $r = 3(1 + \cos \theta)$ **2.** $r = 2 + 3 \sin \theta$

In each of Exercises 3 and 4 show that the origin is not on the graph of the given equation.

    3. $r = 2$ **4.** $r = 3 + \sin \theta$

In each of Exercises 5–14 find the points of intersection of C_1 and C_2. Identify C_1 and C_2, graph them on the same polar coordinate system, and indicate on your figure their points of intersection. Also indicate by shading the graph of the relation $R = \{(r, \theta) \mid P[r, \theta] \text{ is inside } C_1 \text{ and outside } C_2\}$.

    5. C_1: $r = 3 \cos \theta$; C_2: $r = 1 + \cos \theta$

    6. C_1: $r = 4 \cos \theta$; C_2: $r = 2$

    7. C_1: $r = \sin \theta$; C_2: $r = 1 - \cos \theta$

    8. C_1: $r = a(1 + \cos \theta)$; C_2: $r = 2a \cos \theta$

    9. C_1: $r = 1 - \cos \theta$; C_2: $r = 1 + \cos \theta$

10. C_1: $r = 2 \cos \theta$; C_2: $r = 2(1 - \cos \theta)$

11. C_1: $r = 10 \cos \theta$; C_2: $r = 10 \sin \theta$

12. C_1: $r = 6(1 + \sin \theta)$; C_2: $r = 3/(1 - \sin \theta)$

13. C_1: $r = 1 + 2 \cos \theta$; C_2: $r = 4 \cos \theta$

14. C_1: $r = 2(1 - \cos \theta)$; C_2: $r = -6 \cos \theta$

Do Exercises 15–18 as you did Exercises 5–14, except here indicate by shading the graph of the region $R = R_1 \cap R_2$, where R_1 is the region bounded by C_1 and R_2 is the region bounded by C_2.

15. C_1: $r^2 = 4 \cos 2\theta$; C_2: $r^2 = 4 \sin 2\theta$

16. C_1: $r = 4 \cos \theta$; C_2: $r = 6 \cos \theta$

17. C_1: $r^2 = 9 \cos 2\theta$; C_2: $r = 3\sqrt{2} \sin \theta$

18. C_1: $r^2 = 2 \cos \theta$; C_2: $r = 1$

19. Find the points of intersection of the line with equation $\theta = \frac{1}{4}\pi$ and the spiral with equation $r = \theta$ for $\theta \in [-\frac{5}{2}\pi; \frac{5}{2}\pi]$. Graph the line and the spiral.

20. Find the points of intersection of C_1: $r = \sin 2\theta$ and C_2: $r = \cos 2\theta$.

21. Find the points of intersection of C_1: $r = 1 + \sin \theta$ and C_2: $r^2 = \frac{1}{2} \sin \theta$.

7 | VECTORS. LINEAR PROGRAMMING. ADDITION OF ORDINATES

7.1 THE GEOMETRIC STRUCTURE OF VECTORS

In this chapter we denote the *directed line segment* from the point P to the point Q (see Sec. 2.1) by $\overrightarrow{PQ}$ (Fig. 7.1), P being the *initial point* and Q the *terminal point*. The directed line segment from Q to P is oppositely directed from $\overrightarrow{PQ}$ and is denoted by $\overrightarrow{QP}$ or by $-\overrightarrow{PQ}$. The *length* of $\overrightarrow{PQ}$ is denoted by $|\overrightarrow{PQ}|$, and is the distance between the end points P and Q.

If P and Q coincide, we speak of $\overrightarrow{PQ}$ as a *degenerate line segment*.

Two directed nondegenerate line segments $\overrightarrow{PQ}$ and $\overrightarrow{RS}$ are said to have the

FIGURE 7.1 Directed line segment PQ.

same direction if:

    (i)   They lie along parallel lines L_1 and L_2 with (half) arrows pointing in the same direction (Fig. 7.2*a*), or

    (ii)   They lie along the same directed line with arrows pointing in the same direction (Fig. 7.2*b*).

A degenerate line segment has unassigned direction. Subsequently when we refer to a directed line segment $\vec{PQ}$ it is understood that $\vec{PQ}$ is nondegenerate unless stipulated explicitly to the contrary.

Equivalent line segments   In case two directed line segments $\vec{PQ}$ and $\vec{RS}$ have the same length and the same direction, we say they are **equivalent,** for which we write

$$\vec{PQ} \sim \vec{RS} \tag{1}$$

Observe that

$$\vec{PQ} \sim \vec{RS} \;\Rightarrow\; |\vec{PQ}| = |\vec{RS}|$$

but

$$|\vec{PQ}| = |\vec{RS}| \;\not\Rightarrow\; \vec{PQ} \sim \vec{RS}$$

Vector   A **vector** is the set $\mathscr{S}$ of all directed line segments with a given length and a given direction. We denote vectors by lowercase boldface letters as **a**, **b**, **u**, **v**, **w**, and so forth.

Observe that

$$\vec{PQ} \sim \vec{PQ}$$
$$\vec{PQ} \sim \vec{RS} \;\Rightarrow\; \vec{RS} \sim \vec{PQ}$$

and

$$\vec{PQ} \sim \vec{RS} \text{ and } \vec{RS} \sim \vec{UV} \;\Rightarrow\; \vec{PQ} \sim \vec{UV}$$

A relation having these properties is called an *equivalence relation.* Hence equivalence of directed line segments is an equivalence relation, and the set $\mathscr{S}$ of all directed line segments which have the same length and the same direction is an *equivalence class.* Hence *a vector* **v** *is an equivalence class of directed line segments all having a given length and a given direction.*

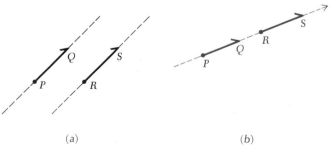

(a)   (b)

FIGURE 7.2   Directed line segments with the same length and direction.

If **v** is a vector and if $\overrightarrow{PQ}$ is a member of the equivalence class **v**, then $\overrightarrow{PQ}$, or any segment equivalent to $\overrightarrow{PQ}$, is a **representative** of the vector **v**.

Vectors **u** and **v** are said to be **equal** in case **u** has a representative $\overrightarrow{PQ}$ and **v** has a representative $\overrightarrow{RS}$ such that $\overrightarrow{PQ} \sim \overrightarrow{RS}$:

$$\mathbf{u} = \mathbf{v} \quad \Longleftrightarrow \quad \text{(a representative of } \mathbf{u}) \sim \text{(a representative of } \mathbf{v}) \tag{2}$$

Sometimes we write $\mathbf{v}(\overrightarrow{PQ})$ to denote "the vector **v** with representative $\overrightarrow{PQ}$." Then (2) can be written as

$$\mathbf{u}(\overrightarrow{PQ}) = \mathbf{v}(\overrightarrow{RS}) \quad \Longleftrightarrow \quad \overrightarrow{PQ} \sim \overrightarrow{RS} \tag{3}$$

The **direction** of a vector **v** is the direction of any representative of **v**. Two vectors **u** and **v** are **parallel** if and only if they have the same or opposite directions.

Vectors such as we have been discussing are called *free vectors* since we are free to choose the initial point of any representative. Sometimes a directed line segment with a fixed initial point is called a *bound vector*. Unless stated to the contrary, any vector we consider in this book is a *free vector*, or simply a *vector*.

The **norm** of a vector **v** is the common length of all its representatives, and is denoted by $\|\mathbf{v}\|$. A **unit vector** is a vector for which $\|\mathbf{v}\| = 1$.

Any degenerate line segment is a representative of the **zero vector,** which we denote by **0**. Observe that

$$\|\mathbf{v}\| > 0 \qquad \text{in case } \mathbf{v} \neq \mathbf{0} \tag{4}$$

and

$$\|\mathbf{v}\| = 0 \qquad \text{in case } \mathbf{v} = \mathbf{0} \tag{5}$$

Using the definitions of the direction of a vector and the norm of a vector, we can write (2) as

$$\mathbf{u} = \mathbf{v} \quad \Longleftrightarrow \quad [\text{the direction of } \mathbf{u} = \text{the direction of } \mathbf{v} \text{ and}$$
$$\text{the norm of } \mathbf{u} = \text{the norm of } \mathbf{v}] \tag{6}$$

We wish to define the *sum* of two vectors **u** and **v** in such a way that the addition of vectors is commutative and associative, and in a way that will fit our intuitive notions of how addition should work. In order to do this let us select a representative $\overrightarrow{PQ}$ of the vector **u**; when this has been done, it is always possible to select a representative of **v** whose initial point is Q. Let the representative of **v**

with initial point Q be denoted by $\overrightarrow{QR}$. Then the sum of **u** and **v** is defined to be the vector **w** with representative $\overrightarrow{PR}$; that is,

$$\mathbf{u} + \mathbf{v} = \mathbf{w} \quad \Longleftrightarrow \quad \mathbf{u}(\overrightarrow{PQ}) + \mathbf{v}(\overrightarrow{QR}) = \mathbf{w}(\overrightarrow{PR}) \tag{7}$$

This definition is illustrated in Fig. 7.3.

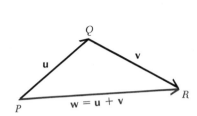

FIGURE 7.3   Addition of vectors.

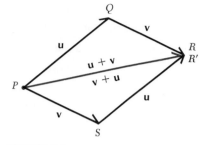

FIGURE 7.4 $\mathbf{u} + \mathbf{v} = \mathbf{v} + \mathbf{u}$.

By considering Fig. 7.4 the student is asked to prove Theorem 7.1 (Exercise 1, page 238).

THEOREM 7.1   *The addition of vectors is commutative:*

$$\mathbf{u} + \mathbf{v} = \mathbf{v} + \mathbf{u} \tag{8}$$

Since a diagonal of the parallelogram which has representatives of **u** and **v** for adjacent sides is a representative of **u** + **v**, it is sometimes said that "vectors are added according to the parallelogram law of addition."

Adding **w** to (**u** + **v**), we obtain (**u** + **v**) + **w**. Proceeding as we did in proving Theorem 7.1, we can prove Theorem 7.2 (Exercise 2, page 238).

THEOREM 7.2   *The addition of vectors is associative:*

$$(\mathbf{u} + \mathbf{v}) + \mathbf{w} = \mathbf{u} + (\mathbf{v} + \mathbf{w}) \tag{9}$$

Subtraction of vectors

Subtraction of vectors is defined to be the inverse of addition (Fig. 7.5):

$$\mathbf{u}(\overrightarrow{PQ}) - \mathbf{v}(\overrightarrow{PR}) = \mathbf{w}(\overrightarrow{RQ}) \iff \mathbf{u}(\overrightarrow{PQ}) = \mathbf{v}(\overrightarrow{PR}) + \mathbf{w}(\overrightarrow{RQ}) \tag{10}$$

or

$$\mathbf{u} - \mathbf{v} = \mathbf{w} \iff \mathbf{u} = \mathbf{v} + \mathbf{w} \tag{11}$$

As a special case of (11) we have

$$\mathbf{u} - \mathbf{u} = \mathbf{0} \iff \mathbf{u} = \mathbf{u} + \mathbf{0} \tag{12}$$

Also

$$\mathbf{u} - \mathbf{v} = \mathbf{0} \iff \mathbf{u} = \mathbf{v} + \mathbf{0} \iff \mathbf{u} = \mathbf{v} \tag{13}$$

The **negative** of $\mathbf{v}(\overrightarrow{PR})$, denoted by $-\mathbf{v}$, is the vector with representative $\overrightarrow{RP}$, so

$$-[\mathbf{v}(\overrightarrow{PR})] = (-\mathbf{v})(\overrightarrow{RP}) \tag{14}$$

If s denotes a scalar (a real number) and **v** a vector, then $s\mathbf{v} = \mathbf{v}s$ is called the

*Scalar multiple
of a vector*   **product** of **v** by s (or a *scalar multiple* of **v**), and is defined as follows:

(i)   The norm of $s\mathbf{v}$ is given by

$$\|s\mathbf{v}\| = |s|\,\|\mathbf{v}\| \tag{15}$$

(ii)   For $s \neq 0$ and $\mathbf{v} \neq \mathbf{0}$ the direction of $s\mathbf{v}$ is the same as the direction of **v** in case $s > 0$ and opposite to that of **v** in case $s < 0$.

(iii)   In case $s = 0$ or $\mathbf{v} = \mathbf{0}$, then $s\mathbf{v} = \mathbf{0}$ (and hence $s\mathbf{v}$ has unassigned direction):

$$s = 0 \text{ or } \mathbf{v} = \mathbf{0} \ \Rightarrow\ s\mathbf{v} = \mathbf{0} \tag{16}$$

As an immediate consequence of this definition it follows that *two vectors are*
Parallel vectors   *parallel if and only if each is a scalar multiple of the other.*

From the definition of $s\mathbf{v}$ the following properties can be established:

$$1\mathbf{v} = \mathbf{v} \tag{17}$$
$$(-1)\mathbf{v} = -\mathbf{v} \tag{18}$$
$$(rs)\mathbf{v} = r(s\mathbf{v}) \tag{19}$$
$$(r + s)\mathbf{v} = r\mathbf{v} + s\mathbf{v} \tag{20}$$
$$s(\mathbf{u} + \mathbf{v}) = s\mathbf{u} + s\mathbf{v} \tag{21}$$

THEOREM   *If $s\mathbf{v} = \mathbf{0}$, then $s = 0$ or $\mathbf{v} = \mathbf{0}$.*
7.3

Proof

Now

$$s\mathbf{v} = \mathbf{0} \ \Rightarrow\ \|s\mathbf{v}\| = 0 \ \Rightarrow\ |s|\,\|\mathbf{v}\| = \mathbf{0} \qquad \text{[by (15)]}$$
$$\Rightarrow\ |s| = 0 \text{ or } \|\mathbf{v}\| = 0$$
$$\Rightarrow\ s = 0 \text{ or } \mathbf{v} = \mathbf{0}$$

THEOREM   *If $s\mathbf{v} = \mathbf{0}$ and $\mathbf{v} \neq \mathbf{0}$, then $s = 0$.*
7.4

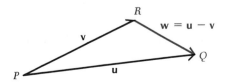

FIGURE 7.5   Subtraction of vectors.

Theorem 7.4 follows immediately from Theorem 7.3.

Let **a** be a given nonzero vector and let **v** be *any* vector parallel to **a**. Then there exists a real number s with the property that

$$\mathbf{v} = s\mathbf{a}$$

We now show that there exists *only one* such real number s. Suppose that there were two real numbers s_1 and s_2 for which

$$\mathbf{v} = s_1\mathbf{a} \quad \text{and} \quad \mathbf{v} = s_2\mathbf{a} \tag{22}$$

Subtracting the second equation in (22) from the first, we get $\mathbf{v} - \mathbf{v} = s_1\mathbf{a} - s_2\mathbf{a}$, which can be written as

$$\mathbf{0} = (s_1 - s_2)\mathbf{a} \tag{23}$$

Since $\mathbf{a} \neq \mathbf{0}$, we have from (23) and Theorem 7.4 that $s_1 - s_2 = 0$, and so $s_1 = s_2$. We have proved Theorem 7.5.

THEOREM 7.5   *Every vector **v** which is parallel to a given nonzero vector **a** can be expressed uniquely by **v** = s**a**.*

Linearly dependent vectors   Two vectors **a** and **b** are said to be **linearly dependent** in case there are scalars s_1 and s_2, *not both zero,* with the property that

$$s_1\mathbf{a} + s_2\mathbf{b} = \mathbf{0} \tag{24}$$

Linearly independent vectors   If there are no scalars s_1 and s_2 other than $s_1 = s_2 = 0$ such that (24) holds, then **a** and **b** are **linearly independent.** From this definition and the fact that two (non-zero) vectors are parallel if and only if each is a scalar multiple of the other, there follows Theorem 7.6.

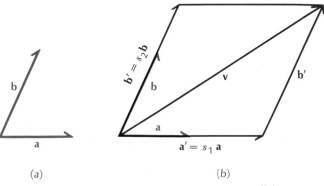

(a)   (b)

FIGURE 7.6   Decomposition of a vector **v** into components parallel to **a** and **b**.

THEOREM 7.6   *Two vectors* **a** *and* **b** *are linearly independent if they are not parallel and neither is the zero vector.*

Suppose **a** and **b** are nonzero vectors. Then in order to have scalars s_1 and s_2, not both zero, such that (24) holds, neither s_1 nor s_2 can be zero. So, if (24) holds for nonzero vectors, then **a** and **b** are parallel, and we can choose representatives of **a** and **b** that are on the *same line*. For this reason it is sometimes said that two *Collinear vectors* nonzero linearly dependent vectors are *collinear*.

THEOREM 7.7   *If* **v** *is any vector in the plane and* **a** *and* **b** *are two given linearly independent vectors, then there exist unique scalars s_1 and s_2 with the property that*

$$\mathbf{v} = s_1\mathbf{a} + s_2\mathbf{b} \tag{25}$$

In Exercise 8 at the end of this section the student is asked to prove Theorem 7.7 with the aid of Fig. 7.6.

If $\mathbf{a}_1, \mathbf{a}_2, \mathbf{a}_3, \ldots, \mathbf{a}_n$ are vectors and $s_1, s_2, s_3, \ldots, s_n$ are scalars, the expression

$$s_1\mathbf{a}_1 + s_2\mathbf{a}_2 + s_3\mathbf{a}_3 + \cdots + s_n\mathbf{a}_n$$

Linear combination of vectors is called a **linear combination** of the vectors $\mathbf{a}_1, \mathbf{a}_2, \ldots, \mathbf{a}_n$. Thus we can read (25) as saying that **v** is a linear combination of **a** and **b**.

Theorem 7.7 tells us that any vector **v** can be written uniquely as the sum of two vectors that are parallel, respectively, to two given nonzero nonparallel vectors **a** and **b**. In the equality (25) and in Fig. 7.6*b*, we call $s_1\mathbf{a}$ the **component** *Components of vectors* **of v parallel to a** and $s_2\mathbf{b}$ the **component of v parallel to b.** When **v** is written in the manner (25) we say that **v** is **decomposed** into components parallel to **a** and **b**.

Three vectors **a**, **b**, and **c** are **linearly dependent** in case there are scalars s_1, s_2, and s_3, *not all zero,* with the property that

$$s_1\mathbf{a} + s_2\mathbf{b} + s_3\mathbf{c} = \mathbf{0} \tag{26}$$

From this definition and Theorem 7.7 there follows Theorem 7.8.

THEOREM 7.8   *Three or more vectors in two-dimensional space are linearly dependent.*

Since every vector **v** in two-dimensional space can be expressed as a linear combination of two linearly independent vectors, we say that two linearly independent vectors **a** and **b** constitute a *basis* for two-dimensional space. For convenience of reference we combine Theorems 7.6 and 7.7 and state the combined theorem in an alternative manner in Theorem 7.9.

THEOREM 7.9 *Any two nonparallel nonzero vectors in two-dimensional space constitute a basis for that space.*

EXERCISES

1. Give a proof for Theorem 7.1 by considering Fig. 7.4.
2. With the aid of Fig. 7.7, prove Theorem 2.2.
3. With the aid of Fig. 7.8, prove that $\mathbf{u} + (-\mathbf{v}) = \mathbf{u} - \mathbf{v}$.
4. Prove (19) for $r > 0$ and $s > 0$.
5. Prove (20).
6. Prove (21) for $s > 0$ with the aid of Figs. 7.9 and 7.10.
7. Prove (21) for $s < 0$ with the aid of Figs. 7.9 and 7.11.
8. Prove Theorem 7.7 with the aid of Fig. 7.6.

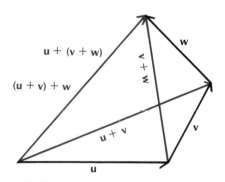

FIGURE 7.7

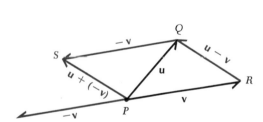

FIGURE 7.8

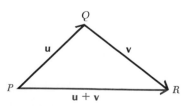

FIGURE 7.9

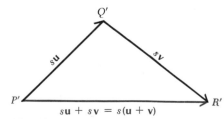

FIGURE 7.10

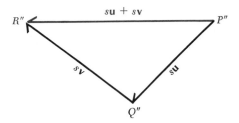

FIGURE 7.11

7.2 THE ALGEBRAIC STRUCTURE OF VECTORS

We now give attention to an algebraic formulation of vectors in two-dimensional euclidean space E_2 where we make use of the familiar two-dimensional rectangular coordinate system.

Since the x axis and the y axis are not parallel, any two vectors parallel, respectively, to these coordinate axes constitute a basis for E_2 (by Theorem 7.9). We find it convenient to use for such a basis two unit vectors which we denote by **i** and **j** and which we define as follows:

Unit vectors
i and j

i has norm 1 and has the same direction as the x axis.

j has norm 1 and has the same direction as the y axis.

From Theorem 7.5 and the definition of $s\mathbf{v}$ [see (15)] we have Theorem 7.10.

THEOREM   *For any nonzero real number c:*
7.10   (i) $c\mathbf{i}$ *is a vector with norm* $|c|$ *and parallel to* **i**.
               (ii) $c\mathbf{j}$ *is a vector with norm* $|c|$ *and parallel to* **j**.

From Theorem 7.7, any vector **v** in E_2 can be written as (see Fig. 7.12)

$$\mathbf{v} = v_1\mathbf{i} + v_2\mathbf{j} \qquad v_1, v_2 \in Re \qquad (27)$$

Vector components
Coordinates of a vector

The vectors $v_1\mathbf{i}$ and $v_2\mathbf{j}$ are called the **vector components** of **v** parallel, respectively, to **i** and **j**. The real numbers v_1 and v_2 are called the **coordinates of v relative to the base vectors i** and **j**, or simply the **coordinates** of **v**. Note that the coordinates of **i** are 1 and 0, and the coordinates of **j** are 0 and 1. That is, $\mathbf{i} = 1\mathbf{i} + 0\mathbf{j}$, and $\mathbf{j} = 0\mathbf{i} + 1\mathbf{j}$. The numbers which we call *coordinates* of a vector are sometimes called the *scalar components* of that vector.

Scalar components

THEOREM   *If* $\mathbf{v} = v_1\mathbf{i} + v_2\mathbf{j}$, *then*
7.11

$$\|\mathbf{v}\| = \sqrt{v_1{}^2 + v_2{}^2} \qquad (28)$$

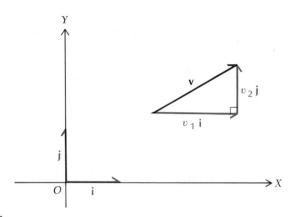

FIGURE 7.12

Proof

The theorem follows directly by applying the Pythagorean theorem to the triangle of Fig. 7.12 and using Theorem 7.10.

To illustrate Theorem 7.11, if $\mathbf{v} = 3\mathbf{i} + 4\mathbf{j}$, then $\|\mathbf{v}\| = \sqrt{3^2 + 4^2} = \sqrt{25} = 5$. From (28) we see that

$$\mathbf{v} = \mathbf{0} \iff v_1 = 0 \text{ and } v_2 = 0 \qquad (29)$$

That is,

$$\mathbf{0} = 0\mathbf{i} + 0\mathbf{j}$$

THEOREM 7.12 *If $P_1(x_1, y_1)$ and $P_2(x_2, y_2)$ are points in E_2, then the vector $\mathbf{v}(\overrightarrow{P_1P_2})$ is given by*

$$\mathbf{v} = (x_2 - x_1)\mathbf{i} + (y_2 - y_1)\mathbf{j} \qquad (30)$$

Proof

With reference to Fig. 7.13, by the parallelogram law for the addition of vectors (see Fig. 7.3), we see that

$$\mathbf{v}(\overrightarrow{P_1P_2}) = \mathbf{v}_1(\overrightarrow{P_1Q}) + \mathbf{v}_2(\overrightarrow{QP_2})$$

where $\mathbf{v}_1(\overrightarrow{P_1Q}) = (x_2 - x_1)\mathbf{i}$ $\mathbf{v}_2(\overrightarrow{QP_2}) = (y_2 - y_1)\mathbf{j}$

From these equalities (30) follows.

To illustrate Theorem 7.12, for $P_1(4, 5)$ and $P_2(7, 11)$, the vector $\mathbf{v}(\overrightarrow{P_1P_2})$ is given by

$$\mathbf{v} = (7 - 4)\mathbf{i} + (11 - 5)\mathbf{j} = 3\mathbf{i} + 6\mathbf{j}$$

In E_2 if the origin is moved by a translation from $O(0, 0)$ to $O'(h, k)$, then the new coordinates of $P(x, y)$ are x', y', where (Sec. 4.4)

$$x' = x - h \qquad y' = y - k \tag{31}$$

Then $\qquad x_2' - x_1' = (x_2 - h) - (x_1 - h) = x_2 - x_1$

and $\qquad y_2' - y_1' = (y_2 - k) - (y_1 - k) = y_2 - y_1$

These results and (30) show that *the coordinates of a vector* **v** (relative to the basis vectors **i** and **j**) *are independent* (or invariant) *of the choice of the initial point of* **v**. Consequently, if a fixed coordinate system is given, each vector is uniquely determined by its coordinates.

Since the coordinates of a vector relative to **i** and **j** are uniquely determined, it follows that for a given rectangular coordinate system there can be established a one-to-one correspondence between vectors in E_2 and ordered pairs of real numbers. Therefore, the study of vectors in E_2 may be based upon the study of ordered pairs of real numbers. *Frequently a vector* **v** *with coordinates* v_1 *and* v_2 *is* denoted by $\langle v_1, v_2 \rangle$. Note that

$$\mathbf{i} = \langle 1, 0 \rangle \qquad \mathbf{j} = \langle 0, 1 \rangle \qquad \mathbf{0} = \langle 0, 0 \rangle$$

THEOREM 7.13   *The coordinates of the sum of two vectors are equal to the sum of the respective coordinates of the vectors.*

Proof

Here, and subsequently, when dealing with two vectors we let them be

$$\mathbf{v_1} = x_1\mathbf{i} + y_1\mathbf{j} = \langle x_1, y_1 \rangle \qquad \text{and} \qquad \mathbf{v_2} = x_2\mathbf{i} + y_2\mathbf{j} = \langle x_2, y_2 \rangle$$

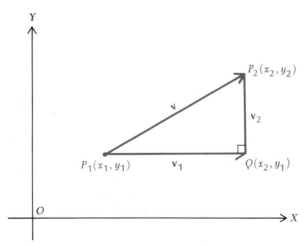

FIGURE 7.13

Then

$$\mathbf{v}_1 + \mathbf{v}_2 = (x_1\mathbf{i} + y_1\mathbf{j}) + (x_2\mathbf{i} + y_2\mathbf{j})$$

$$= (x_1\mathbf{i} + x_2\mathbf{i}) + (y_1\mathbf{j} + y_2\mathbf{j}) \qquad \text{Addition of vectors is}$$
$$\text{associative and commutative}$$

$$= (x_1 + x_2)\mathbf{i} + (y_1 + y_2)\mathbf{j} \qquad \text{Distributive property (20)}$$

$$= \langle x_1 + x_2, y_1 + y_2 \rangle$$

The student is asked to prove in a similar manner Theorems 7.14 and 7.15.

THEOREM 7.14 *If $\mathbf{v}_1 = \langle x_1, y_1 \rangle$ and $\mathbf{v}_2 = \langle x_2, y_2 \rangle$, then*

$$\mathbf{v}_1 - \mathbf{v}_2 = \langle x_1 - x_2, y_1 - y_2 \rangle$$

THEOREM 7.15 *To multiply the vector $\mathbf{v} = v_1\mathbf{i} + v_2\mathbf{j}$ by the real number h, multiply each coordinate of $\mathbf{v}$ by h:*

$$h\mathbf{v} = hv_1\mathbf{i} + hv_2\mathbf{j} = \langle hv_1, hv_2 \rangle$$

To illustrate Theorems 7.13 to 7.15, let $\mathbf{v}_1 = \langle 1, 4 \rangle$, $\mathbf{v}_2 = \langle 6, 9 \rangle$, and $h = 3$. Then $\mathbf{v}_1 + \mathbf{v}_2 = \langle 1, 4 \rangle + \langle 6, 9 \rangle = \langle 7, 13 \rangle$, $\mathbf{v}_1 - \mathbf{v}_2 = \langle 1 - 6, 4 - 9 \rangle = \langle -5, -5 \rangle$, and $h\mathbf{v}_1 = 3\langle 1, 4 \rangle = \langle 3, 12 \rangle$.

As mentioned earlier, we are usually concerned with *free vectors* (see page 233). But sometimes we are concerned with *bound vectors*, especially those whose representatives have the origin for initial point. If $\mathbf{r}$ has $O(0, 0)$ for initial point and $P(x, y)$ for terminal point, then

$$\mathbf{r} = (x - 0)\mathbf{i} + (y - 0)\mathbf{j} = x\mathbf{i} + y\mathbf{j} = \langle x, y \rangle$$

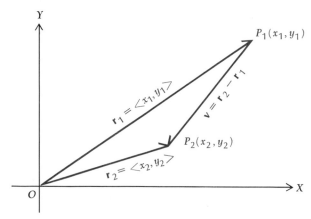

FIGURE 7.14

Position vector   We call $\mathbf{r} = \langle x, y \rangle$ the **position vector** of the point $P(x, y)$. We reserve the use of $\mathbf{r}$ to denote a position vector, and when we speak of a position vector it is to be understood that the vector has only one representative and that the initial point of this representative is at the origin.

Observe that the vector $\mathbf{v}(\overrightarrow{P_1P_2})$ of Theorem 7.12 (see Fig. 7.14) may be considered as $\mathbf{v} = \mathbf{r}_2 - \mathbf{r}_1$, where $\mathbf{r}_1$ and $\mathbf{r}_2$ are the position vectors

$$\mathbf{r}_1 = \langle x_1, y_1 \rangle \qquad \text{and} \qquad \mathbf{r}_2 = \langle x_2, y_2 \rangle$$

THEOREM   *If* $\mathbf{v}_1 = x_1\mathbf{i} + y_1\mathbf{j}$ *and* $\mathbf{v}_2 = x_2\mathbf{i} + y_2\mathbf{j}$, *then*
7.16
$$\mathbf{v}_1 = \mathbf{v}_2 \iff x_1 = x_2 \text{ and } y_1 = y_2$$

Proof

If $\mathbf{v}_1 = \mathbf{v}_2$, then by Theorem 7.14 $\mathbf{v}_1 - \mathbf{v}_2 = \langle x_1 - x_2, y_1 - y_2 \rangle = \mathbf{0}$. Then by (29) we have $x_1 = x_2$ and $y_1 = y_2$. The converse is obvious.

Angle between   The **angle** θ **between** two *nonzero* vectors $\mathbf{u}(\overrightarrow{OP})$ and $\mathbf{v}(\overrightarrow{OQ})$ is the angle POQ
vectors $(0 \le \theta \le \pi)$ and is denoted by $\angle(\mathbf{u}, \mathbf{v})$. If P, O, and Q are collinear, $\angle(\mathbf{u}, \mathbf{v})$ is π or 0 according as O is or is not on the segment PQ.

The **direction angles** and the **direction cosines** of a nonzero vector $\mathbf{v}(\overrightarrow{P_1P_2})$ are the direction angles and the direction cosines of $\overrightarrow{P_1P_2}$.

Let $P_1(x_1, y_1)$ and $P_2(x_2, y_2)$ be two points in E_2, and let α_1 and β_1 be the direction angles of $\overrightarrow{P_1P_2}$ and therefore of $\mathbf{u}(\overrightarrow{P_1P_2})$. From the result (20) of Sec. 3.6 and Theorem 7.12 it follows that

$$\mathbf{u}(\overrightarrow{P_1P_2}) = \langle x_2 - x_1, y_2 - y_1 \rangle = \langle u_1, u_2 \rangle$$

The direction cosines of $\mathbf{u}(\overrightarrow{P_1P_2})$ are given by

$$\cos \alpha_1 = \frac{x_2 - x_1}{\|\mathbf{u}\|} = \frac{u_1}{\|\mathbf{u}\|} \qquad \cos \beta_1 = \frac{y_2 - y_1}{\|\mathbf{u}\|} = \frac{u_2}{\|\mathbf{u}\|} \tag{32}$$

Likewise for $\mathbf{v}(\overrightarrow{Q_1Q_2}) = \langle v_1, v_2 \rangle$ we have

$$\cos \alpha_2 = \frac{v_1}{\|\mathbf{v}\|} \qquad \cos \beta_2 = \frac{v_2}{\|\mathbf{v}\|} \tag{33}$$

From (32) we see that if $\mathbf{u} = \langle u_1, u_2 \rangle$ is a *unit* vector $(\|\mathbf{u}\| = 1)$ then the direction cosines of $\mathbf{u}$ are the coordinates of $\mathbf{u}$.

For the angle $\theta = \angle(\mathbf{u}, \mathbf{v})$ between the nonzero vectors $\mathbf{u}(\overrightarrow{P_1P_2})$ and $\mathbf{v}(\overrightarrow{Q_1Q_2})$, we know from Theorem 3.7 that

$$\cos \theta = \cos \alpha_1 \cos \alpha_2 + \cos \beta_1 \cos \beta_2 \tag{34}$$

Substituting from (32) and (33) in (34), we get

$$\cos\theta = \frac{u_1v_1 + u_2v_2}{\|\mathbf{u}\|\,\|\mathbf{v}\|} \tag{35}$$

For $P_1(1,-1)$ and $P_2(-2,-3)$ we have

$$\mathbf{u}(\overrightarrow{P_1P_2}) = \langle x_2 - x_1,\, y_2 - y_1 \rangle = \langle -3, -2 \rangle \qquad \|\mathbf{u}\| = \sqrt{13}$$

For $P_3(1,-2)$ and $P_4(6, 8)$ we have

$$\mathbf{v}(\overrightarrow{P_3P_4}) = \langle x_4 - x_3,\, y_4 - y_3 \rangle = \langle 5, 10 \rangle \qquad \|\mathbf{v}\| = 5\sqrt{5}$$

Let α_1 and β_1 be the direction angles of $\mathbf{u}$ and let α_2 and β_2 be the direction angles of $\mathbf{v}$. Then

$$\cos\alpha_1 = \frac{-3}{\sqrt{13}} \qquad \cos\beta_1 = \frac{-2}{\sqrt{13}}$$

$$\cos\alpha_2 = \frac{1}{\sqrt{5}} \qquad \cos\beta_2 = \frac{2}{\sqrt{5}}$$

If $\theta = \sphericalangle(\mathbf{u}, \mathbf{v})$, we can use (35) to obtain

$$\cos\theta = \frac{-3(5) + (-2)(10)}{\sqrt{13}\cdot 5\sqrt{5}} = \frac{-15 - 20}{5\sqrt{65}} = \frac{-7}{\sqrt{65}}$$

This result should be compared with the value obtained for $\cos\theta$ in Example 2 of Sec. 3.6 (see Fig. 3.35).

Inner product   The expression $u_1v_1 + u_2v_2$ is called the **inner product** of $\mathbf{u} = \langle u_1, u_2 \rangle$ and $\mathbf{v} = \langle v_1, v_2 \rangle$, and is denoted by $\mathbf{u}\cdot\mathbf{v}$. So

$$\mathbf{u}\cdot\mathbf{v} = u_1v_1 + u_2v_2 \tag{36}$$

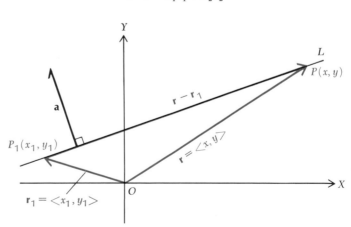

FIGURE 7.15

and
$$\cos \sphericalangle(\mathbf{u}, \mathbf{v}) = \frac{\mathbf{u} \cdot \mathbf{v}}{\|\mathbf{u}\| \, \|\mathbf{v}\|} \tag{37}$$

Scalar product or dot product

The expression $\mathbf{u} \cdot \mathbf{v}$ is also called the **scalar product** or the **dot product** of the vectors $\mathbf{u}$ and $\mathbf{v}$. Note that, as we see from (37), the inner product could be defined by

$$\mathbf{u} \cdot \mathbf{v} = \|\mathbf{u}\| \, \|\mathbf{v}\| \cos \sphericalangle(\mathbf{u}, \mathbf{v})$$

From (37) we obtain Theorem 7.17.

THEOREM 7.17 $\mathbf{u} \perp \mathbf{v} \iff \mathbf{u} \cdot \mathbf{v} = 0.$

THEOREM 7.18   *Let $\mathbf{r}_1 = \langle x_1, y_1 \rangle$ be the position vector of a fixed point $P_1(x_1, y_1)$, let $\mathbf{r} = \langle x, y \rangle$ be the position vector of a (variable) point $P(x, y)$, and let $\mathbf{a} = \langle a_1, a_2 \rangle$ be any nonzero vector. Then $P(x, y)$ is on the line L through $P_1(x_1, y_1)$ and perpendicular to $\mathbf{a}$, if and only if*

Vector equation of a line

$$\mathbf{a} \cdot (\mathbf{r} - \mathbf{r}_1) = 0 \tag{38}$$

Proof

The theorem follows directly from Theorem 7.17 (see Fig. 7.15).

Equation (38) is called a *vector equation* of the line L through $P_1(x_1, y_1)$ and perpendicular to the vector $\mathbf{a} = \langle a_1, a_2 \rangle$. Observe that (38) is equivalent to

$$a_1(x - x_1) + a_2(y - y_1) = 0$$

From an examination of Fig. 7.16 and the definition of the norm of a vector, Theorem 7.19 follows.

THEOREM 7.19   *Let $\mathbf{r}_1 = \langle x_1, y_1 \rangle$ be the position vector of a fixed point $P_1(x_1, y_1)$, let $\mathbf{r} = \langle x, y \rangle$ be the position vector of a (variable) point $P(x, y)$, and let k be any positive real number. Then $P(x, y)$ lies on the circle with center $P_1(x_1, y_1)$ and radius k if and only if*

Vector equation of a circle

$$\|\mathbf{r} - \mathbf{r}_1\| = k \tag{39}$$

Equation (39) is called a *vector equation* of the circle C with center $P_1(x_1, y_1)$ and radius k. Observe that (39) is equivalent to

$$(x - x_1)^2 + (y - y_1)^2 = k^2$$

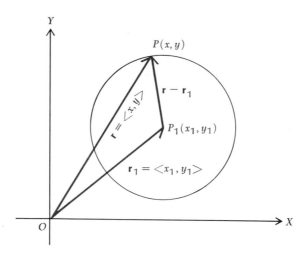

FIGURE 7.16

THEOREM 7.20   *For any vectors* **u** *and* **v** *in* E_2,

$$(\mathbf{u} \cdot \mathbf{v})^2 \le \|\mathbf{u}\|^2 \|\mathbf{v}\|^2 \qquad \text{(the Schwarz inequality)}$$

Proof

The Schwarz inequality is equivalent to

$$(u_1 v_1 + u_2 v_2)^2 \le (u_1^2 + u_2^2)(v_1^2 + v_2^2)$$

or
$$u_1^2 v_1^2 + 2u_1 v_1 u_2 v_2 + u_2^2 v_2^2 \le u_1^2 v_1^2 + u_1^2 v_2^2 + u_2^2 v_1^2 + u_2^2 v_2^2 \qquad (40)$$

Now $0 \le (u_1 v_2 - u_2 v_1)^2$. So

$$0 \le u_1^2 v_2^2 - 2u_1 u_2 v_1 v_2 + u_2^2 v_1^2$$

and
$$2u_1 u_2 v_1 v_2 \le u_1^2 v_2^2 + u_2^2 v_1^2$$

Therefore (40) holds and the theorem is proved.

THEOREM 7.21   *For any vectors* **u**, **v**, *and* **w** *of* E_2:

(i) $\mathbf{u} \cdot (\mathbf{v} + \mathbf{w}) = \mathbf{u} \cdot \mathbf{v} + \mathbf{u} \cdot \mathbf{w}$

(ii) $\mathbf{u} \cdot \mathbf{v} = \mathbf{v} \cdot \mathbf{u}$

(iii) $\|\mathbf{u}\|^2 = \mathbf{u} \cdot \mathbf{u}$

Proof

  (i) We have

$$\mathbf{u} \cdot (\mathbf{v} + \mathbf{w}) = u_1(v_1 + w_1) + u_2(v_2 + w_2)$$ Definition of inner product

$$= u_1v_1 + u_1w_1 + u_2v_2 + u_2w_2$$ Distributive property of real numbers

$$= (u_1v_1 + u_2v_2) + (u_1w_1 + u_2w_2)$$ Properties of real numbers

$$= \mathbf{u} \cdot \mathbf{v} + \mathbf{u} \cdot \mathbf{w}$$ Definition of inner product

  (ii) Similarly, $\mathbf{u} \cdot \mathbf{v} = u_1v_1 + u_2v_2 = v_1u_1 + v_2u_2 = \mathbf{v} \cdot \mathbf{u}$

  (iii) Clearly, $\mathbf{u} \cdot \mathbf{u} = u_1{}^2 + u_2{}^2 = \|\mathbf{u}\|^2$

Triangle inequality

THEOREM *For any two vectors* $\mathbf{u}$ *and* $\mathbf{v}$ *in* E_2,

7.22

$$\|\mathbf{u} + \mathbf{v}\| \leqslant \|\mathbf{u}\| + \|\mathbf{v}\| \qquad (\textit{the triangle inequality})$$

Proof

The Schwarz inequality implies

$$|\mathbf{u} \cdot \mathbf{v}| \leqslant \|\mathbf{u}\| \, \|\mathbf{v}\| \qquad \text{and} \qquad \mathbf{u} \cdot \mathbf{v} \leqslant \|\mathbf{u}\| \, \|\mathbf{v}\| \qquad\qquad (41)$$

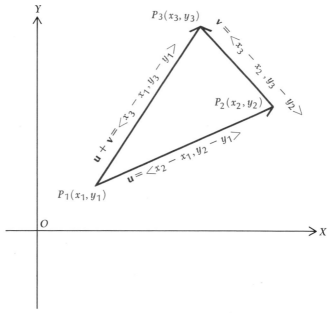

FIGURE 7.17

We have

$$\|\mathbf{u} + \mathbf{v}\|^2 = (\mathbf{u} + \mathbf{v}) \cdot (\mathbf{u} + \mathbf{v}) \qquad \text{By Theorem 7.21(iii)}$$
$$= (\mathbf{u} + \mathbf{v}) \cdot \mathbf{u} + (\mathbf{u} + \mathbf{v}) \cdot \mathbf{v} \qquad \text{By Theorem 7.21(i)}$$
$$= \mathbf{u} \cdot (\mathbf{u} + \mathbf{v}) + \mathbf{v} \cdot (\mathbf{u} + \mathbf{v}) \qquad \text{By Theorem 7.21(ii)}$$
$$= \mathbf{u} \cdot \mathbf{u} + \mathbf{u} \cdot \mathbf{v} + \mathbf{v} \cdot \mathbf{u} + \mathbf{v} \cdot \mathbf{v} \qquad \text{By Theorem 7.21(i)}$$

So

$$\|\mathbf{u} + \mathbf{v}\|^2 = \|\mathbf{u}\|^2 + 2\mathbf{u} \cdot \mathbf{v} + \|\mathbf{v}\|^2 \qquad \text{By Theorem 7.21(ii) and (iii)}$$

From this equality and (41) we get

$$\|\mathbf{u} + \mathbf{v}\|^2 \leqslant \|\mathbf{u}\|^2 + 2\|\mathbf{u}\|\,\|\mathbf{v}\| + \|\mathbf{v}\|^2$$
$$\leqslant (\|\mathbf{u}\| + \|\mathbf{v}\|)^2$$

Therefore

$$\|\mathbf{u} + \mathbf{v}\| \leqslant \|\mathbf{u}\| + \|\mathbf{v}\|$$

Observe that in Theorem 7.22 we have proved the *triangle inequality* referred to in Sec. 2.3. Figure 7.17 indicates the geometric interpretation of Theorem 7.22 in connection with the property of distance (see Sec. 2.3):

$$|P_1 P_3| \leqslant |P_1 P_2| + |P_2 P_3|$$

EXERCISES

1. Prove Theorem 7.14 and give a reason for each step, as was done in the proof of Theorem 7.13.

2. Prove Theorem 7.15, giving a reason for each step.

3. If $\mathbf{v} = \langle v_1, v_2 \rangle$ is a nonzero vector and k is a nonzero real number, use Theorem 7.15 and formulas (33) to prove that $\mathbf{v}$ and $k\mathbf{v}$ have the same direction cosines.

4. For any vectors $\mathbf{u}$, $\mathbf{v}$, and $\mathbf{w}$ of E_2 and any real number k prove (give a reason for each step):

    (a) $(k\mathbf{u}) \cdot \mathbf{v} = k(\mathbf{u} \cdot \mathbf{v})$

    (b) $\mathbf{u} \cdot \mathbf{u} \geqslant 0$, and $\mathbf{u} \cdot \mathbf{u} = 0$ only if $\mathbf{u} = \mathbf{0}$

    (c) $\|\mathbf{u} - \mathbf{v}\|^2 = \|\mathbf{u}\|^2 + \|\mathbf{v}\|^2 - 2\mathbf{u} \cdot \mathbf{v}$

5. If $\mathbf{u}$ and $\mathbf{v}$ are nonzero vectors, use (37) to prove:

    (a) $\mathbf{u} \cdot \mathbf{v} > 0 \iff 0 \leqslant \angle(\mathbf{u}, \mathbf{v}) < \tfrac{1}{2}\pi$

    (b) $\mathbf{u} \cdot \mathbf{v} < 0 \iff \tfrac{1}{2}\pi < \angle(\mathbf{u}, \mathbf{v}) \leqslant \pi$

6. Prove that $\mathbf{i} \cdot \mathbf{i} = 1$, $\mathbf{j} \cdot \mathbf{j} = 1$, and $\mathbf{i} \cdot \mathbf{j} = \mathbf{j} \cdot \mathbf{i} = 0$.

In each of Exercises 7–10 find the vector $\mathbf{v} = \langle v_1, v_2 \rangle = \mathbf{v}(\overrightarrow{P_1 P_2})$ in E_2 for the given points P_1 and P_2, and give the direction cosines on $\mathbf{v}$.

7. $P_1(0, 2)$; $P_2(-3, -2)$ **8.** $P_1(6, -3)$; $P_2(-7, -9)$

9. $P_1(1, 2)$; $P_2(2, 4)$ **10.** $P_1(-7, 5)$; $P_2(1, 0)$

In each of Exercises 11 and 12 find cos $\angle(\mathbf{u}, \mathbf{v})$.

11. $\mathbf{u}(\overrightarrow{P_1 P_2})$, $P_1(1, -1)$, $P_2(-2, -3)$; $\mathbf{v}(\overrightarrow{Q_1 Q_2})$, $Q_1(1, -2)$, $Q_2(6, 8)$

12. $\mathbf{u}(\overrightarrow{P_1 P_2})$, $P_1(1, 1)$, $P_2(4, 5)$; $\mathbf{v}(\overrightarrow{Q_1 Q_2})$, $Q_1(4, 5)$, $Q_2(5, -2)$

In each of Exercises 13–16 find $\mathbf{u} + \mathbf{v}$, $\|\mathbf{u}\|$, $\|\mathbf{v}\|$, $\|\mathbf{u} + \mathbf{v}\|$; represent $\mathbf{u}$, $\mathbf{v}$, and $\mathbf{u} + \mathbf{v}$ in a figure like Fig. 7.17 (choose P_1 to be the origin, if you like), and verify the triangular inequality.

13. $\mathbf{u} = \langle 2, 2 \rangle$; $\mathbf{v} = \langle 3, 4 \rangle$ **14.** $\mathbf{u} = \langle 0, 3 \rangle$; $\mathbf{v} = \langle 3, 0 \rangle$

15. $\mathbf{u} = \langle 5, -2 \rangle$; $\mathbf{v} = \langle 3, -2 \rangle$ **16.** $\mathbf{u} = \langle 3, 5 \rangle$; $\mathbf{v} = \langle -1, -2 \rangle$

In each of Exercises 17 and 18 give a vector equation of the form $\mathbf{a} \cdot (\mathbf{r} - \mathbf{r}_1) = 0$ for the specified line.

17. Through the point $(3, 4)$ and perpendicular to the vector $\langle 5, 6 \rangle$
18. Through the point $(2, 3)$ and perpendicular to the vector $\langle 2, -1 \rangle$
19. Show that the line L through the point $P_1(x_1, y_1)$ and parallel to the vector $\mathbf{b} = \langle b_1, b_2 \rangle$ has the vector equation

$$\mathbf{r} - \mathbf{r}_1 = k \langle b_1, b_2 \rangle$$

20. Give a vector equation of the line through the point $(3, 4)$ and parallel to the vector $\langle 5, 6 \rangle$.

In each of Exercises 21–24 give a vector equation of the form $\|\mathbf{r} - \mathbf{r}_1\| = k$ for the specified circle.

21. With center at $(2, 3)$ and radius 4
22. With center at $(7, 0)$ and radius 9
23. With center at $(0, 0)$ and radius 5
24. With center at $(-6, -4)$ and radius $\frac{1}{2}$

7.3 LINEAR PROGRAMMING

In this section we give a very brief introduction to some of the simpler aspects of a relatively new and quite important branch of mathematics called *linear programming*. We shall make some statements without proof. Proofs of them may be found in any one of several books on the subject. For example, see Walter W. Garvin, "Introduction to Linear Programming," McGraw-Hill Book Company, New York, 1960.

Convex set

Basic to the consideration of linear programming is the concept of convex sets, which we now consider briefly.

A set S of points in a plane is a **convex set** if, whenever P_1 and P_2 are in S, the line segment P_1P_2 is also in S (see Fig. 7.18):

$$S \text{ is convex} \iff [P_1 \in S \text{ and } P_2 \in S \implies P_1P_2 \in S]$$

THEOREM 7.23   *The intersection of two convex sets S_1 and S_2 is a convex set.*

Proof

Let P_1 and P_2 be any two points in $S_1 \cap S_2$ (Fig. 7.19). We want to show that

$$P_1P_2 \subset S_1 \cap S_2$$

Now $P_1P_2 \subset S_1$ since S_1 is convex, and $P_1P_2 \subset S_2$ since S_2 is convex. From the definition of $S_1 \cap S_2$, it follows that $P_1P_2 \subset S_1 \cap S_2$.

In Sec. 3.3 we saw that a nonvertical line L which is the graph of

$$R_1 = \{(x, y) \mid y = mx + b\}$$

divides the coordinate plane into two parts which are the graphs of

$$R_2 = \{(x, y) \mid y > mx + b\} \qquad \text{and} \qquad R_3 = \{(x, y) \mid y < mx + b\}$$

Half plane

The graph of R_2 consists of the points lying *above* L, and the graph of R_3 consists of the points lying *below* L. We call the graph of each of R_2 and R_3 a **half plane.**

If L is a vertical line that is the graph of $\{(x, y) \mid x = a\}$, then the half plane to the *right* of L is the graph of $\{(x, y) \mid x > a\}$ and the half plane to the *left* of L is the graph of $\{(x, y) \mid x < a\}$.

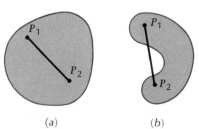

(a)   (b)

FIGURE 7.18   (*a*) A convex set.
(*b*) Not a convex set.

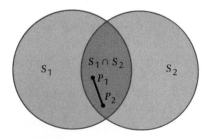

FIGURE 7.19

The graph of the relations

$$R_1 \cup R_2 = \{(x, y) \mid y \geq mx + b\}$$

and

$$R_1 \cup R_3 = \{(x, y) \mid y \leq mx + b\}$$

Closed half plane

Open half plane

are called **closed half planes,** and for this reason the graphs of R_2 and R_3 are sometimes called **open half planes.** Similarly, the graphs of $\{(x, y) \mid x \geq a\}$ and $\{(x, y) \mid x \leq a\}$ are closed half planes.

We assume without proof Theorem 7.24. [For an excellent proof of this (and other theorems mentioned here) see A. M. Glicksman, "An Introduction to Linear Programming and the Theory of Games," p. 35, John Wiley & Sons, Inc., New York, 1963.]

THEOREM 7.24 *Any half plane (open or closed) is a convex set.*

Directly from Theorems 7.23 and 7.24 we have Theorem 7.25.

THEOREM 7.25 *The intersection of any collection of half planes is a convex set.*

Polygonal convex set

The intersection of a finite number of closed half planes is called a **polygonal convex set.**

♦ EXAMPLE 1

Graph

$$S = \{(x, y) \mid x \geq 0 \text{ and } y \geq 0 \text{ and } x + y - 4 \geq 0 \text{ and } 5x + 9y - 45 \leq 0\}$$

Solution

We can write $S = S_1 \cap S_2 \cap S_3 \cap S_4$, where $S_1 = \{(x, y) \mid x \geq 0\}$, $S_2 = \{(x, y) \mid y \geq 0\}$, $S_3 = \{(x, y) \mid x + y - 4 \geq 0\}$, and $S_4 = \{(x, y) \mid 5x + 9y - 45 \leq 0\}$. The graph of S is shown in Fig. 7.20 and is an illustration of a polygonal convex set.

Any polygonal convex set has as *boundary lines* a set of lines

$$L_1: a_1x + b_1y + c_1 = 0$$
$$L_2: a_2x + b_2y + c_2 = 0$$
$$\cdots \cdots \cdots \cdots$$
$$L_n: a_nx + b_ny + c_n = 0$$

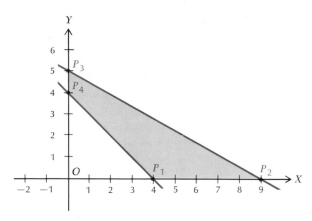

FIGURE 7.20

To illustrate, in Example 1 the boundary lines are

$$L_1: x = 0, \qquad L_2: x + y - 4 = 0, \qquad L_3: y = 0, \qquad L_4: 5x + 9y - 45 = 0$$

If S is a polygonal convex set, the intersection of any boundary line of S with S is called an edge of S. With reference to Example 1 and Fig. 7.20, the edges of S are the segments P_1P_2, P_2P_3, P_3P_4, and P_4P_1. A point in a polygonal convex set S which is common to (that is, is the intersection of) two edges of S is an *Extreme point* **extreme point.** In the set S of Example 1 the extreme points are

$$P_1(4, 0), \qquad P_2(9, 0), \qquad P_3(0, 5), \qquad P_4(0, 4)$$

The basic problem of linear programming (in the plane) is the following: Given a polygonal convex set S and $f(x, y) = ax + by$, $a, b \in Re$, $(x, y) \in S \subset Re \times Re$, find the maximum (greatest) and minimum (least) values of $f(x, y)$.

A famous theorem which appears in subsequent mathematics courses (Weierstrass' theorem on continuous functions) assures us that $f(x, y)$ will attain a maximum value and a minimum value over the polygonal convex set S, and a basic theorem in linear programming tells us that the maximum value and the minimum value will each be attained at some extreme point in S.

● EXAMPLE 2

Find the maximum value and the minimum value of $f_1(x, y)$ and of $f_2(x, y)$ for S of Example 1 where:

  a. $f_1(x, y) = 2x + 3y$
  b. $f_2(x, y) = x - 3y$

Solution

a. We find

$f_1(4, 0) = 2(4) + 3(0) = 8$,   which is the minimum value

$f_1(9, 0) = 18$,   which is the maximum value

$f_1(0, 5) = 15$

$f_1(0, 4) = 12$

b. Here

$f_2(4, 0) = 4$

$f_2(9, 0) = 9$,   which is the maximum value

$f_2(0, 5) = -15$,   which is the minimum value

$f_2(0, 4) = -12$

EXERCISES

In each of Exercises 1–5 graph S and find the extreme points of S. Then find the maximum and minimum values of $f(x, y)$ for S.

1. $S = \{(x, y) \mid x \geqslant 0$ and $y \geqslant 0$ and $y \geqslant -\frac{4}{3}x + 4$ and $y \leqslant -\frac{12}{5}x + 12\}$; $f(x, y) = x + y$

2. $S = \{(x, y) \mid y \geqslant 0$ and $y \leqslant -\frac{1}{2}x + \frac{5}{2}$ and $y \geqslant -\frac{2}{3}x - 2\}$; $f(x, y) = 2x + 3y$

3. $S = \{(x, y) \mid y \geqslant 0$ and $x + y \leqslant 7$ and $-x + 5 \leqslant 10\}$; $f(x, y) = x - y$

4. $S = \{(x, y) \mid x \geqslant 0$ and $y \geqslant 0$ and $x + y - 5 \geqslant 0$ and $x + 3y - 18 \leqslant 0\}$; $f(x, y) = x + 2y$

5. $S = \{(x, y) \mid x \geqslant 0$ and $y \geqslant 4$ and $x + y \geqslant 6$ and $x \leqslant 5$ and $y \leqslant 8\}$; $f(x, y) = x + 2y$

6. The Big Company makes two products, X_1 and X_2. These must be processed on machines m_1 and m_2, X_1 requiring one hour of time on m_1 and 3 hours of time on m_2, X_2 requiring 2 hours of time on m_1 and 1 hour on m_2. To describe the quantities of X_1 and X_2 which may be produced within a week, where x_1 is the quantity of X_1 and x_2 is the quantity of X_2, it is necessary and sufficient that

$$x_1 + 2x_2 \leqslant 100 \qquad 3x_1 + x_2 \leqslant 100 \qquad x_1 \geqslant 0 \qquad x_2 \geqslant 0$$

The company's earnings are \$4.00 per unit on X_1 and \$3.00 per unit on X_2. If E denotes the earnings, then $E = 4x_1 + 3x_2$. Maximize E subject to the restraints listed above.

7. Customer K_1 wants to purchase from 400 to 1,200 units of a certain commodity at \$2.00 each, and customer K_2 wants to purchase from 600 to 1,000 units at \$2.20 each. Delivery charges are 8 cents per unit to K_1 and 16 cents per unit to K_2. If the seller has 2,000 units, find how many he should sell to each of K_1 and K_2 to obtain the maximum proceeds. What is the amount of the maximum proceeds?

7.4 GRAPHING BY ADDITION OF ORDINATES

We sometimes wish to graph a relation $F_3 = \{(x, y) \mid y = F_3(x)\}$, where $F_3(x) = F_1(x) + F_2(x)$. If we first construct the graphs G_1 and G_2 of the relations

$$F_1 = \{(x, y) \mid y = F_1(x)\} \qquad \text{and} \qquad F_2 = \{(x, y) \mid y = F_2(x)\} \qquad (42)$$

respectively, on the same coordinate system, then we can construct the graph G_3 of

$$F_3 = \{(x, y) \mid y = F_1(x) + F_2(x)\}$$

by the *addition of ordinates*. This may be done by actually adding the ordinate y_1 of $P_1(a, y_1)$ on G_1 and the ordinate y_2 of $P_2(a, y_2)$ on G_2 to get the ordinate $y_3 = y_1 + y_2$ of $P_3(a, y_3)$ on G_3. However, a more convenient procedure in most cases is to use a compass, (a pair of) dividers, or a ruler to mark off the ordinates y_1, y_2, and y_3 on a vertical line. Examples 1 and 2 illustrate this method.

◆ EXAMPLE 1

Construct the graph G_3 of the relation $F_3 = \{(x, y) \mid y = \sqrt{4 - x^2} + x, x \in [-2; 2]\}$. Here $F_1(x) = \sqrt{4 - x^2}$ and $F_2(x) = x$.

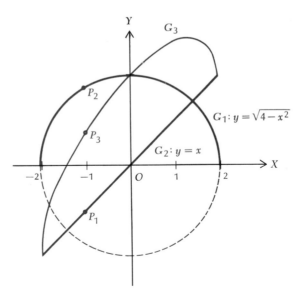

FIGURE 7.21

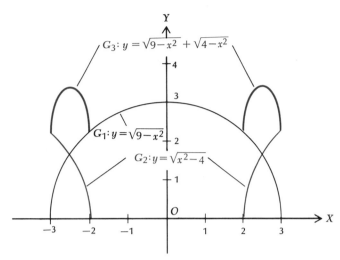

FIGURE 7.22

Solution

The graph G_1 of

$$F_1 = \{(x, y) \mid y = \sqrt{4 - x^2}, x \in [-2; 2]\}$$

is the semicircle of Fig. 7.21, and the graph G_2 of

$$F_2 = \{(x, y) \mid y = x, x \in [-2; 2]\}$$

is the line segment of Fig. 7.21.

For each value of x, say a, belonging to $[-2; 2]$ there are values y_1 and y_2 such that

$$(a, y_1) \in F_1 \qquad (a, y_2) \in F_2 \qquad (a, y_1 + y_2) \in F_3$$

To illustrate, for $P_1(-1, \sqrt{3})$ on G_1 and $P_2(-1, -1)$ on G_2, with dividers we easily locate $P_3(-1, \sqrt{3} - 1)$ on G. In this manner we locate other points which enable us to construct G_3, shown in Fig. 7.21.

Graphing by addition of ordinates is consistent with finding the sum of two functions. Observe that the relations F_1 and F_2 specified above in (42) and also in Example 1 are functions (see Sec. 1.8). If D_{F_1} and D_{F_2} are the domains of F_1

Sum of functions   and F_2 as specified in (42) and if $D_{F_1} \cap D_{F_2} \neq \emptyset$, the **sum** of F_1 and F_2 is denoted by $F_1 + F_2$ and is defined by

$$F_1 + F_2 = \{(x, y) \mid y = F_1(x) + F_2(x), x \in D_{F_1} \cap D_{F_2}\}$$

◆ EXAMPLE 2

If F_1 and F_2 are specified by $F_1(x) = \sqrt{9 - x^2}$ and $F_2(x) = \sqrt{x^2 - 4}$, give a specification for $F_1 + F_2$. Graph F_1, F_2, and $F_1 + F_2$ on the same coordinate system, and give the domain of each of F_1, F_2, and $F_1 + F_2$.

Solution

Here

$$D_{F_1} = [-3; 3] \qquad D_{F_2} = (-\infty; -2] \cup [2; +\infty)$$
$$D_{F_1+F_2} = D_{F_1} \cap D_{F_2} = [-3; 2] \cup [2; 3]$$
$$F_1 + F_2 = \{(x, y) \mid y = \sqrt{9 - x^2} + \sqrt{x^2 - 4}\}$$

The graph of F_1 is the semicircle G_1 shown in Fig. 7.22; the graph G_2 consists of that portion of the hyperbola $H: x^2 - y^2 = 4$ lying in quadrants I and II. The graph G_3 of $F_1 + F_2$ is obtained by the addition of ordinates from G_1 and G_2, and is the heavily drawn curve in Fig. 7.22.

EXERCISES

In each of Exercises 1–10 construct the graphs G_1 of F_1 and G_2 of F_2 for $x \in D_{F_1} \cap D_{F_2}$ on the same coordinate system. If $F_3 = F_1 + F_2$, construct the graph G_3 of F_3 by the addition of ordinates. Give the domain of each of the functions F_1, F_2, and F_3.

1. $F_1(x) = \sqrt{x}$; $F_2(x) = x$ **2.** $F_1(x) = \frac{2}{3}\sqrt{4 - x^2}$; $F_2(x) = \frac{1}{2}x$

3. $F_1(x) = x^3$; $F_2(x) = \frac{1}{3}x$ **4.** $F_1(x) = x^2$; $F_2(x) = 1/x$

5. $F_1(x) = x$; $F_2(x) = 1/x^2$ **6.** $F_1(x) = \sqrt{4 - x^2}$; $F_2(x) = 1/x^2$

7. $F_1(x) = x$; $F_2(x) = \sin x$, $x \in [0; 2\pi]$

8. $F_1(x) = -x$; $F_2(x) = \tan x$, $x \in [-\frac{1}{4}\pi; \frac{1}{4}\pi]$

9. $F_1(x) = \sin x$, $x \in [-\pi; 2\pi]$; $F_2(x) = \cos x$, $x \in [0; 3\pi]$

10. $F_1(x) = \frac{1}{2}\sin x$, $x \in [-2\pi; \pi]$; $F_2(x) = 2 \cos x$, $x \in [-\pi; 2\pi]$

In each of Exercises 11 and 12 show that for the functions F_1 and F_2 whose specifications are given, $D_{F_1} \cap D_{F_2} = \emptyset$, so $F_1 + F_2$ is not defined, and addition of ordinates is of no aid in graphing $F_1 + F_2$.

11. $F_1(x) = \sqrt{4 - x^2}$; $F_2(x) = \sqrt{x^2 - 9}$

12. $F_1(x) = x$, $x \in [-1; 1]$; $F_2(x) = \sqrt{x^2 - 3}$

8 | SOLID ANALYTIC GEOMETRY

This chapter is a brief presentation of the basic concepts of analytic geometry of three dimensions, including planes, lines, and quadric surfaces. It concludes with a presentation of vectors in 3-space, and a projection of that presentation to higher dimensions and more abstract situations.

8.1 THREE-DIMENSIONAL COORDINATE SYSTEMS

Ordered triple   We define an **ordered triple** (of real numbers), which we denote by (a, b, c), to be an ordered pair whose first entry is an ordered pair. That is,

$$(a, b, c) = ((a, b), c) \tag{1}$$

By using (1) and the definition of equality of two ordered pairs (Sec. 1.6), it can be shown that for triples (a, b, c) and (d, e, f),

$$(a, b, c) = (d, e, f) \iff a = d, b = e, c = f$$

Recall that the set of all ordered *pairs* of real numbers is the cartesian product $Re \times Re$. The set of all ordered *triples* of real numbers is the cartesian product $(Re \times Re) \times Re$.

We now describe how the concept of a two-dimensional coordinate system (see Sec. 1.7) can be used to establish a one-to-one correspondence between the set of points of three-dimensional space and the set of ordered triples of real numbers. Through the origin O of a two-dimensional coordinate system S, construct a one-dimensional coordinate system L perpendicular to the plane of S with the origin of L coincident with the origin of S. The directed line L and the coordinate axes of S form a **three-dimensional rectangular coordinate system.**

Three-dimensional coordinate system

The identities of the x axis and the y axis of S are retained, and the one-dimensional coordinate system L is called the z axis. Figure 8.1 shows a three-dimensional coordinate system with the x axis denoted by OX, the y axis by OY, and the z axis by OZ. This is a *left-handed* coordinate system if the x axis is considered as the first axis, the y axis as the second, and the z axis as the third; if the x axis and the y axis are interchanged, the resulting coordinate system is a *right-handed* system.

Left-handed and right-handed systems

The coordinate axes, taken in pairs, determine three planes, called respectively the **xy plane,** the **yz plane,** and the **xz plane.** These planes are referred to as the **coordinate planes.**

Coordinate planes

Let P be any point in three-dimensional space in which a three-dimensional rectangular coordinate system has been constructed, and let the projections of P on the x axis, the y axis, and the z axis be the points U, V, and W, respectively (see Fig. 8.2). Let x_1 be the coordinate of U on the x axis, y_1 the coordinate of V on the y axis, and z_1 the coordinate of W on the z axis. The numbers $x_1, y_1,$ and z_1 are called the **three-dimensional rectangular coordinates,** or simply the **coordinates,** of P. In this way each point P in three-dimensional space has associated with it an *ordered* triple of real numbers (x_1, y_1, z_1).

Coordinates of a point

Conversely, to an ordered triple (x_1, y_1, z_1) of real numbers there can be associated the point that is the intersection of three planes, one perpendicular to

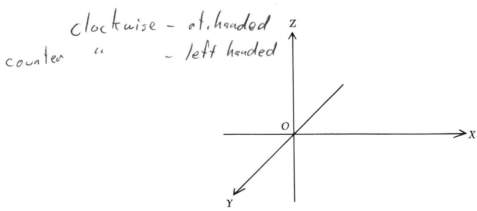

clockwise – rt. handed

counter   "   – left handed

FIGURE 8.1

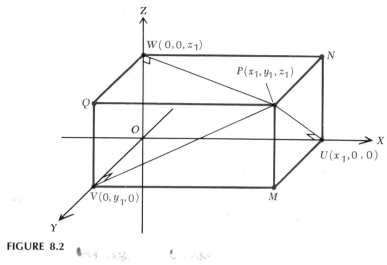

FIGURE 8.2

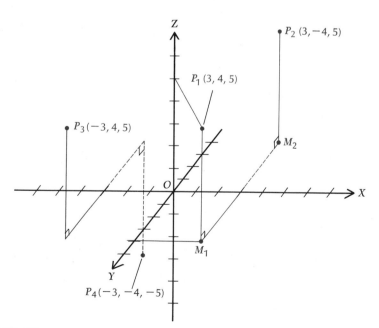

FIGURE 8.3

the x axis at $(x_1, 0, 0)$, the second perpendicular to the y axis at $(0, y_1, 0)$, and the third perpendicular to the z axis at $(0, 0, z_1)$.

We write $P(x_1, y_1, z_1)$ to indicate that P is the point with coordinates x_1, y_1, and z_1; frequently this point is called simply "the point (x_1, y_1, z_1)."

The procedure just described establishes a one-to-one correspondence be-tween the set of points of three-dimensional space and the set of ordered triples of real numbers. Sometimes three-dimensional space is called simply **3-space;** *3-Space* similarly, two-dimensional space is referred to as **2-space.**

2-Space

The coordinate planes divide 3-space into eight regions which are called *Octants* **octants.** The octant in which all three coordinates are positive is called the *first octant.* No particular designation or order is assigned to the other seven octants.

In representing a three-dimensional coordinate system on a plane sheet of paper, as in Figs. 8.1 to 8.3, we usually construct OY through O so that angle XOY is about 135 degrees, and we usually take the unit of length on the y axis about seven-tenths as large as that on the x and z axes. Figure 8.3 shows points $P_1(3, 4, 5)$, $P_2(3, -4, 5)$, $P_3(-3, 4, 5)$, and $P_4(-3, -4, -5)$.

8.2 PROJECTIONS AND SYMMETRY IN THREE DIMENSIONS

Let Π be a plane and let P be a point not on Π. If we draw a line L through P perpendicular to Π, this perpendicular L will intersect Π in a point P' (Fig. 8.4). *Projection of a* The point P' is called the **projection** on Π of P and is denoted by $\text{Proj}_\Pi P$. If P is *point* on Π, then P is its own projection on Π. In Fig. 8.2, M is the projection of P on the xy plane, N is the projection of P on the xz plane, and Q is the projection of P on the yz plane.

Let P_1P_2 be a (directed) segment on a directed line L, and let P_1' and P_2' be the respective projections on a plane Π of the points P_1 and P_2. The segment $P_1'P_2'$

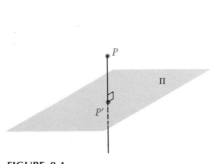

FIGURE 8.4

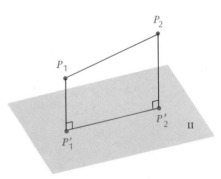

FIGURE 8.5

Projection of a segment   is **the projection on** Π **of the segment** P_1P_2 (Fig. 8.5), and is denoted by Proj_Π P_1P_2. In Fig. 8.2, MU is the projection of PN on the xy plane; in Fig. 8.3, Proj_{xy} $P_1P_2 = M_1M_2$, where Proj_{xy} denotes the projection on the xy plane.

Two points P and Q are **symmetric with respect to a plane** Π if and only if Π bisects the line segment PQ and is perpendicular to PQ. The points (a, b, c) and $(-a, b, c)$ are symmetric with respect to the yz plane; the points (a, b, c) and $(a, b, -c)$ are symmetric with respect to the xy plane. In Fig. 8.3, $P_1(3, 4, 5)$ and $P_2(3, -4, 5)$ are symmetric with respect to the xz plane.

A set of points G is **symmetric with respect to a plane** Π if and only if corresponding to each point $P_1 \in G$ there is a point $P_2 \in G$ with the property that P_1 and P_2 are symmetric with respect to Π. Thus G is symmetric with respect to the yz plane if and only if

$$P_1(x_1, y_1, z_1) \in G \;\;\Rightarrow\;\; P_2(-x_1, y_1, z_1) \in G$$

8.3 THE DISTANCE FORMULA AND THE SPHERE

In considering distance in 3-space we sometimes need the fact that the square of the length of a diagonal of a rectangular parallelepiped is equal to the sum of the squares of the lengths of its three edges a, b, c (Fig. 8.6):

$$d^2 = a^2 + b^2 + c^2 \tag{2}$$

This result follows from two applications of the Pythagorean theorem. We use the equality (2) to prove the following theorem.

THEOREM 8.1   *If $P_1(x_1, y_1, z_1)$ and $P_2(x_2, y_2, z_2)$ are points (in 3-space), then the distance $|P_1P_2|$ between P_1 and P_2 is given by*

Distance formula

$$|P_1P_2| = \sqrt{(x_2 - x_1)^2 + (y_2 - y_1)^2 + (z_2 - z_1)^2} \tag{3}$$

directed

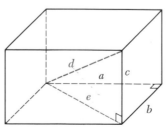

FIGURE 8.6 $e^2 = a^2 + b^2$; $d^2 = e^2 + c^2 = a^2 + b^2 + c^2$.

Proof

Construct a rectangular parallelepiped with faces parallel to the coordinate planes and with P_1 and P_2 as ends of a diagonal (see Fig. 8.7). The edges are then parallel to the coordinate axes. The length of the edges parallel to the x axis is the same as the length of $\text{Proj}_{OX} P_1 P_2$; the length of the edges parallel to the y axis is the same as the length of $\text{Proj}_{OY} P_1 P_2$; the length of the edges parallel to the z axis is the same as the length of $\text{Proj}_{OZ} P_1 P_2$. Referring to Fig. 8.7, we observe that

$$|P_1 A| = \text{length of Proj}_{OX} P_1 P_2 = |x_2 - x_1|$$
$$|AB| = \text{length of Proj}_{OY} P_1 P_2 = |y_2 - y_1|$$
$$|BP_2| = \text{length of Proj}_{OZ} P_1 P_2 = |z_2 - z_1|$$

Using $a = |x_2 - x_1|$, $b = |y_2 - y_1|$, and $c = |z_2 - z_1|$ in (2), we obtain

$$|P_1 P_2|^2 = (x_2 - x_1)^2 + (y_2 - y_1)^2 + (z_2 - z_1)^2$$

from which (3) follows.

To illustrate, the distance $|P_1 P_2|$ between the points $P_1(4, 1, -6)$ and $P_2(-4, -3, 2)$ is given by

$$|P_1 P_2| = \sqrt{(-4-4)^2 + (-3-1)^2 + (2+6)^2} = \sqrt{64 + 16 + 64} = 12$$

Observe that the *distance formula* (3) for 3-space is a generalization of the distance formula for 2-space (see Sec. 2.2), namely, $d = \sqrt{(x_2 - x_1)^2 + (y_2 - y_1)^2}$.

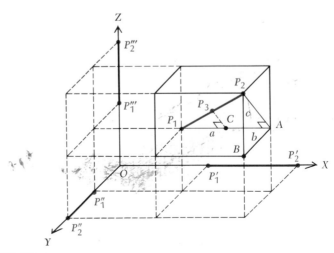

FIGURE 8.7

Many other results in 3-space are similar to, or are generalizations of, familiar results in 2-space. We now prove Theorem 8.2 in which we extend the point of division formulas of 2-space (see Exercise 17 of Sec. 2.4) to 3-space.

THEOREM 8.2   If $P_3(x_3, y_3, z_3)$ *divides the line segment from* $P_1(x_1, y_1, z_1)$ *to* $P_2(x_2, y_2, z_2)$ *in the ratio* t, *then*

$$
\begin{aligned}
x_3 &= x_1 + t(x_2 - x_1) \\
y_3 &= y_1 + t(y_2 - y_1) \\
z_3 &= z_1 + t(z_2 - z_1)
\end{aligned}
\tag{4}
$$

Proof

One possible orientation of P_1, P_2, and P_3 in accordance with the hypothesis that

$$
\frac{\overline{P_1 P_3}}{\overline{P_1 P_2}} = t \qquad \text{or} \qquad \overline{P_1 P_3} = t\,\overline{P_1 P_2}
\tag{5}
$$

is shown in Fig. 8.7. Using Fig. 8.7 as a guide, construct a plane through P_3 perpendicular to the x axis, and hence perpendicular to $P_1 A$ (the line through P_1 parallel to the x axis) at the point C. The right triangles $P_1 C P_3$ and $P_1 A P_2$ are similar. Therefore, by (5),

$$
\frac{\overline{P_1 C}}{\overline{P_1 A}} = \frac{\overline{P_1 P_3}}{\overline{P_1 P_2}} = t
\tag{6}
$$

Observing that $\overline{P_1 C} = x_3 - x_1$ and $\overline{P_1 A} = x_2 - x_1$, we conclude from (6) that

$$
x_3 - x_1 = t(x_2 - x_1) \qquad \text{so} \qquad x_3 = x_1 + t(x_2 - x_1)
$$

In a similar way we can establish the formulas for y_3 and z_3.

The student is asked to prove the special case of Theorem 8.2 which is expressed in Theorem 8.3.

THEOREM 8.3   If $P_3(x_3, y_3, z_3)$ *is the midpoint of the line segment joining* $P_1(x_1, y_1, z_1)$ *and* $P_2(x_2, y_2, z_2)$, *then*

Midpoint formulas

$$
x_3 = \frac{x_1 + x_2}{2} \qquad y_3 = \frac{y_1 + y_2}{2} \qquad z_3 = \frac{z_1 + z_2}{2}
\tag{7}
$$

Recall from Sec. 1.6 that a *relation R* in *Re* (the set of real numbers) is a set of ordered pairs whose entries are members of *Re*; that is, a relation in *Re* is a subset of *Re* $\times$ *Re*. Since there is a one-to-one correspondence between members

Relation in 3-space

of the cartesian product $Re \times Re$ and the points in a plane, we agree to identify $Re \times Re$ with 2-space. From the definition (1) of an ordered triple, it follows that we can consider a set of ordered triples as a *relation* whose domain is a subset of 2-space and whose range is a subset of Re; we call such a relation a **relation in 3-space.** Thus, a relation in 3-space is a subset of $(Re \times Re) \times Re$. Since there is a one-to-one correspondence between the cartesian product $(Re \times Re) \times Re$ and the set of points in three-dimensional space, we agree to identify $(Re \times Re) \times Re$ with 3-space.

Graph of a relation in 3-space

The **graph of a relation R in 3-space** is defined to be the set G of points in 3-space with the property that

$$P(a, b, c) \in G \iff (a, b, c) \in R$$

We use S_{xyz} to denote a sentence in the three variables x, y, and z for which the universe is Re, analogous to our use of S_{xy} in Sec. 1.8, and we say that

$$R = \{(x, y, z) \mid S_{xyz}\}$$

is a relation in 3-space determined by the sentence S_{xyz}. To illustrate,

$$R = \{(x, y, z) \mid x^2 + y^2 + z^2 = 16\}$$

is a relation in 3-space determined by the sentence $x^2 + y^2 + z^2 = 16$. The point $P(3, 2, \sqrt{3})$ belongs to the graph of R, because $(3, 2, \sqrt{3}) \in R$. From the distance formula (3) it follows that the graph of R is a sphere with center at the origin $O(0, 0, 0)$ and radius 4. Analogous to our procedure in 2-space, we denote this sphere by

$$S: x^2 + y^2 + z^2 = 16$$

Observe the distinction between the graphs of

$$R_1 = \{x \mid x = 2\} \qquad R_2 = \{(x, y) \mid x = 2\} \qquad R_3 = \{(x, y, z) \mid x = 2\}$$

Each of these sets is specified by the sentence $x = 2$; but the graph of R_1 is a single *point* on the coordinate line (x axis); the graph of R_2 is a *line* in 2-space perpendicular to the x axis at the point $(2, 0)$; the graph of R_3 is a *plane* in 3-space perpendicular to the x axis at the point $(2, 0, 0)$.

In Sec. 2.7 we saw that the circle with center at $C(h, k)$ and radius r is the graph of $(x - h)^2 + (y - k)^2 = r^2$. Similarly, by using the distance formula (3) and the familiar definition of a sphere, it follows that the sphere with center at $C(h, k, l)$ and radius r is the graph of

$$(x - h)^2 + (y - k)^2 + (z - l)^2 = r^2 \tag{8}$$

▶ EXAMPLE

Find an equation of the sphere which has the segment joining $P_1(2, -2, 4)$ and $P_2(4, 8, -6)$ for a diameter.

Solution

Using the midpoint formulas (7), we find that the center of the sphere is $C(3, 3, -1)$. Using the distance formula (3), we find $r = \sqrt{51}$, so by (8) we have that

$$(x - 3)^2 + (y - 3)^2 + (z + 1)^2 = 51$$

is an equation of the sphere.

EXERCISES

In each of Exercises 1–6 graph the given point on a three-dimensional rectangular coordinate system, and find its distance from (*a*) the *x* axis; (*b*) the *y* axis; (*c*) the *z* axis; and (*d*) the origin.

1. $(1, \sqrt{2}, \sqrt{3})$ **2.** $(6, 3, 2)$ **3.** $(2, 3, -6)$

4. $(-5, -4, -12)$ **5.** $(8, -6, 0)$ **6.** $(-2, 1, 2)$

In each of Exercises 7–10 graph the given point P_1 and give the coordinates of the projections M, N, Q of P_1 on the xy, xz, and yz planes, respectively. Also, give the coordinates of the projections U, V, W of P_1 on the x, y, and z axes, respectively.

7. $P_1(3, 4, 5)$ **8.** $P_1(-3, 6, 7)$

9. $P_1(-4, -5, -2)$ **10.** $P_1(7, \quad 6, 8)$

In each of Exercises 11–14 find the point P_2 for which P_2 and the given point P_1 are symmetric with respect to the given plane.

11. $P_1(2, -3, 4)$; xz plane   **12.** $P_1(3, 2, 1)$; yz plane

13. $P_1(-4, -6, -7)$; xy plane   **14.** $P_1(4, 2, -6)$; xy plane

In each of Exercises 15–16 graph P_1 and P_2 on the same coordinate system. Give the projections P_1' and P_2' of P_1 and P_2 on the xy plane, and on your graph indicate $\text{Proj}_{xy} P_1 P_2$.

15. $P_1(3, 2, 5)$; $P_2(7, 4, 9)$ **16.** $P_1(3, -2, 4)$; $P_2(5, -4, 6)$

In each of Exercises 17–20 find the distance $|P_1 P_2|$.

17. $P_1(5, 2, 2)$; $P_2(8, 5, 4)$ **18.** $P_1(1, 1, 1)$; $P_2(2, 0, 3)$

19. $P_1(4, 6, -8)$; $P_2(3, 5, 7)$ **20.** $P_1(-3, -2, 1)$; $P_2(3, 2, -1)$

21. Observe that the graph of $\{(x, y, z) \mid x = 0 \text{ and } y = 0\}$ is the z axis. Write a relation whose graph is the x axis; whose graph is the y axis.

In each of Exercises 22 and 23 describe the graph of the given relation.

22. $\{(x, y, z) \mid x = 7\}$ **23.** $\{(x, y, z) \mid x = 5 \text{ and } y = 6\}$

In each of Exercises 24 and 25 find the point P_3 that divides the line segment from P_1 to P_2 in the ratio t.

24. $P_1(1, -1, 1); P_2(2, -3, 2); t = -\frac{1}{3}$ **25.** $P_1(5, 2, 2); P_2(8, 5, 4); t = \frac{2}{3}$

In each of Exercises 26 and 27 find the midpoint of the segment joining the two given points.

26. $P_1(1, 2, 3); P_2(4, 5, 6)$ **27.** $P_1(-3, -2, -1); P_2(-6, -5, -4)$

28. Find an equation of a set of points S which has the property that each point of S is equidistant from $P_1(5, 2, 2)$ and $P_2(8, 5, 4)$. $3x + 3y + 2z = 36$

29. Show that the points $(-1, -3, 7)$, $(-2, -2, 9)$, and $(1, 3, 5)$ are the vertices of a right triangle.

In each of Exercises 30–33 determine whether or not the given equation is an equation of a sphere; if it is, give the center and radius.

30. $x^2 + y^2 + z^2 + 2x + 4y + 6z + 1 = 0$

31. $x^2 + y^2 + z^2 - 2x + 4y - 6z - 4 = 0$

32. $3x^2 + 3y^2 + 3z^2 + 5x - 6y + 7z = 0$

33. $x^2 + y^2 + z^2 + 2x + 4y + 6z + 20 = 0$

34. Find an equation of the sphere for which the segment joining $P_1(-2, 3, -1)$ and $P_2(4, 5, -3)$ is a diameter.

8.4 DIRECTION ANGLES, DIRECTION COSINES, AND DIRECTION NUMBERS

Here we extend to 3-space the concepts of direction angles, direction cosines, and direction numbers which we studied in Sec. 3.6 for 2-space. Recall that in Sec. 3.6 we defined the angle between two *intersecting* lines L_1 and L_2. If L_1 and L_2 are parallel, then the angle between them is either 0 or π.

In 2-space two lines either intersect or are parallel. In 3-space there is another possibility: lines L_1 and L_2 may neither intersect nor be parallel. If L_1 and L_2 are neither intersecting nor parallel, the angle between L_1 and L_2 is defined to be the angle between lines L_1' and L_2' passing through the origin with L_1' parallel to L_1 and L_2' parallel to L_2. (If L_1 and L_2 are directed lines then of course L_1' has the same direction as L_1 and L_2' has the same direction as L_2.)

Direction angles   If L is a *directed* line, the **direction angles** α, β, γ of L are the angles with the following properties (recall that the coordinate axes are directed lines):

α is the angle between L and the x axis.
β is the angle between L and the y axis.
γ is the angle between L and the z axis.

Direction cosines   One possible orientation of L is shown in Fig. 8.8. The cosines of the direction angles, cos α, cos β, cos γ, are called the **direction cosines** of the directed line L.

If L is an undirected line, it has two sets of direction angles, one set for each of the two possible choices of direction for L (analogous to the situation for 2-space depicted in Fig. 3.31). If the two sets of direction angles are $\{\alpha_1, \beta_1, \gamma_1\}$ and $\{\alpha_2, \beta_2, \gamma_2\}$, then

$$\alpha_2 = \pi - \alpha_1 \qquad \beta_2 = \pi - \beta_1 \qquad \gamma_2 = \pi - \gamma_1$$

Since cos $\alpha_2 = \cos (\pi - \alpha_1) = -\cos \alpha_1$, cos $\beta_2 = -\cos \beta_1$, and cos $\gamma_2 = -\cos \gamma_1$, an undirected line has two sets of direction cosines, with the members of one set being the negatives of the members of the other set.

Suppose that the directed line L passes through the origin, and let $P(a, b, c)$ be a point on L. Designating the distance $|OP|$ by d, we have (see Fig. 8.8)

$$d^2 = a^2 + b^2 + c^2 \qquad \cos \alpha = \frac{a}{d} \qquad \cos \beta = \frac{b}{d} \qquad \cos \gamma = \frac{c}{d}$$

Hence
$$\cos^2 \alpha + \cos^2 \beta + \cos^2 \gamma = \frac{a^2 + b^2 + c^2}{d^2} = 1$$

We have proved Theorem 8.4.

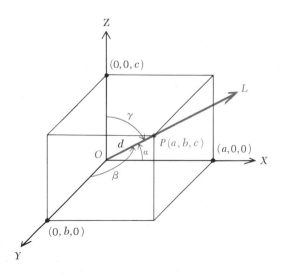

FIGURE 8.8

THEOREM *The sum of the squares of the direction cosines of a line is*
8.4   *equal to 1:*

$$\cos^2 \alpha + \cos^2 \beta + \cos^2 \gamma = 1 \tag{9}$$

Let $P_1(x_1, y_1, z_1)$ and $P_2(x_2, y_2, z_2)$ be two (distinct) points on the line L directed from P_1 to P_2 (one possible orientation is shown in Fig. 8.9), and let $d = |P_1P_2|$. Then

$$\cos \alpha = \frac{x_2 - x_1}{d} \qquad \cos \beta = \frac{y_2 - y_1}{d} \qquad \cos \gamma = \frac{z_2 - z_1}{d} \tag{10}$$

▶ EXAMPLE 1

Find the direction cosines of the line L through $P_1(0, -2, 7)$ and $P_2(3, 4, 1)$.
   a. If L is directed from P_1 to P_2
   b. If L is undirected

Solution

   a. Using (3), we find $d = |P_1P_2| = 9$. Then using (10), we obtain $\cos \alpha = \frac{1}{3}$, $\cos \beta = \frac{2}{3}$, $\cos \gamma = -\frac{2}{3}$. Observe that these values satisfy the equality (9).

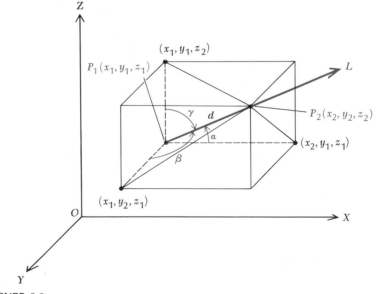

FIGURE 8.9

b. For L undirected, $\cos \alpha = \frac{1}{3}$, $\cos \beta = \frac{2}{3}$, $\cos \gamma = -\frac{2}{3}$, or $\cos \alpha = -\frac{1}{3}$, $\cos \beta = -\frac{2}{3}$, $\cos \gamma = \frac{2}{3}$.

EXAMPLE 2

If, for a line L, $\alpha = 60°$ and $\beta = 135°$, find the possible values for γ.

Solution

Theorem 8.4 tells us that

$$\cos^2 60° + \cos^2 135° + \cos^2 \gamma = 1$$

or

$$\tfrac{1}{4} + \tfrac{1}{2} + \cos^2 \gamma = 1$$

Therefore, $\cos^2 \gamma = \frac{1}{4}$, so $\cos \gamma = \pm \frac{1}{2}$, and $\gamma = 60°$ or $\gamma = 120°$.

THEOREM 8.5   *Let L_1 be a directed line with direction angles $\alpha_1, \beta_1, \gamma_1$; let L_2 be a directed line with direction angles $\alpha_2, \beta_2, \gamma_2$; and let θ be the angle between L_1 and L_2. Then*

$$\cos \theta = \cos \alpha_1 \cos \alpha_2 + \cos \beta_1 \cos \beta_2 + \cos \gamma_1 \cos \gamma_2 \quad (11)$$

The student is asked to give a proof of Theorem 8.5 in Exercise 13 of this section (use the proof of Theorem 3.7 as a model).

Theorem 8.6 follows from Theorem 8.5 when we recall the definition of the angle between two undirected lines (see Sec. 3.6).

THEOREM 8.6   *If L_1 and L_2 are undirected lines with direction angles $\alpha_1, \beta_1, \gamma_1$ and $\alpha_2, \beta_2, \gamma_2$, respectively, and if θ is the angle between L_1 and L_2, then*

$$\cos \theta = |\cos \alpha_1 \cos \alpha_2 + \cos \beta_1 \cos \beta_2 + \cos \gamma_1 \cos \gamma_2| \quad (12)$$

If $\cos \alpha$, $\cos \beta$, and $\cos \gamma$ are direction cosines of a directed line L, then three real numbers l, m, n which have the property that, for some *positive* real number k,

$$l = k \cos \alpha \qquad m = k \cos \beta \qquad n = k \cos \gamma \quad (13)$$

Direction numbers

are called **direction numbers** of L. If L is an undirected line, then k may be any *nonzero* real number. When two ordered triples (l_1, m_1, n_1) and (l_2, m_2, n_2) are related so that $l_2 = k l_1$, $m_2 = k m_1$, and $n_2 = k n_1$, we say that *the second triple is proportional to the first triple*, the constant of proportionality being k. Thus we see that an ordered triple (l, m, n) of real numbers is a set of direction numbers of a *directed* line L if and only if (l, m, n) is proportional to the triple of direction cosines $(\cos \alpha, \cos \beta, \cos \gamma)$ of L, with a *positive* constant of proportionality. If L is *undirected*, the only restriction on the constant of proportionality is that it not be zero.

Proceeding as we did in Sec. 3.6 for a directed line L in 2-space, we can establish the following formulas for a *directed* line L in 3-space (see Exercise 14, page 273):

$$
\cos \alpha = \frac{l}{\sqrt{l^2 + m^2 + n^2}}
$$
$$
\cos \beta = \frac{m}{\sqrt{l^2 + m^2 + n^2}} \tag{14}
$$
$$
\cos \gamma = \frac{n}{\sqrt{l^2 + m^2 + n^2}}
$$

For an *undirected* line L in 3-space either Eqs. (14) hold or

$$
\cos \alpha = \frac{l}{-\sqrt{l^2 + m^2 + n^2}}
$$
$$
\cos \beta = \frac{m}{-\sqrt{l^2 + m^2 + n^2}} \tag{15}
$$
$$
\cos \gamma = \frac{n}{-\sqrt{l^2 + m^2 + n^2}}
$$

will be true.

◆ EXAMPLE 3

The numbers $2, -2$, and 1 are direction numbers for a line L. Find the direction cosines of L.

   a. If L is directed
   b. If L is undirected

Solution

   a. Here $l = 2$, $m = -2$, $n = 1$, and $l^2 + m^2 + n^2 = 9$. Using (14) we find $\frac{2}{3}, -\frac{2}{3}$, and $\frac{1}{3}$ as the direction cosines of L.
   b. By use of (13) and (14) we see that the triple $(\frac{2}{3}, -\frac{2}{3}, \frac{1}{3})$ or the triple $(-\frac{2}{3}, \frac{2}{3}, -\frac{1}{3})$ is a set of direction cosines for L.

If L is a line directed from $P_1(x_1, y_1, z_1)$ and $P_2(x_2, y_2, z_2)$, it follows from (10) that *the triple l, m, n, where*

$$
l = x_2 - x_1 \qquad m = y_2 - y_1 \qquad n = z_2 - z_1 \tag{16}
$$

is a set of direction numbers for L.

▶ EXAMPLE 4

Find direction cosines of the line L through $P_1(-5, 4, 8)$ and $P_2(1, 2, 11)$:
   a. If L is directed from P_1 to P_2
   b. If L is undirected

Solution

   a. Using (16), we find $l = 6$, $m = -2$, $n = 3$. Further, using (3), we find $d = |P_1P_2|$ to be 7. Then

$$\cos \alpha = \tfrac{6}{7} \qquad \cos \beta = -\tfrac{2}{7} \qquad \cos \gamma = \tfrac{3}{7}$$

   b. For L undirected, the direction cosines may have the values just listed or their negatives, respectively.

From formulas (16) it follows that if a line L passes through the origin and has direction numbers a, b, c, then the point $P(a, b, c)$ is on L; also, if L is directed, then it is directed from $O(0, 0, 0)$ to $P(a, b, c)$.

The following theorem is an immediate consequence of the definition of direction numbers of a line.

THEOREM 8.7   *If a line L has a set of direction numbers (l, m, n), then for any real number k ($k > 0$ if L is directed, $k \neq 0$ if L is undirected), the triple (kl, km, kn) is a set of direction numbers of L.*

We agree that when we speak simply of a line, we mean an undirected line unless specifically stated otherwise.

Closely related to Theorem 8.7 is Theorem 8.8, which the student is asked to prove in Exercise 15 of this section.

THEOREM 8.8   *If lines L_1 and L_2 have direction numbers (l_1, m_1, n_1) and (l_2, m_2, n_2), respectively, then L_1 and L_2 are parallel if and only if the triple (l_1, m_1, n_1) is proportional to the triple (l_2, m_2, n_2):*

$$L_1 \parallel L_2 \iff l_1 = kl_2, \; m_1 = km_2, \; n_1 = kn_2$$

for some real number k.

▶ EXAMPLE 5

Show that the line L_1 through $P_1(2, 3, 0)$ and $P_2(2, -9, 5)$ and the line L_2 through $P_3(-8, -3, -10)$ and $P_4(-8, 9, -15)$ are parallel.

Solution

Using (16), we get $(0, -12, 5)$ for a set of direction numbers of L_1 and $(0, 12, -5)$ for a set of direction numbers of L_2. Since these triples are proportional, Theorem 8.8 tells us that L_1 is parallel to L_2.

Using formulas (14) and Theorems 8.5 and 8.6, we get Theorem 8.9.

THEOREM 8.9 *If (l_1, m_1, n_1) is a set of direction numbers of L_1 and (l_2, m_2, n_2) is a set of direction numbers of L_2, and if θ is the angle between L_1 and L_2, then*

$$\cos \theta = \frac{l_1 l_2 + m_1 m_2 + n_1 n_2}{\sqrt{l_1{}^2 + m_1{}^2 + n_1{}^2} \ \sqrt{l_2{}^2 + m_2{}^2 + n_2{}^2}} \qquad (17)$$

if L_1 and L_2 are directed, and

$$\cos \theta = \frac{|l_1 l_2 + m_1 m_2 + n_1 n_2|}{\sqrt{l_1{}^2 + m_1{}^2 + n_1{}^2} \ \sqrt{l_2{}^2 + m_2{}^2 + n_2{}^2}} \qquad (18)$$

if L_1 and L_2 are undirected.

If θ is the angle between lines L_1 and L_2, then

$$L_1 \perp L_2 \iff \theta = 90° \text{ and } \cos \theta = 0$$

From this fact and Theorem 8.9, we have Theorem 8.10.

THEOREM 8.10 *L_1 is perpendicular to L_2 if and only if*

$$l_1 l_2 + m_1 m_2 + n_1 n_2 = 0 \qquad (19)$$

where (l_1, m_1, n_1) are direction numbers of L_1 and (l_2, m_2, n_2) are direction numbers of L_2.

▸ EXAMPLE 6

If $(0, 5, 1)$ is a set of direction numbers of L_1 and $(-3, 4, -2)$ is a set of direction numbers of L_2, find a set of direction numbers of a line L that is perpendicular to both L_1 and L_2.

Solution

Let (l, m, n) be a set of direction numbers of L. By Theorem 8.10 we have

$$L \perp L_1 \iff 5m + n = 0$$
$$L \perp L_2 \iff -3l + 4m - 2n = 0$$

Now

$$5m + n = 0 \quad \text{and} \quad -3l + 4m - 2n = 0 \quad \Longleftrightarrow \quad n = -5m = -\tfrac{15}{14}l$$

We may let l be any nonzero number. Let $l = 14$; then we find $(14, 3, -15)$ as a set of direction numbers of L.

EXERCISES

In each of Exercises 1–4 find a set of direction numbers and the set of direction cosines of the line through P_1 and P_2 that is directed from P_1 to P_2.

1. $P_1(7, -1, -2)$; $P_2(-1, -4, 3)$ **2.** $P_1(0, 0, 0)$; $P_2(6, 3, 2)$

3. $P_1(2, 4, 6)$; $P_2(0, 7, 12)$ **4.** $P_1(-6, 3, 5)$; $P_2(2, 4, 1)$

5. Find the direction cosines and the direction angles of the line through $P_1(1, 0, 1)$ and $P_2(3, 2\sqrt{2}, -1)$ that is directed from P_1 to P_2.

6. Which of the following triples can be direction angles of a line?
   (a) $45°, 135°, 90°$ (b) $60°, 135°, 120°$
   (c) $60°, 45°, 60°$ (d) $45°, 60°, 30°$

7. A line makes an angle of 60 degrees with the x axis and an angle of 45 degrees with the y axis. What angle does it make with the z axis?

8. If a line L has direction numbers 1, 2, 3, find a set of direction cosines of L.

9. Show that the line determined by $P_1(3, 2, 10)$ and $P_2(5, -1, 4)$ is parallel to the line determined by $P_3(3, -4, -2)$ and $P_4(1, -1, 4)$.

10. Find the cosine of the angle θ between the line through $P_1(2, 4, 0)$ and $P_2(0, 0, 4)$ directed from P_1 to P_2 and the line through $P_3(2, -1, -1)$ and $P_4(2, 2, 3)$ directed from P_3 to P_4.

11. Show that the line L_1 with $(1, -6, 5)$ for direction numbers and the line L_2 with $(8, 3, 2)$ for direction numbers are perpendicular.

12. If $(3, -2, 1)$ is a set of direction numbers of line L_1 and $(4, -1, -7)$ is a set of direction numbers of L_2, find a set of direction numbers of a line L such that $L \perp L_1$ and $L \perp L_2$.

13. Prove Theorem 8.5.

14. Establish formulas (14) and (15).

15. Prove Theorem 8.8.

8.5 LINES IN 3-SPACE

Since a set of direction numbers determines a set of parallel lines, a point and a set of direction numbers determine one and only one line. Let us consider the line L through the point $P_1(x_1, y_1, z_1)$ with direction numbers l, m, n, and let

$P(x, y, z)$ be any point in 3-space distinct from P_1. The line L' through P and P_1 will coincide with L if and only if each set of direction numbers of L' is proportional to each set of direction numbers of L. Since $x - x_1, y - y_1, z - z_1$ are direction numbers of the line through $P(x, y, z)$ and $P_1(x_1, y_1, z_1)$, we have that

$$P \in L \iff x - x_1 = tl, \; y - y_1 = tm, \; z - z_1 = tn$$

where t is a nonzero real number. This means that if $P(x, y, z)$ is a point on L distinct from $P_1(x_1, y_1, z_1)$, then there is a nonzero real number t for which

$$x = x_1 + tl \qquad y = y_1 + tm \qquad z = z_1 + tn \tag{20}$$

and, if t is any nonzero real number, then the point $P(x, y, z)$ whose coordinates are given by (20) is on the line L. If we take $P(x, y, z)$ to coincide with $P_1(x_1, y_1, z_1)$, then clearly (20) holds with $t = 0$. Consequently, when, in Eqs. (20), x_1, y_1, z_1, l, m, and n are given constants and t is a variable whose universe is Re, then Eqs. (20) associate with each value of the variable t the coordinates (x, y, z) of a point on L; conversely, with each point $P(x, y, z)$ on L, the equations associate a value of the variable t. We call the variable t a *parameter* and we call Eqs. (20) **parametric equations** of the line L which has (l, m, n) as a set of direction numbers and which passes through the point $P_1(x_1, y_1, z_1)$. We also speak of Eqs. (20) as a **parametric representation** of the line L.

Parametric equations of a line

To illustrate, if L has direction numbers $-4, 3, -4$ and passes through the point $P_1(8, -3, 10)$, parametric equations of L are

$$x = 8 - 4t \qquad y = -3 + 3t \qquad z = 10 - 4t \tag{21}$$

Using the parametric representation (21), we can find coordinates of other points on L by assigning values to t: $t = 2$ gives the point $P_2(0, 3, 2)$; $t = -2$ gives the point $P_3(16, -9, 18)$.

As an example of how a parametric representation of a line can be used, let us find the point Q on the line L with parametric equations (21) with the property that Q is in the yz plane. For Q to be in the yz plane, its x coordinate must be zero. Now, for $P(x, y, z)$ on L,

$$x = 0 \iff 8 - 4t = 0 \iff t = 2$$

Substituting 2 in place of t in (21), we find that $Q(0, 3, 2)$ is the point of intersection of L and the yz plane. Similarly, we find that $R(4, 0, 6)$ is the point of intersection of L and the xz plane, and that $S(-2, \frac{9}{2}, 0)$ is the point of intersection of L and the xy plane.

If we know a parametric representation of a line L in 3-space, the graph of L on a coordinate system may be indicated by graphing the points Q, R, and S in which L intersects the coordinate planes and drawing the line joining these points.

Recall that $x_2 - x_1$, $y_2 - y_1$, and $z_2 - z_1$ are direction numbers of the line through $P_1(x_1, y_1, z_1)$ and $P_2(x_2, y_2, z_2)$, so

$$x = x_1 + (x_2 - x_1)t \qquad y = y_1 + (y_2 - y_1)t \qquad z = z_1 + (z_2 - z_1)t \qquad (22)$$

is a parametric representation of the line through P_1 and P_2.

EXERCISES

In each of Exercises 1–3 find parametric equations of the line L through the given two points, find the points of intersection Q, R, S with the yz, xz, and xy planes, respectively, and graph L on a coordinate system.

1. $P_1(2, 3, 4)$; $P_2(5, 7, 9)$ **2.** $P_1(1, -6, -2)$; $P_2(-1, 1, 1)$

3. $P_1(3, 0, 4)$; $P_2(0, 4, 5)$

In each of Exercises 4–7 for the line L with the given parametric equations, find a set of direction numbers of L and two points P_1 and P_2 on L, and graph L.

4. $x = 8 - 6t$; $y = -2 + 9t$; $z = 4 + 7t$

5. $x = -5 + 2t$; $y = 3 + t$; $z = 0 + 5t$

6. $x = 2$; $y = t$; $z = 4 + 3t$ **7.** $x = 7 + 3t$; $y = 4 - 3t$; $z = -2 - 5t$

In each of Exercises 8 and 9 eliminate the parameter t from the given parametric representation of a line L to obtain two equations of the form $a_1 x + b_1 y + c_1 z + d_1 = 0$, $a_2 x + b_2 y + c_2 z + d_2 = 0$.

8. $x = t + 1$; $y = 2t$; $z = 1 - \frac{3}{2}t$ **9.** $x = \frac{1}{2}t$; $y = (t - 1)/3$; $z = 6t + 5$

In each of Exercises 10–13 show that the lines L_1 and L_2 intersect, find the point of intersection $P_1(x_1, y_1, z_1)$, and find a parametric representation of the line L_3 that passes through P_1 such that $L_3 \perp L_1$ and $L_3 \perp L_2$.

10. L_1: $x = 10 + 6s$; $y = -7 - 2s$; $z = 7 + 3s$
       L_2: $x = 3 + 5t$; $y = 5 + 8t$; $z = -t$

Hint: To show that L_1 and L_2 intersect, find values of s and t such that

$$10 + 6s = 3 + 5t \qquad \text{and} \qquad -7 - 2s = 5 + 8t$$

and then show that these same values of s and t satisfy $7 + 3s = -t$.

11. L_1: $x = -2 + 5s$; $y = 2 + 3s$; $z = -2$ DON'T INTERSECT
       L_2: $x = 3 + 5t$; $y = 5 + 8t$; $z = -t$

12. L_1: $x = 8 + 3s$; $y = -2 - s$; $z = 5 + 2s$
       L_2: $x = 11 + 3t$; $y = -11 - 5t$; $z = 5 + t$

13. L_1: $x = 3 + 4s$; $y = 0$; $z = \frac{7}{4} + 3s$
   L_2: $x = 0$; $y = -10 + 2t$; $z = -3 + \frac{1}{2}t$

In each of Exercises 14–17 show that the lines L_1 and L_2 do not intersect. Find the perpendicular distance d between L_1 and L_2.

14. L_1: $x = 1 + s$; $y = 1 + s$; $z = 1 + s$
   L_2: $x = -1 + t$; $y = -6 - 8t$; $z = 2 - 2t$

Hint: To show that L_1 and L_2 do *not* intersect, find values of s and t such that

$$1 + s = -1 + t \qquad \text{and} \qquad 1 + s = -6 - 8t$$

and then show that these values of s and t do *not* satisfy

$$1 + s = 2 - 2t$$

To find d, let L_3, with l, m, and n for direction numbers, be the line perpendicular to both L_1 and L_2. Show that $(l, m, n) = (2, 1, -3)$, so that L_3 has

$$x - x' = 2p \qquad y - y' = 1p \qquad z - z' = -3p$$

for a parametric representation, (x', y', z') being a point on L_3. Next find a point $P_1(x_1, y_1, z_1)$ on L_1 and a point $P_2(x_2, y_2, z_2)$ on L_2 that are also on L_3. This may be done by finding values of s and t such that

$$\frac{(1 + s) - (-1 + t)}{2} = \frac{(1 + s) - (-6 - 8t)}{1} = \frac{(1 + s) - (2 - 2t)}{-3}$$

In this manner get $s = -\frac{2}{3}$ and $t = -\frac{2}{3}$, which determine $P_1(\frac{1}{3}, \frac{1}{3}, \frac{1}{3})$ and $P_2(-\frac{5}{3}, -\frac{2}{3}, \frac{10}{3})$. Then $d = |P_1P_2| = \sqrt{14}$.

15. L_1: $x = 2s$; $y = 3 + 2s$; $z = -1 + s$
   L_2: $x = t$; $y = t$; $z = t$

16. L_1: $x = 1 + 4s$; $y = -2 - 3s$; $z = 3 + s$
   L_2: $x = -1 + t$; $y = 2$; $z = 1 - 3t$

17. L_1: $x = 1 + 2s$; $y = -2 + s$; $z = 3 + s$
   L_2: $x = -2 - 3t$; $y = 2 + t$; $z = -1 + 2t$

8.6 PLANES IN 3-SPACE

In this section we make use of the following theorems from solid geometry.
   (i)   Through a given point P_1 on a line L there is one and only one plane Π perpendicular to L (Fig. 8.10).
   (ii) A point P different from P_1 is on the plane described in (i) if and only if the line through P and P_1 is perpendicular to L.

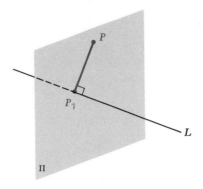

FIGURE 8.10

Normal to a plane

The line L is called the **normal** to the plane Π at P_1.

Let Π be any plane in 3-space and let L be the normal to Π at the point $P_1(x_1, y_1, z_1)$. Suppose that L has direction numbers (a, b, c), and let $P(x \ y, z)$ be any point in 3-space distinct from P_1. From (ii) we have that

$$P(x, y, z) \in \Pi \iff (\text{line } PP_1) \perp L$$

and from Theorem 8.10 it follows that

$$(\text{line } PP_1) \perp L \iff a(x - x_1) + b(y - y_1) + c(z - z_1) = 0$$

If P coincides with P_1 so that $x - x_1 = 0$, $y - y_1 = 0$, and $z - z_1 = 0$, clearly $a(x - x_1) + b(y - y_1) + c(z - z_1) = 0$. We have proved Theorem 8.11.

THEOREM 8.11 *If the line L has direction numbers (a, b, c) and is normal to the plane Π at the point $P_1(x_1, y_1, z_1)$, then Π is the graph of*

$$a(x - x_1) + b(y - y_1) + c(z - z_1) = 0 \tag{23}$$

An equation of the form

$$ax + by + cz + d = 0 \tag{24}$$

where $a, b, c,$ and d are real numbers with not all of $a, b,$ and c zero, is called an *equation of the first degree in $x, y,$ and z*. Since Eq. (23) may be written in the form (24) with $d = -(ax_1 + by_1 + cz_1)$, we have proved Theorem 8.12.

THEOREM 8.12 *Every plane is the graph of an equation of the first degree in three variables.*

Conversely, we now prove that the graph of every equation of the first degree in x, y, and z is a plane. Let (x_1, y_1, z_1) be an ordered triple for which $ax_1 + by_1 + cz_1 + d = 0$. Subtracting this equality from (24), we get $ax - ax_1 + by - by_1 + cz - cz_1 = 0$, which is equivalent to (23). From this result and Theorem 8.11 there follows Theorem 8.13.

THEOREM 8.13   *The graph of an equation of the first degree in x, y, and z,*

$$ax + by + cz + d = 0$$

is a plane perpendicular to a line with direction numbers (a, b, c).

A number k is an x intercept of a graph G if and only if $P(k, 0, 0) \in G$. A y intercept and a z intercept of a graph G are defined similarly.

Trace of a graph   The set of points that constitutes the intersection of a graph G and one of the coordinate planes is called the **trace** of G in that coordinate plane. If a plane Π intersects a coordinate plane, without being coincident with it, the trace of G in that plane is a line. The trace of a sphere S in a coordinate plane is either a circle, a point, or the empty set.

In case a plane Π does not pass through the origin, its x, y, and z intercepts

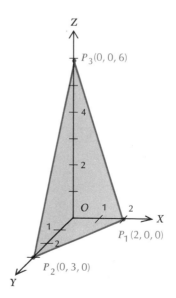

FIGURE 8.11

and its traces in the coordinate planes are helpful in indicating the graph of Π on a coordinate system. To illustrate, let Π be the graph of

$$3x + 2y + z - 6 = 0$$

For Π the x intercept is 2, the y intercept is 3, and the z intercept is 6. Thus the graph of Π passes through the three points $P_1(2, 0, 0)$, $P_2(0, 3, 0)$, and $P_3(0, 0, 6)$. The trace of Π in the xz plane is the line in that plane which passes through P_1 and P_3; the trace of Π in the yz plane is the line in that plane which passes through the points P_2 and P_3; the trace of Π in the xy plane is the line in that plane which passes through the points P_1 and P_2. Observe that the trace of Π in the xy plane is the graph of

$$\{(x, y, z) \mid 3x + 2y + z - 6 = 0\} \cap \{(x, y, z) \mid z = 0\}$$
$$= \{(x, y, z) \mid 3x + 2y + z - 6 = 0 \text{ and } z = 0\}$$
$$= \{(x, y, z) \mid 3x + 2y - 6 = 0 \text{ and } z = 0\}$$

Similar results obtain for the other two traces. The graph of Π, showing the intercepts and the traces, is indicated in Fig. 8.11.

▶ EXAMPLE 1

Find an equation of the plane Π which passes through the point $P_1(1, -3, 2)$ and which is perpendicular to the line through the points $P_2(0, 0, 3)$ and $P_1(1, -3, 2)$.

Solution

With the use of formulas (16) we find that $(1, -3, -1)$ is a set of direction numbers of the line normal to Π. Then by Theorem 8.11 we have that

$$1(x - 1) - 3(y + 3) - 1(z - 2) = 0$$

or

$$x - 3y - z - 8 = 0$$

is an equation of Π.

Angle between planes

The **angle θ between two planes** is the angle between two lines that are perpendicular, respectively, to the two planes, $0 \leq \theta \leq \frac{1}{2}\pi$. Thus, the angle θ between the planes

$$\Pi_1 : a_1 x + b_1 y + c_1 z + d_1 = 0$$

and

$$\Pi_2 : a_2 x + b_2 y + c_2 z + d_2 = 0$$

is given by

$$\cos \theta = \frac{|a_1 a_2 + b_1 b_2 + c_1 c_2|}{\sqrt{a_1{}^2 + b_1{}^2 + c_1{}^2} \, \sqrt{a_2{}^2 + b_2{}^2 + c_2{}^2}} \qquad (25)$$

From Theorem 8.8 we have

$$\Pi_1 \parallel \Pi_2 \iff a_1 = ka_2, \; b_1 = kb_2, \; c_1 = kc_2$$

for some nonzero real number k (26)

and from Theorem 8.10 we have

$$\Pi_1 \perp \Pi_2 \iff a_1a_2 + b_1b_2 + c_1c_2 = 0 \tag{27}$$

♦   EXAMPLE 2

Find an equation of the plane Π which passes through the points $P_1(2, 1, -1)$ and $P_2(1, 1, 2)$ and which is perpendicular to the plane with equation $7x + 4y - 4z + 30 = 0$.

Solution

Theorem 8.11 tells us that

$$a(x - 2) + b(y - 1) + c(z + 1) = 0 \tag{28}$$

is an equation of the plane through $P_1(2, 1, -1)$ and normal to the line through P_1 with direction numbers (a, b, c). Since we wish (28) to be an equation of a plane perpendicular to the plane with equation $7x + 4y - 4z + 30 = 0$, (27) tells us that we must choose a, b, and c so that

$$7a + 4b - 4c = 0 \tag{29}$$

Further, since the graph of (28) is to pass through $P_4(1, 1, 2)$, we must have

$$a(1 - 2) + b(1 - 1) + c(2 + 1) = 0 \tag{30}$$

Solving the pair of equations (29) and (30) for a and b in terms of c, we get

$$a = 3c \qquad b = -\tfrac{17}{4}c$$

where c can be any real number. If we choose c to be 4, we have $a = 12$, $b = -17$, $c = 4$; and using these values in (28), we obtain

$$12(x - 2) - 17(y - 1) + 4(z + 1) = 0$$

or

$$12x - 17y + 4z - 3 = 0$$

as an equation of Π.

EXERCISES

In each of Exercises 1–4 find the x, y, and z intercepts of the plane whose equation is given. With the use of these intercepts draw the traces of the plane on the coordinate planes and thereby indicate the graph of the plane on a coordinate system.

1. $x + 2y + 3z = 6$ **2.** $6x + 5y + 6z - 30 = 0$

3. $2x + y + 3z + 12 = 0$ **4.** $4x + 5y = 20$

5. Find an equation of the plane whose x, y, and z intercepts are 2, -3, and -1, respectively.

6. Find an equation of the plane through the point $P_1(-1, 1, 7)$ and perpendicular to a line having $(6, -1, 5)$ for a set of direction numbers.

7. Find an equation of the plane through the point $P_1(1, -3, 2)$ and perpendicular to the line joining the points $P_2(1, -3, 4)$ and $P_3(0, 0, 3)$.

8. Find an equation of the plane passing through the points $P_1(2, 1, 3)$, $P_2(1, 3, 2)$, and $P_3(-1, 2, 4)$.

9. Find an equation of the plane passing through the point $P_1(3, -1, 2)$ and perpendicular to both of the planes Π_1: $2x - 3y + z = 4$ and Π_2: $x + 2y + 3z = 5$.

10. Find an equation of the plane through $P_1(1, 1, 1)$ and $P_2(-2, 1, 3)$ and perpendicular to the plane Π: $3x - 4y + z = 6$.

11. Find the point of intersection of the planes Π_1: $x + y + 2z = 7$, Π_2: $x + y + z = 5$, and Π_3: $3x - 2y + z = 1$.

In each of Exercises 12–15 equations of two planes Π_1 and Π_2 are given. Determine whether Π_1 and Π_2 are parallel or perpendicular. If neither, find the cosine of the angle between Π_1 and Π_2.

12. $2x - 2y + z - 2 - 0$; $4x \quad 4y + 2z - 5 = 0$

13. $x + 2y + 3z - 6 = 0$; $2x + 5y - 4z - 10 = 0$

14. $x + 4y - 8z - 9 = 0$; $x - 2y + 2z - 9 = 0$

15. $3x + 4y + 12 = 0$; $5x - 12y - 30 = 0$

16. Construct on the same coordinate system the graphs of the planes Π_1: $2x + 3y + 4z = 12$ and Π_2: $10x + 15y + 6z = 30$. From this graph observe that Π_1 and Π_2 appear to intersect in a line L. By considering the traces of Π_1 and Π_2, first in the yz plane and then in the xz plane, we can determine that Π_1 and Π_2 have the points $P_1(0, \frac{8}{7}, \frac{15}{7})$ and $P_2(\frac{12}{7}, 0, \frac{15}{7})$ in common. Now, using (22), we get

$$x = \tfrac{12}{7}t \qquad y = \tfrac{8}{7} - \tfrac{8}{7}t \qquad z = \tfrac{15}{7} \qquad\qquad (*)$$

for a parametric representation of the line L through P_1 and P_2. The student is asked to substitute the expressions for x, y, and z given by (*) in the equations of Π_1 and Π_2, and show that the two resulting equations are identities in t. Hence, the line L through P_1 and P_2 lies in both planes Π_1 and Π_2, and is their line of intersection. The line L is the graph of the relation

$$R = \{(x, y, z) \mid 2x + 3y + 4z - 12 = 0 \text{ and } 10x + 15y + 6z - 30 = 0\}$$

If a line L is the graph of

$$\{(x, y, z) \mid a_1x + b_1y + c_1z + d_1 = 0 \text{ and } a_2x + b_2x + c_2z + d_2 = 0\}$$

we say that L is the *graph of the system*

$$a_1x + b_1y + c_1z + d_1 = 0 \qquad a_2x + b_2y + c_2z + d_2 = 0$$

Two-plane representation of a line

and we call this system a *two-plane representation* of the line L.

17. Write a two-plane representation of the line L passing through $P_1(2, 1, 5)$, perpendicular to a line L_1 with direction numbers $(3, -1, 4)$, and perpendicular to a line L_2 with direction numbers $(-2, 5, 1)$.

18. If, in the parametric representation (20) of line L, we have $l \neq 0$, $m \neq 0$, and $n \neq 0$, we can write

$$\frac{x - x_1}{l} = \frac{y - y_1}{m} = \frac{z - z_1}{n}$$

Symmetric representation of a line

We call this the *symmetric representation* of the line L passing through the point $P_1(x_1, y_1, z_1)$ and having (l, m, n) for a set of direction numbers. Observe that this symmetric representation consists of the three equations

$$\frac{x - x_1}{l} = \frac{y - y_1}{m} \qquad \frac{x - x_1}{l} = \frac{z - z_1}{n} \qquad \frac{y - y_1}{m} = \frac{z - z_1}{n}$$

Each of these is an equation of a plane perpendicular to a coordinate plane, and these planes are called the *projection planes* of the line L.

Find a symmetric representation of the line L with the two-plane representation $x - y + 2z = 6$, $x + y - z = 12$. Graph L, and on this graph indicate the projection planes of L.

8.7 QUADRIC SURFACES

Surface

Quadric surface

A set of points in 3-space that is the graph of a relation determined by a single equation $E(x, y, z) = 0$ in the variables x, y, and z is a **surface.** We have studied two types of surfaces, namely, spheres (Sec. 8.3) and planes (Sec. 8.6). A **quadric surface** is a surface that is the graph of a (polynomial) equation of the second degree in the variables x, y, and z.

Plane section of a surface

The set of points that constitutes the intersection of a surface S and a plane Π is called a **plane section** of S. If Π is perpendicular to a line L, we say that the plane section is perpendicular to L. Note that the trace of a surface S in a co-ordinate plane is a plane section perpendicular to one of the coordinate axes.

In graphing a surface S it is usually advantageous to find the x, y, and z intercepts of S (Sec. 8.6) and to study various plane sections of S, especially the plane sections of S that are perpendicular to the coordinate axes (including the traces of S in the coordinate planes). <u>*Any plane section of a quadric surface is a conic section or two parallel lines*</u> (see Sec. 5.1).

For a given surface S with equation $E(x, y, z) = 0$, a plane section perpendicular to a coordinate axis is the graph of one of the relations

$$R_1 = \{(x, y, z) \mid E(r, y, z) = 0 \text{ and } x = r\}$$
$$R_2 = \{(x, y, z) \mid E(x, s, z) = 0 \text{ and } y = s\}$$
$$R_3 = \{(x, y, z) \mid E(x, y, t) = 0 \text{ and } z = t\}$$

where r, s, and t are real numbers. If R_1 is not the empty set, its graph is the plane section of S perpendicular to the x axis at the point $P_1(r, 0, 0)$. Similar statements pertain to R_2 and R_3. Hence the plane sections of S perpendicular to the x axis, the y axis, and the z axis are determined by the respective systems

$$
\begin{array}{ccc}
x = r & y = s & z = t \\
E(r, y, z) = 0 & E(x, s, z) = 0 & E(x, y, t) = 0
\end{array}
$$

A sphere is a quadric surface since it is the graph of an equation of the second degree, namely, $(x - h)^2 + (y - k)^2 + (z - l)^2 = r^2$. For the sphere

$$S: \ x^2 + y^2 + z^2 = 9$$

the traces of S in the xy, yz, and xz planes are the graphs of the respective systems

$$
C_1: \begin{array}{c} z = 0 \\ x^2 + y^2 = 9 \end{array}
\qquad
C_2: \begin{array}{c} x = 0 \\ y^2 + z^2 = 9 \end{array}
\qquad
C_3: \begin{array}{c} y = 0 \\ x^2 + z^2 = 9 \end{array}
$$

C_1, C_2, and C_3 are circles in the xy, yz, and xz planes, respectively. The graph of S, with C_1, C_2, and C_3 indicated, is shown in Fig. 8.12. The plane section of S determined by the plane Π: $z = 2$ is the graph of the system

$$
C_4: \begin{array}{c} z = 2 \\ x^2 + y^2 + 4 = 9 \end{array}
\qquad \text{or} \qquad
\begin{array}{c} z = 2 \\ x^2 + y^2 = 5 \end{array}
$$

C_4 is also shown in Fig. 8.12.

We now study a type of quadric surface called a *quadric cylinder*. Consider a curve C that lies in a plane Π, and let S be the set of all lines intersecting C and perpendicular to Π. The set of all points on the lines of the set S is called a (right) *Cylindrical* **cylindrical surface,** or briefly, a **cylinder** (for example, see Figs. 8.13 and 8.14). *surface* The curve C is called the **directrix** of the cylinder, and each line in S is called an **element** of S. The elements of a cylinder are parallel to each other, since each is perpendicular to the plane Π. A cylinder is often named after its directrix; to illustrate, a cylinder whose directrix is a parabola is a parabolic cylinder (for example, see Fig. 8.14).

Let $E(x, y)$ be an expression containing no variable other than x and y. Then

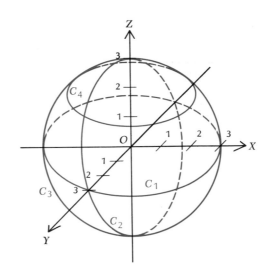

FIGURE 8.12

the graph of

$$R_4 = \{(x, y, z) \mid E(x, y) = 0\}$$

is a cylinder with elements parallel to the z axis and with its directrix C the graph of $\{(x, y) \mid E(x, y) = 0\}$. Similar descriptions of the graphs of

$$R_5 = \{(x, y, z) \mid E(y, z) = 0\}$$
and
$$R_6 = \{(x, y, z) \mid E(x, z) = 0\}$$

as cylinders may be given. A coordinate system in 3-space can always be chosen so that the plane containing the directrix of a given cylinder is one of the co-ordinate planes, and so that the directrix is the graph of one of the relations $\{(x, y) \mid E(x, y) = 0\}$, $\{(y, z) \mid E(y, z) = 0\}$, $\{(z, x) \mid E(z, x) = 0\}$.

Quadric cylinder   A cylinder is a **quadric cylinder** *if its directrix is a conic section.* To illustrate, the cylinders

$$K_1, \text{ the graph of } \{(x, y, z) \mid x^2 + (y - 3)^2 = 4\}$$
and
$$K_2, \text{ the graph of } \{(x, y, z) \mid y^2 = 9x\}$$

are quadric cylinders. A finite portion of the graph of the quadric (circular) cylinder K_1 appears in Fig. 8.13, and a finite portion of the graph of the quadric (parabolic) cylinder K_2 appears in Fig. 8.14. To graph (a finite portion of) K_2 we first construct a portion of the parabola C which is the graph of $\{(x, y) \mid y^2 = 9x\}$, and then draw a set of line segments with a selected length, say 4, extending from C in the direction of the positive z axis. The ends of these segments, which are in the plane Π: $z = 4$, determine a plane section C' of K_2 which is perpendicular to the elements of K_2 (and which is called a *normal* section of K_2).

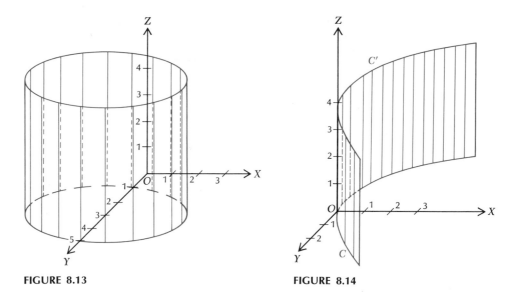

FIGURE 8.13   **FIGURE 8.14**

The graph of $\{(x, y, z) \mid y = \sin x\}$ is an interesting cylinder, but it is not a quadric cylinder (and therefore not a quadric surface); the student is asked to construct this graph in Exercise 2 at the end of this section.

A group of quadric surfaces called *degenerate quadric surfaces* are illustrated by the graphs of the relations in Table 8.1. The student is asked to construct the graphs of R_7 to R_{11} in Exercise 1 at the end of this section.

In addition to the sphere, the quadric cylinders, and the degenerate quadric surfaces which are illustrated in Table 8.1, there are *six standard quadric surfaces*. We give the equations and graphs of all six of these, with a detailed discussion of one of the six called the ellipsoid. The student should supply a

TABLE 8.1

RELATION	GRAPH
$R_7 = \{(x, y, z) \mid (x-3)^2 + y^2 + z^2 = 0\}$	The point $(3, 0, 0)$
$R_8 = \{(x, y, z) \mid (x-2)^2 + (y-1)^2 = 0\}$	The line through $(2, 1, 0)$ and $\perp$ to the xy plane
$R_9 = \{(x, y, z) \mid (x-4)^2 = 9\}$	Two parallel planes, Π_1: $x - 4 = 3$ and Π_2: $x - 4 = -3$
$R_{10} = \{(x, y, z) \mid \frac{1}{4}x^2 - \frac{1}{9}y^2 = 0\}$	Two intersecting planes, Π_1: $\frac{1}{2}x - \frac{1}{3}y = 0$ and Π_2: $\frac{1}{2}x + \frac{1}{3}y = 0$
$R_{11} = \{(x, y, z) \mid (x+5)^2 = 0\}$	The single plane, Π: $x + 5 = 0$

similar discussion of the other five. Here a, b, and c denote positive real numbers.

The student should recall the statements concerning symmetry made in Sec. 8.2. There we concluded that a graph G is symmetric with respect to the yz plane if and only if

$$P_1(x_1, y_1, z_1) \in G \quad \Rightarrow \quad P_2(-x_1, y_1, z_1) \in G \tag{31}$$

Now (31) is true if and only if x occurs in *even powers* only in an equation of G. Therefore *a quadric surface S is symmetric with respect to the yz plane if and only if x occurs to even powers only in an equation of S.* Similar statements hold regarding symmetry with respect to the other two coordinate planes.

The *ellipsoid E* which has

$$\frac{x^2}{a^2} + \frac{y^2}{b^2} + \frac{z^2}{c^2} = 1 \tag{32}$$

for an equation is shown in Fig. 8.15.

E is symmetric with respect to each of the coordinate planes; it has a and $-a$ for x intercepts, b and $-b$ for y intercepts, and c and $-c$ for z intercepts.

The trace of E in each of the coordinate planes is an ellipse, the trace in the xy plane being the graph of the system

$$\frac{x^2}{a^2} + \frac{y^2}{b^2} = 1 \qquad z = 0$$

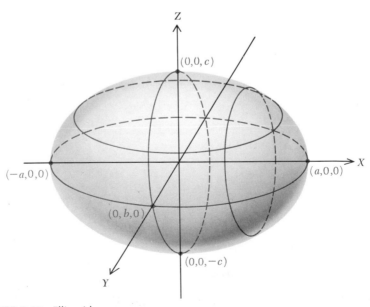

FIGURE 8.15 Ellipsoid.

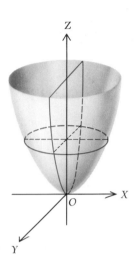

FIGURE 8.16 Elliptic paraboloid.

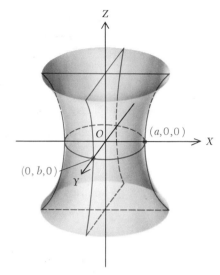

FIGURE 8.17 Hyperboloid of one sheet.

The plane sections of E perpendicular to the x axis, the y axis, and the z axis are determined by the respective systems:

$$\left.\begin{array}{l} x = r \\[2mm] \dfrac{y^2}{b^2} + \dfrac{z^2}{c^2} = 1 - \dfrac{r^2}{a^2} \end{array}\right\}$$

This is an ellipse if $r^2 < a^2$,
a point if $r^2 = a^2$,
the null set if $r^2 > a^2$.

$$\left.\begin{array}{l} y = s \\[2mm] \dfrac{x^2}{a^2} + \dfrac{z^2}{c^2} = 1 - \dfrac{s^2}{b^2} \end{array}\right\}$$

This is an ellipse if $s^2 < b^2$,
a point if $s^2 = b^2$,
the null set if $s^2 > b^2$.

$$\left.\begin{array}{l} z = t \\[2mm] \dfrac{x^2}{a^2} + \dfrac{y^2}{b^2} = 1 - \dfrac{t^2}{c^2} \end{array}\right\}$$

This is an ellipse if $t^2 < c^2$,
a point if $t^2 = c^2$,
the null set if $t^2 > c^2$.

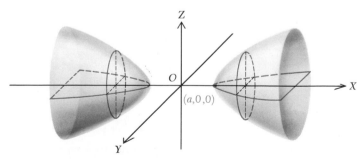

FIGURE 8.18 Hyperboloid of two sheets.

TABLE 8.2

NAME OF SURFACE	EQUATION	GRAPH IN
(ii) Elliptic paraboloid	$\dfrac{x^2}{a^2}+\dfrac{y^2}{b^2}=cz$	Fig. 8.16
(iii) Hyperboloid of one sheet	$\dfrac{x^2}{a^2}+\dfrac{y^2}{b^2}-\dfrac{z^2}{c^2}=1$	Fig. 8.17
(iv) Hyperboloid of two sheets	$\dfrac{x^2}{a^2}-\dfrac{y^2}{b^2}-\dfrac{z^2}{c^2}=1$	Fig. 8.18
(v) Cone	$\dfrac{x^2}{a^2}+\dfrac{y^2}{b^2}-\dfrac{z^2}{c^2}=0$	Fig. 8.19
(vi) Hyperbolic paraboloid	$\dfrac{x^2}{a^2}-\dfrac{y^2}{b^2}=cz$	Fig. 8.20

Information regarding the remaining five standard quadric surfaces is given in Table 8.2 and in the related figures.

Interchanging the symbols x, y, and z in any of the equations of a quadric surface does not affect the type of surface. Such an interchange simply changes the designations of the coordinate axes.

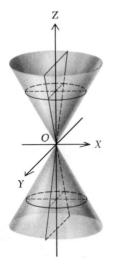

FIGURE 8.19 Cone.

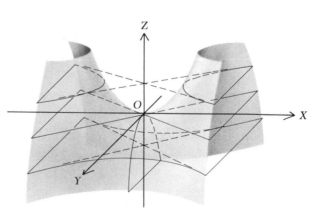

FIGURE 8.20 Hyperbolic paraboloid.

EXERCISES

1. In Table 8.1 there are listed five relations $R_7, \ldots, R_{11}$. Construct the graph of each of these relations.

2. Construct the graph of $\{(x, y, z) \mid y = \sin x, x \in [0; 2\pi]\}$.

In each of Exercises 3–8 identify and construct the graph of the given relation.

3. $\{(x, y, z) \mid x^2 + y^2 = 16 \text{ and } z = 0\}$

4. $\{(x, y, z) \mid x^2 + y^2 = 16 \text{ and } z = 4\}$

5. $\{(x, y, z) \mid x^2 + y^2 = 16\}$ **6.** $\{(x, y, z) \mid xy = 6 \text{ and } z = 0\}$

7. $\{(x, y, z) \mid xy = 6 \text{ and } z = -3\}$ **8.** $\{(x, y, z) \mid xy = 6\}$

In each of the following exercises identify and construct the graph of the given equation in 3-space.

9. $x^2 - 4x + y^2 = 0$ **10.** $z^2 - 6z + y^2 = 0$

11. $x^2 - 4y = 0$ **12.** $4x^2 + 9y^2 = 36$

13. $x^2 + y^2 + z^2 = 25$ **14.** $x^2 + 9y^2 + 4z^2 = 36$

15. $9x^2 + 16y^2 - z^2 = 144$ **16.** $16x^2 - 9y^2 - z^2 = 144$

17. $x^2 + 9y^2 - z^2 = 0$ **18.** $-x^2 + y^2 + 4z^2 = 0$

19. $\frac{1}{4}x^2 + \frac{1}{9}y^2 = z$ **20.** $\frac{1}{4}x^2 - \frac{1}{9}y^2 = z$

21. $\frac{1}{4}x^2 - \frac{1}{9}y^2 = 0$ **22.** $x^2 + y^2 = 9x$

23. $x^2 + y^2 = 9z$ **24.** $x^2 + z^2 = y^2 - 2y + 1$

8.8 VECTORS IN 3-SPACE

Most of the material in Sec. 7.1 regarding the geometric structure of vectors in 2-space carries over to the geometric structure of vectors in 3-space. If P and Q are points in three-dimensional space, the symbol $\overrightarrow{PQ}$ denotes the *directed line segment* from P to Q, with initial point P and terminal point Q. As in 2-space, the length of $\overrightarrow{PQ}$ is denoted by $|\overrightarrow{PQ}|$. The concept of *same direction* for two directed line segments in 3-space is the same as that in 2-space given in Sec. 7.1. Also, as we did in Sec. 7.1, we say that two directed line segments in 3-space are **equivalent** if and only if they have the same length and the same direction. A **vector v** in 3-space is an equivalence class of directed line segments in 3-space, all having a given length and a given direction.

If **v** is a vector and if $\overrightarrow{PQ}$ is a member of the equivalence class **v**, then $\overrightarrow{PQ}$, or any segment equivalent to $\overrightarrow{PQ}$, is a representative of the vector **v**. We write $\mathbf{v}(\overrightarrow{PQ})$ to denote "the vector **v** with representative $\overrightarrow{PQ}$."

One very basic difference between vectors in 2-space and vectors in 3-space stems from the fact that in 2-space three directed line segments lie in a single plane, while in 3-space three directed line segments need not (and usually do not) lie in a single plane.

The definition of the **sum** of vectors in 3-space has the same form as in 2-space, and the basic properties

$$\mathbf{u} + \mathbf{v} = \mathbf{v} + \mathbf{u} \tag{33}$$
$$(\mathbf{u} + \mathbf{v}) + \mathbf{w} = \mathbf{u} + (\mathbf{v} + \mathbf{w}) \tag{34}$$

are the same. These properties are established in the same way as they were in Sec. 7.1 for 2-space except the proof of (34) must be adapted to take into account the fact mentioned in the preceding paragraph. The student is asked to prove (34) in Exercise 1, page 298, with the aid of Fig. 8.21.

The **norm** of a vector **v** is the common length of all its representatives and is denoted by $\|\mathbf{v}\|$. The **direction** of **v** is the direction of any one of its representatives, and two vectors **v** and **u** are parallel if and only if they have the same or opposite directions.

The definition of the product $s\mathbf{v}$ of **v** by a scalar s is the same as that given by statements (15) and (16) in Sec. 7.1. Multiplication of a vector by a scalar has the following properties:

$$1\mathbf{v} = \mathbf{v} \tag{35}$$
$$(-1)\mathbf{v} = -\mathbf{v} \tag{36}$$
$$(rs)\mathbf{v} = r(s\mathbf{v}) \tag{37}$$
$$(r + s)\mathbf{v} = r\mathbf{v} + s\mathbf{v} \tag{38}$$
$$s(\mathbf{u} + \mathbf{v}) = s\mathbf{u} + s\mathbf{v} \tag{39}$$
$$s\mathbf{v} = 0 \quad \Rightarrow \quad s = 0 \text{ or } \mathbf{v} = \mathbf{0} \tag{40}$$
$$s\mathbf{v} = 0 \text{ and } \mathbf{v} \neq \mathbf{0} \quad \Rightarrow \quad s = 0 \tag{41}$$

These properties are established in the same way as they were for 2-space.

The concepts of equality of vectors and subtraction of vectors carry over without modification from 2-space to 3-space.

Let **u** and **v** be two nonzero vectors that are *not* parallel, and select respective representatives $\overrightarrow{PQ}$ and $\overrightarrow{PR}$ of **u** and **v** that have a common initial point P. The two directed line segments $\overrightarrow{PQ}$ and $\overrightarrow{PR}$ determine a plane Π, and we say that Π is *a plane determined by the vectors* **u** *and* **v**.

We say that a vector **v** is **parallel to a plane** Π if every representative of **v** is parallel to (or lies in) Π.

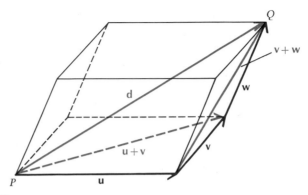

FIGURE 8.21

Theorems 7.5 and 7.6 hold for vectors in 3-space since the concept of linear independence of vectors is the same in 3-space as in 2-space. However, for 3-space, Theorem 7.7 must be slightly modified, as expressed in Theorem 8.14.

THEOREM 8.14   *Every vector **v** that is parallel to a plane determined by two given linearly independent vectors **a** and **b** can be expressed as*

$$\mathbf{v} = s_1\mathbf{a} + s_2\mathbf{b} \tag{42}$$

*where s_1 and s_2 are uniquely determined scalars. Conversely, if a vector **v** can be expressed by (42), where **a** and **b** are linearly independent, then **v** is parallel to a plane determined by **a** and **b**.*

The concept of the decomposition of a vector **v** into components $s_1\mathbf{a}$ parallel to **a** and $s_2\mathbf{b}$ parallel to **b** in accord with (42) carries over to 3-space.

Recall that three vectors **a**, **b**, and **c** are **linearly dependent** in case there are scalars s_1, s_2, and s_3, not all zero, for which

$$s_1\mathbf{a} + s_2\mathbf{b} + s_3\mathbf{c} = \mathbf{0} \tag{43}$$

Suppose **a**, **b**, **c** are nonzero vectors and that no two of them are parallel. Then, in order to have scalars s_1, s_2, s_3 so that (43) holds, no one of the scalars can be zero. Therefore, if (43) holds and if **a**, **b**, **c** are nonzero with no two of them parallel, any one of them can be written as a linear combination of the other two. Thus, it follows from Theorem 8.14 that, if **a**, **b**, and **c** are linearly dependent, then they have representatives that lie in the same plane. When three vectors have representatives that lie in the same plane we say that the vectors are

coplanar. If nonzero vectors **a**, **b**, and **c** are coplanar, then it follows from Theorem 7.8 that **a**, **b**, and **c** are linearly dependent.

If there are no scalars s_1, s_2, s_3, other than $s_1 = s_2 = s_3 = 0$, for which (43) holds, then **a**, **b**, and **c** are **linearly independent.** From this definition and the remarks in the preceding paragraph we have Theorem 8.15.

THEOREM
8.15
*Three vectors **a**, **b**, and **c** are linearly independent if and only if they are not coplanar and none is the zero vector.*

THEOREM
8.16
*If **a**, **b**, and **c** are three linearly independent vectors in 3-space, then for any vector **v** in 3-space there is a unique set of scalars (s_1, s_2, s_3) for which*

$$\mathbf{v} = s_1\mathbf{a} + s_2\mathbf{b} + s_3\mathbf{c} \qquad (44)$$

In Exercise 2 at the end of this section, the student is asked to prove this theorem with the aid of Fig. 8.22. A proof similar to that of Theorem 7.7 can be constructed.

Theorem 8.16 says that any vector **v** in 3-space can be written uniquely as the sum of three vectors which are parallel, respectively, to three given nonzero noncoplanar vectors **a**, **b**, and **c**. In the equality (44), and in Fig. 8.22*b*, we call $s_1\mathbf{a}$, $s_2\mathbf{b}$, and $s_3\mathbf{c}$ the **components of v parallel, respectively,** to **a**, **b**, and **c**. When **v** is written in the manner (44), we say that **v** is **decomposed** into components parallel to **a**, **b**, and **c**.

Four vectors **a**, **b**, **c**, and **d** are **linearly dependent** in case there are scalars s_1, s_2, s_3, s_4, not all zero, for which

$$s_1\mathbf{a} + s_2\mathbf{b} + s_3\mathbf{c} + s_4\mathbf{d} = \mathbf{0} \qquad (45)$$

From this definition and Theorem 8.16 there follows Theorem 8.17.

THEOREM
8.17
Four or more vectors in 3-space are linearly dependent.

Since every vector **v** in 3-space can be expressed as a linear combination of three linearly independent vectors, we say that three linearly independent vectors **a**, **b**, and **c** constitute a *basis* for 3-space. Using the term "basis," we give a combined alternative statement of Theorems 8.15 and 8.16 in Theorem 8.18.

THEOREM
8.18
Any three noncoplanar nonzero vectors in 3-space constitute a basis for that space.

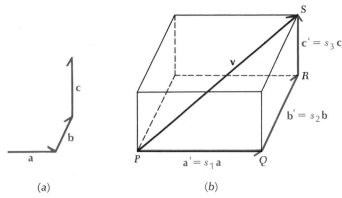

FIGURE 8.22   Decomposition of a vector **v** into components parallel to **a**, **b**, and **c**.

Let us denote the 3-space which we studied in previous sections of this chapter by E_3. Any three vectors parallel, respectively, to the x axis, the y axis, and the z axis form a basis for E_3. We find it convenient to choose for such a basis three unit vectors which we denote by **i**, **j**, and **k**, and which we define as follows:

Unit vectors
i, j, and k

i has norm 1 and has direction that of the x axis.
j has norm 1 and has direction that of the y axis.
k has norm 1 and has direction that of the z axis.

From Theorem 7.5 and the definition of $s\mathbf{v}$ we have Theorem 8.19.

THEOREM   *For any nonzero real number c:*
8.19
     (i)   *$c\mathbf{i}$ is a vector with norm $|c|$ and parallel to* **i**.
     (ii)   *$c\mathbf{j}$ is a vector with norm $|c|$ and parallel to* **j**.
     (iii)   *$c\mathbf{k}$ is a vector with norm $|c|$ and parallel to* **k**.

By Theorem 8.16 any vector **v** in E_3 can be written as (see Fig. 8.23)

$$\mathbf{v} = v_1\mathbf{i} + v_2\mathbf{j} + v_3\mathbf{k} \tag{46}$$

where v_1, v_2, and v_3 are uniquely determined scalars.

Vector components of **v** and coordinates of **v** are defined for vectors in E_3 as they were in Sec. 7.2 for vectors in E_2. We denote a three-dimensional vector **v** with coordinates v_1, v_2, and v_3 by $\langle v_1, v_2, v_3 \rangle$. Note that

$$\mathbf{i} = \langle 1, 0, 0 \rangle \qquad \mathbf{j} = \langle 0, 1, 0 \rangle \qquad \mathbf{k} = \langle 0, 0, 1 \rangle \qquad \mathbf{0} = \langle 0, 0, 0 \rangle$$

For E_3, Theorems 8.20, 8.21, 8.22(i), 8.22(ii), 8.23, and 8.24 correspond, respectively, to Theorems 7.11 to 7.16 for E_2. Their proofs are similar, and the student is asked to give these proofs in Exercises 3–8 on page 298.

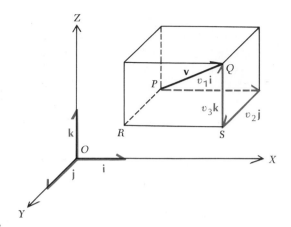

FIGURE 8.23

THEOREM 8.20   *If* $\mathbf{v} = v_1\mathbf{i} + v_2\mathbf{j} + v_3\mathbf{k}$, *then*

$$\|\mathbf{v}\| = \sqrt{v_1{}^2 + v_2{}^2 + v_3{}^2} \qquad (47)$$

THEOREM 8.21   *If* $P_1(x_1, y_1, z_1)$ *and* $P_2(x_2, y_2, z_2)$ *are points in* E_3, *then the vector* $\mathbf{v}(\overrightarrow{P_1P_2})$ *is given by*

$$\mathbf{v} = (x_2 - x_1)\mathbf{i} + (y_2 - y_1)\mathbf{j} + (z_2 - z_1)\mathbf{k} \qquad (48)$$

THEOREM 8.22   *If* $\mathbf{v}_1 = \langle x_1, y_1, z_1 \rangle$ *and* $\mathbf{v}_2 = \langle x_2, y_2, z_2 \rangle$, *then*
   (i) $\mathbf{v}_1 + \mathbf{v}_2 = \langle x_1 + x_2, y_1 + y_2, z_1 + z_2 \rangle$
   (ii) $\mathbf{v}_1 - \mathbf{v}_2 = \langle x_1 - x_2, y_1 - y_2, z_1 - z_2 \rangle$

THEOREM 8.23   *To multiply the vector* $\mathbf{v} = v_1\mathbf{i} + v_2\mathbf{j} + v_3\mathbf{k}$ *by the real number* h, *multiply each coordinate of* $\mathbf{v}$ *by* h:

$$h\mathbf{v} = hv_1\mathbf{i} + hv_2\mathbf{j} + hv_3\mathbf{k} = \langle hv_1, hv_2, hv_3 \rangle$$

THEOREM 8.24   *If* $\mathbf{v}_1 = x_1\mathbf{i} + y_1\mathbf{j} + z_1\mathbf{k}$ *and* $\mathbf{v}_2 = x_2\mathbf{i} + y_2\mathbf{j} + z_2\mathbf{k}$, *then*

$$\mathbf{v}_1 = \mathbf{v}_2 \iff x_1 = x_2, \ y_1 = y_2, \ z_1 = z_2$$

    To illustrate Theorems 8.20 to 8.23, let $\mathbf{v}_1 = 3\mathbf{i} + 2\mathbf{j} + 6\mathbf{k} = \langle 3, 2, 6 \rangle$, $\mathbf{v}_2 = \langle 5, 4, 7 \rangle$, and $h = 4$. Then $\|\mathbf{v}_1\| = \sqrt{9 + 4 + 36} = \sqrt{49} = 7$, $\mathbf{v}_1 + \mathbf{v}_2 = \langle 3 + 5, 2 + 4, 6 + 7 \rangle = 8\mathbf{i} + 6\mathbf{j} + 13\mathbf{k}$, $\mathbf{v}_1 - \mathbf{v}_2 = \langle 3 - 5, 2 - 4, 6 - 7 \rangle = \langle -2, -2, -1 \rangle = -2\mathbf{i} - 2\mathbf{j} - \mathbf{k}$, and $h\mathbf{v}_1 = 4\mathbf{v}_1 = 4\langle 3, 2, 6 \rangle = \langle 12, 8, 24 \rangle = 12\mathbf{i} + 8\mathbf{j} + 24\mathbf{k}$.

As in E_2, we reserve the use of the symbol **r** to denote a *position vector* of a point P. When we speak of a position vector it is to be understood that the vector has only one representative and that the initial point of this representative is the origin $O(0, 0, 0)$ and the terminal point is P. Observe that the vector $\mathbf{v}(\overrightarrow{P_1P_2})$ of Theorem 8.21 may be considered as $\mathbf{v} = \mathbf{r}_2 - \mathbf{r}_1$, where $\mathbf{r}_1 = \langle x_1, y_1, z_1 \rangle$ and $\mathbf{r}_2 = \langle x_2, y_2, z_2 \rangle$.

The **direction angles** and the **direction cosines** of a nonzero vector $\mathbf{v}(\overrightarrow{P\,P_2})$ are the direction angles and the direction cosines of $\overrightarrow{P_1P_2}$. Let $P_1(x_1, y_1, z_1)$ and $P_2(x_2, y_2, z_2)$ be two points in E_3, and let $\alpha_1, \beta_1, \gamma_1$ be direction angles of $\overrightarrow{P_1P_2}$ and therefore of $\mathbf{u}(\overrightarrow{P_1P_2})$. From (10) and Theorem 8.21 it follows that for

$$\mathbf{u}(\overrightarrow{P_1P_2}) = \langle x_2 - x_1, y_2 - y_1, z_2 - z_1 \rangle = \langle u_1, u_2, u_3 \rangle$$

the direction cosines of $\mathbf{u}(\overrightarrow{P_1P_2})$ are given by

$$\cos \alpha_1 = \frac{x_2 - x_1}{\|\mathbf{u}\|} = \frac{u_1}{\|\mathbf{u}\|} \qquad \cos \beta_1 = \frac{y_2 - y_1}{\|\mathbf{u}\|} = \frac{u_2}{\|\mathbf{u}\|} \qquad \cos \gamma_1 = \frac{z_2 - z_1}{\|\mathbf{u}\|} = \frac{u_3}{\|\mathbf{u}\|} \tag{49}$$

Similarly, for $\mathbf{v}(\overrightarrow{Q_1Q_2}) = \langle v_1, v_2, v_3 \rangle$ we have

$$\cos \alpha_2 = \frac{v_1}{\|\mathbf{v}\|} \qquad \cos \beta_2 = \frac{v_2}{\|\mathbf{v}\|} \qquad \cos \gamma_2 = \frac{v_3}{\|\mathbf{v}\|} \tag{50}$$

If $\theta = \measuredangle(\mathbf{u}, \mathbf{v})$, using (11), (49), and (50), we get

$$\cos \theta = \frac{u_1v_1 + u_2v_2 + u_3v_3}{\|\mathbf{u}\|\,\|\mathbf{v}\|} \tag{51}$$

Observe that if $\mathbf{u} = \langle u_1, u_2, u_3 \rangle$ is a unit vector, so that $\|\mathbf{u}\| = 1$, then from (49) we have that the direction cosines of $\mathbf{u}$ are the coordinates of the vector $\mathbf{u}$.

For $P_1(2, 4, 0)$ and $P_2(0, 0, 4)$, we have

$$\mathbf{u}(\overrightarrow{P_1P_2}) = \langle x_2 - x_1, y_2 - y_1, z_2 - z_1 \rangle = \langle -2, -4, 4 \rangle \qquad \|\mathbf{u}\| = 6$$

For $P_3(2, -1, -1)$ and $P_4(2, 2, 3)$, we have

$$\mathbf{v}(\overrightarrow{P_3P_4}) = \langle 2 - 2, 2 - (-1), 3 - (-1) \rangle = \langle 0, 3, 4 \rangle \qquad \|\mathbf{v}\| = 5$$

Let $\alpha_1, \beta_1, \gamma_1$ be the direction angles of $\mathbf{u}$ and let $\alpha_2, \beta_2, \gamma_2$ be the direction angles of $\mathbf{v}$. Then

$$\cos \alpha_1 = \tfrac{-2}{6} = -\tfrac{1}{3} \qquad \cos \beta_1 = \tfrac{-4}{6} = -\tfrac{2}{3} \qquad \cos \gamma_1 = \tfrac{4}{6} = \tfrac{2}{3}$$
$$\cos \alpha_2 = 0 \qquad \cos \beta_2 = \tfrac{3}{5} \qquad \cos \gamma_2 = \tfrac{4}{5}$$

If $\theta = \measuredangle(\mathbf{u}, \mathbf{v})$, Eq. (51) can be used to obtain

$$\cos \theta = \frac{-2(0) + (-4)(3) + 4(4)}{(6)(5)} = \frac{-12 + 16}{30} = \frac{2}{15}$$

Inner product

The expression $u_1 v_1 + u_2 v_2 + u_3 v_3$ is called the **inner product** of $\mathbf{u} = \langle u_1, u_2, u_3 \rangle$ and $\mathbf{v} = \langle v_1, v_2, v_3 \rangle$ and is denoted by $\mathbf{u} \cdot \mathbf{v}$. Thus

$$\mathbf{u} \cdot \mathbf{v} = u_1 v_1 + u_2 v_2 + u_3 v_3 \tag{52}$$

and

$$\cos \measuredangle (\mathbf{u}, \mathbf{v}) = \frac{\mathbf{u} \cdot \mathbf{v}}{\|\mathbf{u}\| \, \|\mathbf{v}\|} \tag{53}$$

Scalar or dot product

The expression $\mathbf{u} \cdot \mathbf{v}$ is also called the **scalar product** or the **dot product** of the vectors $\mathbf{u}$ and $\mathbf{v}$. Note that, as we see from (53), the inner product could be defined by

$$\mathbf{u} \cdot \mathbf{v} = \|\mathbf{u}\| \, \|\mathbf{v}\| \cos \measuredangle (\mathbf{u}, \mathbf{v})$$

From (53) we obtain Theorem 8.25.

THEOREM 8.25 $\mathbf{u} \perp \mathbf{v} \iff \mathbf{u} \cdot \mathbf{v} = 0$.

THEOREM 8.26 *Let* $\mathbf{r}_1 = \langle x_1, y_1, z_1 \rangle$ *be the position vector of a fixed point* $P_1(x_1, y_1, z_1)$, *let* $\mathbf{r} = \langle x, y, z \rangle$ *be the position vector of a variable point* $P(x, y, z)$, *and let* $\mathbf{a} = \langle a_1, a_2, a_3 \rangle$ *be any nonzero vector. Then* $P(x, y, z)$ *is on the plane* Π *through* $P_1(x_1, y_1, z_1)$ *and perpendicular to* $\mathbf{a}$ *if and only if*

Vector equation of a plane

$$\mathbf{a} \cdot (\mathbf{r} - \mathbf{r}_1) = 0 \tag{54}$$

Proof

The theorem follows directly from Theorems 8.21 and 8.25 (see Fig. 8.24).

Equation (54) is called a *vector equation* of the plane Π through $P_1(x_1, y_1, z_1)$ and perpendicular to the vector $\mathbf{a} = \langle a_1, a_2, a_3 \rangle$. Observe that (54) is equivalent to

$$a_1(x - x_1) + a_2(y - y_1) + a_3(z - z_1) = 0$$

We call this last equation a *scalar coordinate form* of an equation of the plane Π.

THEOREM 8.27 *Let* $\mathbf{r}_1 = \langle x_1, y_1, z_1 \rangle$ *be the position vector of a fixed point* $P_1(x_1, y_1, z_1)$, *let* $\mathbf{r} = \langle x, y, z \rangle$ *be the position vector of a variable point* $P(x, y, z)$, *and let* k *be any positive real number. Then* $P(x, y, z)$ *lies on the sphere with center* $P_1(x_1, y_1, z_1)$ *and radius* k *if and only if*

Vector equation of a sphere

$$\|\mathbf{r} - \mathbf{r}_1\| = k \tag{55}$$

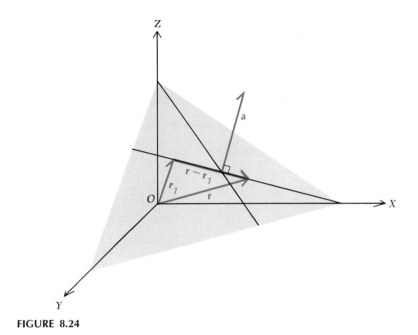

FIGURE 8.24

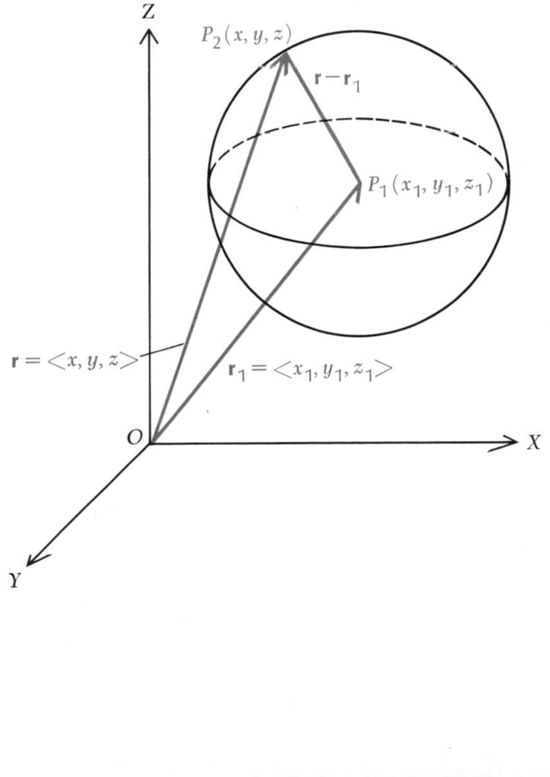

FIGURE 8.25

Proof

The theorem follows directly from Theorems 8.20 and 8.21 (see Fig. 8.25).

Equation (55) is called a *vector equation* of the sphere with center $P_1(x_1, y_1, z_1)$ and radius k. Note that (55) is equivalent to

$$(x - x_1)^2 + (y - y_1)^2 + (z - z_1)^2 = k^2$$

We call this equation a *scalar coordinate form* of an equation of the sphere.

EXERCISES

1. If **u**, **v**, and **w** are noncoplanar vectors in 3-space, prove (34) with the aid of Fig. 8.21.

2. With the aid of Fig. 8.22, prove Theorem 8.16.

3. Give a proof of Theorem 8.20 (it is similar to the proof of Theorem 7.11).

4. Give a proof of Theorem 8.21 (it is similar to the proof of Theorem 7.12).

5. Give a proof of Theorem 8.22(i) (it is similar to the proof of Theorem 7.13).

6. Give a proof of Theorem 8.22(ii) (it is similar to the proof of Theorem 7.14).

7. Give a proof of Theorem 8.23 (it is similar to the proof of Theorem 7.15).

8. Give a proof of Theorem 8.24 (it is similar to the proof of Theorem 7.16).

9. For the sphere S with center at $P_1(1, 2, 3)$ and with radius k give:

(*a*) An equation of S in vector form

(*b*) An equation of S in scalar coordinate form

10. For the plane Π through the point $P_1(2, 4, 5)$ and perpendicular to the vector $\langle 1, -2, 3 \rangle$ give:

(*a*) An equation of Π in vector form

(*b*) An equation of Π in scalar coordinate form

11. Prove the theorem: Let $\mathbf{r}_1 = \langle x_1, y_1, z_1 \rangle$ be the position vector of a fixed point $P_1(x_1, y_1, z_1)$, let $\mathbf{r} = \langle x, y, z \rangle$ be the position vector of a variable point $P(x, y, z)$, and let $\mathbf{a} = \langle a_1, a_2, a_3 \rangle$ be a constant vector. Then the line L through P_1 and parallel to **a** has

$$\mathbf{r} - \mathbf{r}_1 = t\mathbf{a}$$

for a vector equation, or vector parametric representation. Here t is a variable with universe Re.

12. How do we write the vector parametric representation of Exercise 11 as a parametric representation like that in Sec. 8.5?

13. For the line L through $P_1(6, 5, 4)$ and parallel to $\mathbf{a} = \langle 1, 3, -2 \rangle$ give:

(*a*) A vector parametric representation

(*b*) A parametric representation like that in Sec. 8.5

8.9 A FORWARD GLANCE

We have presented the analytic geometry of 2-space and 3-space with the aid of visual representations (figures and graphs), and have assumed an acquaintance with points, lines, and planes and a prior knowledge of geometric topics like the Pythagorean theorem and the law of cosines. But we could have begun by *defining* a point in 2-space to be an ordered pair of numbers, defining a circle to be a set of points satisfying an equation of the form $(x - x_1)^2 + (y - y_1)^2 = r^2$, and defining a line as a set of points satisfying an equation of the type $ax + by + c = 0$. Similarly, in 3-space we could have *defined* a point to be an ordered triple of numbers, defined a sphere to be a set of points satisfying an equation of the form $(x - x_1)^2 + (y - y_1)^2 + (z - z_1)^2 = r^2$, and defined a plane as a set of points satisfying an equation of the type $ax + by + cz + d = 0$. By such procedure all geometric theorems would appear as algebraic theorems.

This algebraic approach is the approach which is used in studying spaces of four and higher dimensions and more abstract spaces where visual interpretations are not readily available. Vector concepts and symbolism facilitate this manner of generalizing geometric concepts to higher dimensions, as indicated in the discussion below.

Analogous to an ordered pair like (a, b) and an ordered triple like (a, b, c), there are ordered sets of n real numbers. An ordered set of n objects is called an *ordered n-tuple*.

Vector space V_n   The **vector space** V_n (over the field of real numbers Re) is the algebraic system consisting of all ordered n-tuples $\mathbf{x} = \langle x_1, x_2, \ldots, x_n \rangle$ with $x_i \in Re$, together with the operations of addition of n-tuples and multiplication of n-tuples by real numbers, as defined below. These n-tuples are called **vectors,** and the real numbers x_i are called **coordinates** of $\mathbf{x}$. If $\mathbf{x} = \langle x_1, x_2, \ldots, x_n \rangle$ and $\mathbf{y} = \langle y_1, y_2, \ldots, y_n \rangle$, then

$$\mathbf{x} = \mathbf{y} \iff x_i = y_i \qquad i = 1, 2, \ldots, n$$

Addition of $\mathbf{x}$ and $\mathbf{y}$ (the determination of the *sum* $\mathbf{x} + \mathbf{y}$) is defined by

$$\mathbf{x} + \mathbf{y} = \langle x_1 + y_1, x_2 + y_2, \ldots, x_n + y_n \rangle \tag{56}$$

and **scalar multiplication** (the determination of the *product* of $\mathbf{x}$ by any real number k) is defined by

$$k\mathbf{x} = \langle kx_1, kx_2, \ldots, kx_n \rangle \tag{57}$$

By using the field properties of real numbers it can be shown that the following properties hold for the vector space V_n:

(i) $\mathbf{x} + \mathbf{y} = \mathbf{y} + \mathbf{x}$ for all $\mathbf{x}, \mathbf{y} \in V_n$

(ii) $\mathbf{x} + (\mathbf{y} + \mathbf{z}) = (\mathbf{x} + \mathbf{y}) + \mathbf{z}$ for all $\mathbf{x}, \mathbf{y}, \mathbf{z} \in V_n$

(iii)   There is a unique vector $\mathbf{0} = \langle 0, 0, \ldots, 0 \rangle$ with the property that

$$\mathbf{x} + \mathbf{0} = \mathbf{0} + \mathbf{x} = \mathbf{x} \qquad \text{for all } \mathbf{x} \in V_n$$

(iv)   For each $\mathbf{x} \in V_n$ there is a unique $(-\mathbf{x}) \in V_n$ such that

$$\mathbf{x} + (-\mathbf{x}) = (-\mathbf{x}) + \mathbf{x} = \mathbf{0}$$

For all real numbers r and s and for all vectors $\mathbf{x}, \mathbf{y} \in V_n$ we have

(v) $(r + s)\mathbf{x} = r\mathbf{x} + s\mathbf{x}$
(vi) $r(\mathbf{x} + \mathbf{y}) = r\mathbf{x} + r\mathbf{y}$
(vii) $r(s\mathbf{x}) = (rs)\mathbf{x}$
(viii) $1\mathbf{x} = \mathbf{x}$

Just as we associated a point $P(x_1, x_2)$ with the position vector $\mathbf{r} = \langle x_1, x_2 \rangle$ in 2-space, and a point $P(x_1, x_2, x_3)$ with the position vector $\mathbf{r} = \langle x_1, x_2, x_3 \rangle$ in 3-space, we can associate a "point" $P(x_1, x_2, x_3, \ldots, x_n)$ with the vector $\mathbf{r} = \langle x_1, x_2, x_3, \ldots, x_n \rangle$, called the position vector of P.

In n-space we have n axes, the x_1 axis being the set of all vectors of the form $\langle x_1, 0, \ldots, 0 \rangle$, where x_1 is any real number, and so forth. A coordinate plane in n-space may be defined to be the set of all points for which some two of the n coordinates take on any real values, and the remaining $n - 2$ coordinates are zero.

A vector space V_n may be made a euclidean space E_n (referred to subsequently as n-space) in which we have distance and angles (so-called "metric" concepts) through the introduction of the concept of an inner product. Such an inner product may be defined in a variety of ways. The (standard) **inner product** $\mathbf{x} \cdot \mathbf{y}$ of the vectors $\mathbf{x} = \langle x_1, x_2, \ldots, x_n \rangle$ and $\mathbf{y} = \langle y_1, y_2, \ldots, y_n \rangle$ is defined by

Inner product in n-space

$$\mathbf{x} \cdot \mathbf{y} = x_1 y_1 + x_2 y_2 + \cdots + x_n y_n$$

With the use of this inner product we define the *norm* or *length* $\|\mathbf{x}\|$ of $\mathbf{x}$ by

$$\|\mathbf{x}\| = \sqrt{\mathbf{x} \cdot \mathbf{x}} = \sqrt{x_1{}^2 + x_2{}^2 + \cdots + x_n{}^2}$$

The **distance** $d(\mathbf{x}, \mathbf{y})$ between two vectors $\mathbf{x}$ and $\mathbf{y}$ is defined by

Distance in n-space

$$d(\mathbf{x}, \mathbf{y}) = \|\mathbf{x} - \mathbf{y}\| = \sqrt{(x_1 - y_1)^2 + (x_2 - y_2)^2 + \cdots + (x_n - y_n)^2}$$

and it can be shown that this distance has the four basic properties of distance that we discussed in Sec. 2.3. A **sphere** in n-space is defined to be the set of points satisfying an equation of the form

$$\|\mathbf{r} - \mathbf{r}_1\| = k$$

for fixed $\mathbf{r}_1$ and constant k (compare with Theorems 7.19 and 8.27).

Recall that in 2-space and in 3-space we proved (with the aid of the law of cosines) that if $\theta = \measuredangle(\mathbf{x}, \mathbf{y})$ for nonzero vectors $\mathbf{x}$ and $\mathbf{y}$, then

$$\cos \theta = \frac{\mathbf{x} \cdot \mathbf{y}}{\|\mathbf{x}\| \, \|\mathbf{y}\|} \qquad 0 \leqslant \theta \leqslant \pi \tag{58}$$

From the definitions given above of inner product and norm in n-space, we see that the expression

$$\frac{\mathbf{x} \cdot \mathbf{y}}{\|\mathbf{x}\| \, \|\mathbf{y}\|} \tag{59}$$

is also meaningful in n-space. This fact suggests that for nonzero vectors $\mathbf{x}$ and $\mathbf{y}$ in n-space we might define $\measuredangle (\mathbf{x, y})$ to be the number (between 0 and π) whose cosine is given by (59). But such a definition would be acceptable only in case

$$-1 \leqslant \frac{\mathbf{x} \cdot \mathbf{y}}{\|\mathbf{x}\| \, \|\mathbf{y}\|} \leqslant 1 \tag{60}$$

The inequalities (60) are indeed true for n-space, since it can be shown that the Schwarz inequality (Theorem 7.20)

$$|\mathbf{x} \cdot \mathbf{y}| \leqslant \|\mathbf{x}\| \, \|\mathbf{y}\| \tag{61}$$

holds in n-space, and (60) is a consequence of (61).

Accordingly, if $\mathbf{x}$ and $\mathbf{y}$ are nonzero vectors in euclidean n-space E_n, we define $\measuredangle(\mathbf{x, y})$ to be the number θ for which

$$\cos \theta = \frac{\mathbf{x} \cdot \mathbf{y}}{\|\mathbf{x}\| \, \|\mathbf{y}\|} \qquad 0 \leqslant \theta \leqslant \pi \tag{62}$$

We read the symbols $\measuredangle(\mathbf{x, y})$ as "the angle between $\mathbf{x}$ and $\mathbf{y}$." If either $\mathbf{x}$ or $\mathbf{y}$ is **0**, we define $\cos \theta$ to be 0.

Orthogonal vectors   Two vectors in E_n are said to be **orthogonal** or perpendicular in case the cosine of the "angle between the vectors" is zero. From the definition of the preceding paragraph, it follows that the zero vector is orthogonal to any vector, and that

$$\mathbf{x} \text{ and } \mathbf{y} \text{ are orthogonal} \iff \mathbf{x} \cdot \mathbf{y} = 0 \tag{63}$$

A **plane** in n-space is defined to be the set of all points satisfying an equation of the form

$$\mathbf{a} \cdot (\mathbf{r} - \mathbf{r_1}) = 0$$

for fixed $\mathbf{a}$ and $\mathbf{r_1}$ (compare with Theorems 7.18 and 8.26).

EXERCISES

1. Using the field properties of real numbers, verify that the set of all n-tuples $\mathbf{x} = \langle x_1, x_2, \ldots, x_n \rangle$ with addition defined by (56) and scalar multiplication defined by (57) has the properties (i) to (viii).

2. Using the formula $d(\mathbf{x}, \mathbf{y}) = \|\mathbf{x} - \mathbf{y}\|$, verify that the triangle in E_4 with vertices $P_1(-1, 7, -3, 0)$, $P_2(3, 0, -3, 1)$, and $P_3(4, 7, -3, 5)$ is isosceles.

3. Find a vector in E_4 which is orthogonal to the vectors $\mathbf{x} = \langle 0, 0, 3, 1 \rangle$, $\mathbf{y} = \langle 2, -3, 0, -1 \rangle$, and $\mathbf{z} = \langle -1, 2, 1, 1 \rangle$ and which has 0 for its second coordinate. $\langle\ 0, 1, 1, -3\ \rangle$

4. As you progress in your study of mathematics you will observe that mathematical entities other than ordered pairs, ordered triples, and n-tuples are called vectors. Indeed, a (abstract linear) *vector space* V over a field F is any set of objects with members $\mathbf{x}, \mathbf{y}, \mathbf{z}, \ldots$ called vectors with an operation called *addition* for which properties (i) to (iv) hold (with V for V_n), and with an operation called *scalar multiplication* for which properties (v) to (viii) hold. Notable among such vector spaces is the *space of functions* $\mathbf{f}, \mathbf{g}, \mathbf{h}$, and so forth, all with a common domain D. In this space of (real) functions (over the real field), *addition* of any two functions (with domain D)

Space of functions

$$\mathbf{f} = \{(x, y) \mid y = f(x)\} \qquad \text{and} \qquad \mathbf{g} = \{(x, y) \mid y = g(x)\}$$

is defined by

$$\mathbf{f} + \mathbf{g} = \{(x, y) \mid y = f(x) + g(x)\} \tag{*}$$

and *scalar multiplication* is defined by

$$k\mathbf{x} = \{(x, y) \mid y = kf(x)\} \tag{**}$$

Here k is any real number. Using the definitions (*) and (**), show (using the field properties of real numbers) that the properties (i) to (viii) hold for this space of real functions.

| APPENDIX

VALUES OF SINES, COSINES, AND TANGENTS

ANGLE, DEGREES	SINE	COSINE	TANGENT	ANGLE, DEGREES	SINE	COSINE	TANGENT
1	0.0175	1.00	0.0175	45	0.707	0.707	1.00
2	0.0349	0.999	0.0349	46	0.719	0.695	1.04
3	0.0523	0.999	0.0524	47	0.731	0.682	1.07
4	0.0698	0.998	0.0699	48	0.743	0.669	1.11
5	0.0872	0.996	0.0875	49	0.755	0.656	1.15
6	0.105	0.995	0.105	50	0.766	0.643	1.19
7	0.122	0.993	0.123	51	0.777	0.629	1.23
8	0.139	0.990	0.141	52	0.788	0.616	1.28
9	0.156	0.988	0.158	53	0.799	0.602	1.33
10	0.174	0.985	0.176	54	0.809	0.588	1.38
11	0.191	0.982	0.194	55	0.819	0.574	1.43
12	0.208	0.978	0.213	56	0.829	0.559	1.48
13	0.225	0.974	0.231	57	0.839	0.545	1.54
14	0.242	0.970	0.249	58	0.848	0.530	1.60
15	0.259	0.966	0.268	59	0.857	0.515	1.66
16	0.276	0.961	0.287	60	0.866	0.500	1.73
17	0.292	0.956	0.306	61	0.875	0.485	1.80
18	0.309	0.951	0.325	62	0.883	0.469	1.88
19	0.326	0.946	0.344	63	0.891	0.454	1.96
20	0.342	0.940	0.364	64	0.899	0.438	2.05
21	0.358	0.934	0.384	65	0.906	0.423	2.14
22	0.375	0.927	0.404	66	0.914	0.407	2.25
23	0.391	0.921	0.424	67	0.921	0.391	2.36
24	0.407	0.914	0.445	68	0.927	0.375	2.48
25	0.423	0.906	0.466	69	0.934	0.358	2.61
26	0.438	0.899	0.488	70	0.940	0.342	2.75
27	0.454	0.891	0.510	71	0.946	0.326	2.90
28	0.469	0.883	0.532	72	0.951	0.309	3.08
29	0.485	0.875	0.554	73	0.956	0.292	3.27
30	0.500	0.866	0.577	74	0.961	0.276	3.49
31	0.515	0.857	0.601	75	0.966	0.259	3.73
32	0.530	0.848	0.625	76	0.970	0.242	4.01
33	0.545	0.839	0.649	77	0.974	0.225	4.33
34	0.559	0.829	0.675	78	0.978	0.208	4.70
35	0.574	0.819	0.700	79	0.982	0.191	5.14
36	0.588	0.809	0.727	80	0.985	0.174	5.67
37	0.602	0.799	0.754	81	0.988	0.156	6.31
38	0.616	0.788	0.781	82	0.990	0.139	7.12
39	0.629	0.777	0.810	83	0.993	0.122	8.14
40	0.643	0.766	0.839	84	0.995	0.105	9.51
41	0.656	0.755	0.869	85	0.996	0.0872	11.4
42	0.669	0.743	0.900	86	0.998	0.0698	14.3
43	0.682	0.731	0.933	87	0.999	0.0523	19.1
44	0.695	0.719	0.966	88	0.999	0.0349	28.6
45	0.707	0.707	1.00	89	1.00	0.0175	57.3

ANSWERS TO ODD-NUMBERED EXERCISES

1. (a) T; (b) F; (c) T; (d) T; (e) T; (f) F.
3. $\{a, b\}$, $\{a\}$, $\{b\}$, $\emptyset$. All except $\{a, b\}$.
5. $\{1, 2, 3\}$, $\{1, 2, 4\}$.
7. (a) $\emptyset$; (b) $\{1, 2, 3, 4, 5, 6, 7, 8, 9\}$; (c) $\{a, b, c, 1, 2, 3\}$; (d) $\{a\}$.
9. $A \cap B = \{3, 4\}$; $A \cap C = \{4\}$; $B \cap C = \{4, 5, 6\}$; $A \cup B = \{1, 2, 3, 4, 5, 6\}$;
   $A \cup C = \{1, 2, 3, 4, 5, 6, 7\}$; $B \cup C = \{3, 4, 5, 6, 7\}$.
11. $A \cap B = \{c, d, e\}$; $A \cup B = \{a, b, c, d, e, f, g\}$.

1. No.   3. No.   5. Yes.
7. There is at least one rational number whose square is 2.
9. If $a \neq 0$ and $b \neq 0$, then $a \cdot b \neq 0$.
11. (a) $\{1, 2, 3, 4, 5, 6, 7, 8, 9, \ldots, 23\}$; (b) $\{1, 2, 3, 4\}$.
13. (a) $\{3\}$; (b) $\emptyset$.   15. $\{6\}$; $\emptyset$.   17. $\{-2, -1, 0, 1\}$.
19. I.   21. $\{7\}$.   23. $\{-2, -1, 1, 2\}$.

1. $\overline{P_1 P_2} = 4$; $|P_1 P_2| = 4$.   3. $\overline{P_1 P_2} = -11$; $|P_1 P_2| = 11$.
5. $\overline{P_1 P_2} = -3k$; $|P_1 P_2| = 3k$.   7. $\overline{P_1 P_2} = -2$; $|P_1 P_2| = 2$.
9. $P_1(4)$; $P_2(-4)$.   11. $P(2)$.

Sec. 1.5, pages 17–18

1. The points between $P_1(3)$ and $P_2(5)$, including $P_2(5)$.

3. The points $P_1(-4)$ and $P_2(4)$.

5. The points $P_1(-1)$ and $P_2(3)$.

7. The points between $P_1(-3)$ and $P_2(7)$, including $P_1(-3)$ and $P_2(7)$.

9. The points to the left of $P_1(3)$ and the points to the right of $P_2(5)$.

11. (a) $\{x \mid x > 2\}$; (b) $\{x \mid -3 \leqslant x < 4\} = \{x \mid x \geqslant -3 \text{ and } x < 4\}$; (c) $\{x \mid |x| = 5\} = \{x \mid x = 5 \text{ or } x = -5\}$; (d) $\{x \mid |x - 1| \geqslant 5\} = \{x \mid x \leqslant -4 \text{ or } x \geqslant 6\}$.

19. $(-1; 4)$.   **21.** $[2; +\infty)$.

23. $A \cap B = \{x \mid 3 \leqslant x \leqslant 5\} = [3; 5]$; $A \cup B = \{x \mid -2 < x \leqslant 11\} = (-2; 11]$.

25. $A \cap B = \{x \mid 9 < x \leqslant 11\} = (9; 11]$; $A \cup B = (-\infty; -3) \cup (6; +\infty)$.

Sec. 1.6, pages 20–21

1. $(1, 1), (1, 2), (1, 3), (2, 1), (2, 2), (2, 3), (3, 1), (3, 2), (3, 3)$.

3. Domain $R_1 = \{1, 2\}$, domain $R_2 = \{1\}$, domain $R_3 = \{2\}$; range $R_1 = \{1, 2\}$, range $R_2 = \{2\}$, range $R_3 = \{1\}$.

5. (a) $R_1 = \{(1, 1), (2, 2), (3, 3), (4, 4)\}$; (b) $R_2 = \{(1, 2), (1, 3), (1, 4), (2, 3), (2, 4), (3, 4)\}$; (c) $R_3 = \{(2, 4), (3, 3), (4, 2)\}$; (d) $R_4 = \{(2, 1), (3, 1), (3, 2), (4, 1), (4, 2), (4, 3)\}$.

7. $U \times U = \{(1, 1), (1, 2), (1, 3), (1, 4), (1, 5), (2, 1), (2, 2), (2, 3), (2, 4), (2, 5), (3, 1), (3, 2), (3, 3), (3, 4), (3, 5), (4, 1), (4, 2), (4, 3), (4, 4), (4, 5), (5, 1), (5, 2), (5, 3), (5, 4), (5, 5)\}$.

9. Domain of $R_1 = \{1, 2, 3, 4, 5\}$, range of $R_1 = \{1, 2, 3, 4, 5\}$; domain of $R_2 = \{2, 3, 4, 5\}$, range of $R_2 = \{1, 2, 3, 4\}$; domain of $R_3 = \{1, 2\}$, range of $R_3 = \{1, 4\}$.

11. $U \times V = \{(1, 1), (1, 2), (1, 3), (1, 4), (2, 1), (2, 2), (2, 3), (2, 4), (3, 1), (3, 2), (3, 3), (3, 4)\}$.

13. Domain of $R_1 = \{1, 2, 3\}$, range of $R_1 = \{2, 3, 4\}$; domain of $R_2 = \{1, 2, 3\}$, range of $R_2 = \{1, 2, 3\}$; domain of $R_3 = \{1, 2\}$, range of $R_3 = \{3, 4\}$.

Sec. 1.8, pages 30–32

1. $E(4, 2), F(-4, 5), G(-2, -3), H(2, -2), I(-5, 0), J(0, -5)$.

5. $P(x_1, y_1)$ is in quadrant II $\iff$ $x_1 < 0$ and $y_1 > 0$; $P(x_1, y_1)$ is in quadrant III $\iff$ $x_1 < 0$ and $y_1 < 0$; $P(x_1, y_1)$ is in quadrant IV $\iff$ $x_1 > 0$ and $y_1 < 0$.

7. $(0, 0), (a, 0), (a, a), (0, a)$.

9. (a) $R_1 = \{(1, 1), (2, 2), (3, 3), (4, 4), (5, 5), (6, 6)\}$; (b) $R_2 = \{(1, 5), (2, 4), (3, 3), (4, 2), (5, 1)\}$; (c) $R_3 = \{(1, 4), (2, 5), (3, 6)\}$; (d) $R_4 = \{(1, 1), (4, 2)\}$.

11. Domain $= \{3\}$; range $= (-\infty; 0)$.   **13.** Domain $= [-1; 3]$; range $= [-2; 6]$.

15. Domain $= (-\infty; +\infty)$; range $= (-\infty; +\infty)$.

17. Domain $= \{4\}$; range $= (-\infty; +\infty)$.   **19.** Domain $= \{4\}$; range $= \{5\}$.

21. Domain $= (-\infty; +\infty)$; range $= [0; +\infty)$.

23. Domain $= (-\infty; +\infty)$; range $= [0; +\infty)$.

25. Domain $= (-\infty; +\infty)$; range $= [3; +\infty)$.

27. Range $= (-\infty; 0) \cup (0; +\infty)$.

29. $(1, 4)$.   **31.** (a, b).

33. (a) Graph of R_1 is the union of the graphs of $\{(x, y) \mid y = x^2\}$ and $\{(x, y) \mid x = 2\}$; (b) graph of R_2 is the intersection of the graphs of $\{(x, y) \mid y = x^2\}$ and $\{(x, y) \mid y = 4\}$, the point $(2, 4)$, and the point $(-2, 4)$; (c) graph of R_3 is the same as the graph of R_2.

35. Not a function. Domain $= Re$; range $= \{-2, 2\}$.

37. A function. Domain $= [-5; 5]$; range $= [0; 5]$.

39. Not a function.

Sec. 2.4, pages 41–42

1. (a) $M_1(3, 0)$, $M_2(4, 0)$, $\overline{M_1M_2} = 1$, $|M_1M_2| = 1$; $N_1(0, -2)$, $N_2(0, 5)$, $\overline{N_1N_2} = 7$, $|N_1N_2| = 7$. (b) $M_1(6, 0)$, $M_2(-3, 0)$, $\overline{M_1M_2} = -9$, $|M_1M_2| = 9$; $N_1(0, 8)$, $N_2(0, -1)$, $\overline{N_1N_2} = -9$, $|N_1N_2| = 9$.

3. (a) 10; (b) $\sqrt{37}$; (c) $4\sqrt{10}$; (d) $\sqrt{85}$; (e) $2\sqrt{10}$; (f) $\sqrt{2(a^2 + b^2)}$.

5. (a) Scalene; (b) isosceles; (c) equilateral; (d) isosceles; (e) the triangle in each of parts a and d is a right triangle.

13. Not on the same line.

15. On the same line.   **19.** $(2, 5)$.   **21.** $(-2, -\frac{2}{3})$; $(3, 3\frac{2}{3})$.

Sec. 2.6, pages 46–47

1. 73.   **3.** $\frac{27}{2}$.   **7.** 25.

11. No; area $P_1P_2P_3 = 3$.

13. Det is a function whose domain is $\mathscr{A}_2$, the set of all arrays like (10), and whose range is Re.

Sec. 2.9, pages 57–59

1. Domain $= [-3; 1]$, range $= [-4; 0]$; x intercept is -1, y intercepts are $-2 - \sqrt{3}$ and $-2 + \sqrt{3}$.

3. Domain $= [-\sqrt{5}; \sqrt{5}]$, range $= [-\sqrt{5}; \sqrt{5}]$; x intercepts are $\sqrt{5}$ and $-\sqrt{5}$, y intercepts are $\sqrt{5}$ and $-\sqrt{5}$.

5. (a) The graph of R_1 is the union of the graphs of $\{(x, y) \mid x^2 + y^2 = 5\}$ and $\{(x, y) \mid x = 1\}$. (b) The graph of R_2 is the intersection of the graphs of $\{(x, y) \mid x^2 + y^2 = 5\}$ and $\{(x, y) \mid x = 1\}$. $R_2 = \{(1, 2), (1, -2)\}$.

7. $(x - 5)^2 + y^2 = 4$; $x^2 + y^2 - 10x + 21 = 0$.

9. $(x + 3)^2 + (y + 4)^2 = \frac{4}{9}$; $x^2 + y^2 + 6x + 8y + \frac{221}{9} = 0$.

11. $(x + 2)^2 + (y - 3)^2 = 37$; $x^2 + y^2 + 4x - 6y - 24 = 0$.

13. Circle; center at $(0, -5)$, radius $= 10$.   **15.** Circle; center at $(-\frac{5}{6}, 1)$, radius $= \frac{7}{6}$.

17. Null set.   **19.** Circle; center at $(\frac{1}{6}, \frac{1}{3})$, radius $= \frac{1}{6}\sqrt{17}$.

21. $x^2 + y^2 + 2x + 4y = 20$; center at $(-1, -2)$, radius $= 5$.

23. $x^2 + y^2 - 4x - 4y - 8 = 0$.   **25.** $x^2 + y^2 - 12x + 4y - 41 = 0$.

27. The x intercepts are $5\sqrt{3}$ and $-5\sqrt{3}$; the y intercepts are 5 and -15.

29. Domain $= [-5; 5]$, range $= [-5; 5]$; R is not a function.

31. Domain $= [-10; -5]$, range $= [-5\sqrt{3}; 5\sqrt{3}]$; R is not a function.

33. $R = \{(x, y) \mid x^2 + y^2 = 100, y \in [5\sqrt{2}; 5]\}$.

35. Angle with vertex at $(3, 4)$ and initial side along the segment from $(3, 4)$ to $(3, 0)$.

Sec. 2.11, pages 65–66

1. Domain $= (-3; 3)$; range $= (-3; 3)$.   **3.** Domain $= [-4; 4]$; range $= [-4; 4]$.

5. (a) $x^2 + y^2 = 49$; (b) $x^2 + y^2 < 49$; (c) $x^2 + y^2 > 49$; (d) $(x - 3)^2 + (y - 4)^2 > 36$.

7. Domain $= [3; 4]$; range $= [-4; 4]$.   **11.** $(x - \frac{2}{3})^2 + (y - \frac{1}{3})^2 = \frac{5}{9}$.

13. $x^2 + y^2 + x - 10y - 30 = 0$.   **15.** $5x^2 + 5y^2 - x - 17y + 8 = 0$.

Sec. 3.1, pages 75–76

1. (*a*) $\alpha \doteq 18°$; (*b*) $\alpha \doteq 162°$.

3. $m = 2$; $\alpha \doteq 63°$.   **5.** $m = -2$; $\alpha \doteq 117°$.

7. $m = -\frac{4}{5}$; $\alpha \doteq 141°$.   **9.** Perpendicular.

11. Parallel.   **25.** Yes; yes.

31. $m = -1$.   **33.** $m = -\frac{3}{2}$.

Sec. 3.2, pages 83–86

1. $y = 4$.   **3.** $x = -5$.

9. $2x - 3y - 12 = 0$.   **11.** $3x - 4y + 11 = 0$.

13. $3x - 5y + 18 = 0$.   **15.** $x\sqrt{3} + y - 4 - 3\sqrt{3} = 0$.

17. $x\sqrt{3} - y - 1 - 10\sqrt{13} = 0$.   **19.** $x - 8y + 25 = 0$.

21. $3x + 2y + 1 = 0$.   **23.** $2x + y + 3 = 0$.

25. x intercept is -2, y intercept is -5; $m = -\frac{5}{2}$.

27. x intercept is -7, y intercept is $-\frac{7}{2}$; $m = \frac{1}{2}$.

29. x intercept is -3, y intercept is -7; $m = -\frac{7}{3}$.

31. $3x - 2y + 1 = 0$.

33. $12x - 7y + 1 = 0$; yes; because the coordinates of the point satisfy the equation of the line.

35. $(\frac{11}{2}, \frac{9}{2})$.   **37.** $(3, -1)$.

39. $(3, \frac{1}{2})$.   **41.** (*a*) $x - 2y - 5 = 0$; (*b*) $2x + y + 5 = 0$.

45. x intercept is 0; y intercept is 0.

47. x intercept is $\frac{2}{3}$; y intercepts are 2 and -2.

49. x intercepts are -3, 4, and -4; y intercepts are 4 and -4.

51. Domain $= [1; 3]$; range $= [-\frac{4}{3}; 0]$.

53. Domain $= (-\infty; +\infty)$; range $= (-\infty; 2] \cup (4; +\infty)$.

55. $5x + 9y - 2 = 0$.

57. (*a*) $y = 0$, $3x + 2y - 12 = 0$, $3x - y + 6 = 0$; (*b*) $x = 0$, $2x - 3y + 4 = 0$, $x + 3y - 4 = 0$; (*c*) $3x - 4y + 6 = 0$, $3x + 5y - 12 = 0$, $6x + y - 6 = 0$.

59. (*a*) $2cx + (a + b)y - ac - bc = 0$, $cx + (2a - b)y - ac = 0$, $cx + (2b - a)y - bc = 0$; (*b*) $x = 0$, $bx - cy - ab = 0$, $ax - cy - ab = 0$; (*c*) $x = (a + b)/2$, $2ax - 2cy = a^2 - c^2$, $2bx - 2cy = b^2 - c^2$.

Sec. 3.3, pages 91–92

1. Above, on, below.   **3.** Above, below, above.

Sec. 3.4, pages 94–95

1. $d = 7$.   **3.** $d = \frac{1}{2}$.

5. $d = \frac{134}{13}$.   **7.** $d = \frac{66}{13}$.

9. $d = 2$.   **11.** $x + 7y + 3 = 0$; $7x - y - 17 = 0$.

13. $\frac{9}{5}$.   **15.** 35.

Sec. 3.5, page 97

1. Radical axis: $y = x$; points of intersection $P_1(0, 0)$, $P_2(1, 1)$.

3. $(5, 3)$, $(-3, -5)$.

Sec. 3.6, pages 107–108

1. $\dfrac{1}{\sqrt{5}}, \dfrac{2}{\sqrt{5}}$.

3. $-\dfrac{8}{\sqrt{89}}, \dfrac{5}{\sqrt{89}}$.

5. $m = -A/B$; $(-B, A)$ is a set of direction numbers; $\dfrac{-B}{\sqrt{A^2 + B^2}}, \dfrac{A}{\sqrt{A^2 + B^2}}$ is a set of direction cosines.

9. $(2, 0)$.

11. Lines are coincident; no unique solution.

13. $(0, k)$, where k is any nonzero real number.

15. $90°$. **17.** $45°$. **21.** $\tan \theta = 1$.

23. $\tan A = -\frac{5}{3}$; $\tan B = 4$; $\tan C = 1$.

Sec. 3.7, page 111

1. $x = 2 + 3t$; $y = 3 + 4t$. **3.** $x = 3 - 3t$; $y = 0 + 4t$.

5. Direction numbers $(-6, 9)$; point $(8, -2)$.

7. Direction numbers $(0, 1)$; point $(2, 0)$.

9. (a) $m = -\frac{3}{2}$; (b) $m = \frac{1}{2}$; (c) slope not defined; (d) $m = -1$.

11. $3x - 4y - 10 = 0$.

13. $P(-3, 5)$. **15.** $P(3, 0)$.

17. $\cos \theta = 3/\sqrt{885}$, $\sin \theta = 24/\sqrt{885}$, $\tan \theta = 8$.

Sec. 3.8, pages 113–114

1. $x - y + 2 = 0$. **3.** $4x + y = 0$.

5. $2x + y + 11 = 0$. **7.** $13x + 5y - 1 = 0$.

11. $k = -8$. **13.** $29x + 17y + 9 = 0$; $13x - 31y + 33 = 0$.

15. $x - y = 0$; $7x - y = 38$; $x - 7y + 38 = 0$.

Sec. 3.9, page 116

1. $6x - 5y + 2 = 0$. **3.** $5x - 7y = 0$.

5. $y = -3x + t$. **7.** $\frac{1}{2}x + y/t = 1$.

9. $y - 4 = m(x - 3)$.

Sec. 4.2, pages 123–124

1. Vertex $(0, 0)$, focus $(4, 0)$, length of latus rectum $= 16$, end points of latus rectum $(4, 8)$ and $(4, -8)$, equation of directrix $x = -4$; symmetric with respect to the x axis; domain $= [0; +\infty)$, range $= (-\infty; +\infty)$.

3. Vertex $(0, 0)$, focus $(0, \frac{5}{2})$, length of latus rectum $= 10$, end points of latus rectum $(-5, \frac{5}{2})$ and $(5, \frac{5}{2})$, equation of directrix $y = -\frac{5}{2}$; symmetric with respect to the y axis; domain $= (-\infty; +\infty)$, range $= [0; +\infty)$.

5. Vertex $(0, 0)$, focus $(0, -\frac{5}{12})$, length of latus rectum $= \frac{5}{3}$, end points of latus rectum $(-\frac{5}{6}, -\frac{5}{12})$ and $(\frac{5}{6}, -\frac{5}{12})$; symmetric with respect to the y axis; domain $= (-\infty; +\infty)$, range $= (-\infty; 0]$.

7. Vertex $(0, 0)$, focus $(-\frac{3}{2}, 0)$, length of latus rectum $= 6$, end points of latus rectum $(-\frac{3}{2}, 3)$ and $(-\frac{3}{2}, -3)$, equation of directrix $x = \frac{3}{2}$; symmetric with respect to the x axis; domain $= (-\infty; 0]$, range $= (-\infty; +\infty)$.

9. $y^2 = 28x$. **11.** $x^2 = 8y$.

13. $y^2 = -8x$. **15.** $x^2 = 16y$.

19. $x^2 = -12y$.

Sec. 4.3, pages 126–127

1. Domain $= (-\infty; +\infty)$; range $= (-\infty; +\infty)$.

3. Domain $= (-\infty; +\infty)$; range $= (-\infty; +\infty)$.

5. Domain $= (0; 8)$; range $= (-2; 4)$.

7. Domain $= (-\infty; +\infty)$; range $= (-\infty; +\infty)$.

9. Domain $= \{0, 1\}$; range $= \{0, 3\}$.

11. Domain $= (-\infty; +\infty)$; range $= (-\infty; +\infty)$.

Sec. 4.4, pages 133–134

1. $(y + 1)^2 = 4(x - 2)$, vertex $(2, -1)$, focus $(3, -1)$, end points of latus rectum $(3, 1)$ and $(3, -3)$, equation of directrix $x = 1$, equation of axis $y = -1$.

3. $x^2 = -20(y - 2)$, vertex $(0, 2)$, focus $(0, -3)$.

5. $(x - \frac{2}{3})^2 = 2(y - \frac{10}{9})$, vertex $(\frac{2}{3}, \frac{10}{9})$, focus $(\frac{2}{3}, \frac{29}{18})$.

7. $y = x^2 - x$. **9.** $(x - 3)^2 = -4(y - 2)$.

11. $(0, 0)$, $(4, 4)$. **13.** $(-2, 2)$, $(2, 2)$.

15. (a) Since R_1 is the union of the relations $\{(x, y) \mid y^2 = 4x\}$ and $\{(x, y) \mid x^2 = 4y\}$, the graph of R_1 consists of the parabola which is the graph of $\{(x, y) \mid y^2 = 4x\}$ and the parabola which is the graph of $\{(x, y) \mid x^2 = 4y\}$. (b) Since R_2 is the intersection of the relations $\{(x, y) \mid y^2 = 4x\}$ and $\{(x, y) \mid x^2 = 4y\}$, the graph of R_2 consists of the points of intersection of the parabolas specified in (a).

17. $x^2 - 4xy + 4y^2 + 40x + 20y - 100 = 0$; vertex $(2, 1)$.

19. $y = -x^2 + 2$. **21.** $y = x^2 - 2x + 1$.

23. $y = x^2 - 2x - 1$. **25.** $x^2 = 4y$.

29. Greatest value of y is 72; highest point is $(6, 72)$.

31. Least value of y is 4; lowest point is $(3, 4)$.

Sec. 4.5, pages 143–145

1. Center $(0, 0)$, vertices $(0, 5)$ and $(0, -5)$, foci $(0, 3)$ and $(0, -3)$, end points of minor axis $(4, 0)$ and $(-4, 0)$, length of latus rectum $= \frac{32}{5}$, end points of latera recta $(-\frac{16}{5}, 3)$, $(\frac{16}{5}, 3)$, $(-\frac{16}{5}, -3)$, and $(\frac{16}{5}, -3)$; domain $= [-4; 4]$, range $= [-5; 5]$.

3. Center $(0, 0)$, vertices $(0, 5)$ and $(0, -5)$, foci $(0, \sqrt{21})$ and $(0, -\sqrt{21})$, end points of minor axis $(2, 0)$ and $(-2, 0)$, length of latus rectum $= \frac{8}{5}$, end points of latera recta $(\frac{4}{5}, \sqrt{21})$, $(-\frac{4}{5}, \sqrt{21})$, $(-\frac{4}{5}, -\sqrt{21})$, and $(\frac{4}{5}, -\sqrt{21})$; domain $= [-2; 2]$, range $= [-5; 5]$.

5. Center $(0, 0)$, vertices $(2, 0)$ and $(-2, 0)$, foci $(1, 0)$ and $(-1, 0)$, end points of minor axis $(0, \sqrt{3})$ and $(0, -\sqrt{3})$, length of latus rectum $= 3$, end points of latera recta $(1, \frac{3}{2})$, $(-1, \frac{3}{2})$, $(-1, -\frac{3}{2})$, and $(1, -\frac{3}{2})$; domain $= [-2; 2]$, range $= [-\sqrt{3}; \sqrt{3}]$.

7. $\frac{1}{16}x^2 + \frac{1}{25}y^2 = 1$. **9.** $49x^2 + 16y^2 = 784$.

11. $\frac{1}{64}x^2 + \frac{1}{12}y^2 = 1$. **13.** $7x^2 + 3y^2 = 55$.

15. $3x^2 + 4y^2 = 108$. **17.** $x^2 + y^2 = 25$.

19. Ellipse with equation $(x - 1)^2/9 + (y + 2)^2/25 = 1$. Center $(1, -2)$, vertices $(1, 3)$ and $(1, -7)$, foci $(1, 2)$ and $(1, -6)$.

21. Point.

23. Null set.

25. Ellipse.

27. $(x + 1)^2/9 + (y + 1)^2/25 = 1$.

29. Domain $= (-\infty; +\infty)$; range $= (-\infty; +\infty)$.

31. Domain $= (-\infty; +\infty)$; range $= (-\infty; +\infty)$.

33. Domain $= (-\frac{12}{5}; \frac{12}{5})$; range $= (3; 5)$.

35. $9(x - 3)^2 + 5(y - 2)^2 = 180$.

Sec. 4.7, pages 154–156

1. Center $(0, 0)$, vertices $(4, 0)$ and $(-4, 0)$, foci $(2\sqrt{7}, 0)$ and $(-2\sqrt{7}, 0)$, length of latus rectum $= 6$; end points of latera recta $(2\sqrt{7}, 3)$, $(-2\sqrt{7}, 3)$, $(-2\sqrt{7}, -3)$, and $(2\sqrt{7}, -3)$; equations of asymptotes $y = \pm(\sqrt{3}/2)x$; domain $= (-\infty; -4] \cup [4; +\infty)$, range $= (-\infty; +\infty)$.

3. Center $(0, 0)$, vertices $(0, \sqrt{5})$ and $(0, -\sqrt{5})$, foci $(0, 3)$ and $(0, -3)$, length of latus rectum $= 8/\sqrt{5}$; end points of latera recta $(4/\sqrt{5}, 3)$, $(-4/\sqrt{5}, 3)$, $(-4/\sqrt{5}, -3)$, and $(4/\sqrt{5}, -3)$; equations of asymptotes $y = \pm(\sqrt{5}/2)x$; domain $= (-\infty; +\infty)$, range $= (-\infty; -\sqrt{5}] \cup [\sqrt{5}; +\infty)$.

5. Center $(0, 0)$, vertices $(3, 0)$ and $(-3, 0)$, foci $(\sqrt{13}, 0)$ and $(-\sqrt{13}, 0)$, length of latus rectum $= \frac{8}{3}$; end points of latera recta $(\sqrt{13}, \frac{4}{3})$, $(-\sqrt{13}, \frac{4}{3})$, $(-\sqrt{13}, -\frac{4}{3})$, and $(\sqrt{13}, -\frac{4}{3})$; equations of asymptotes $y = \pm\frac{2}{3}x$; domain $= (-\infty; -3] \cup [3; +\infty)$, range $= (-\infty; +\infty)$.

7. $\frac{1}{9}x^2 - \frac{16}{81}y^2 = 1$.

9. $5x^2 - 2y^2 = 80$.

11. $4x^2 - 5y^2 = 16$.

13. $9x^2 - 16y^2 = 144$.

15. $(x + 1)^2/16 - (y - 3)^2/25 = 1$.

17. $\frac{1}{16}x^2 - \frac{1}{20}y^2 = 1$.

19. Hyperbola with equation $(x - 2)^2/4 - (y + 3)^2/5 = -1$; equations of asymptotes $y + 3 = \pm(\sqrt{5}/2)(x - 2)$.

21. Hyperbola with equation $(x - 1)^2/9 - (y + 1)^2/3 = 1$; equations of asymptotes $y + 1 = \pm(1/\sqrt{3})(x - 1)$.

23. Two lines with equations $x + 2y - 1 = 0$ and $x - 2y - 1 = 0$.

25. Two lines with equation $(x - 1)^2/4 - (y + 3)^2/9 = 0$.

33. Vertices $(-a/\sqrt{2}, a/\sqrt{2})$ and $(a/\sqrt{2}, -a/\sqrt{2})$.

35. (a) $xy = 12$; (b) $xy = 35$.

37. Domain $= (-\infty; +\infty)$; range $= (-\infty; +\infty)$.

41. $c = 6{,}000$.

43. $x'y' = 4$.

Sec. 4.8, page 161

1. $y^2 = 2x$.

3. $y = \frac{1}{8}(x - 3)^2 - 4$.

5. $(x - 3)^2/16 + \frac{1}{9}y^2 = 1$.

7. $x = 1 - 2y^2$.

9. $y = 12/x$.

Sec. 5.1, pages 166–167

1. Line with equation $2x + y = 8$.

3. Parabola with equation $(x - 4)^2 = -16(y - 1)$.

5. Ellipse with equation $9x^2 + 25y^2 - 225 = 0$.

7. (a) Domain $= (-\infty; +\infty)$, range $= [-4; +\infty)$; (b) domain $= (-\infty; +\infty)$, range $= (-4; +\infty)$; (c) domain $= (-1; 3)$, range $= (-4; 0)$.

Sec. 5.2, pages 172–173

1. $5y'^2 - x'^2 = 16$.   **3.** $\frac{1}{4}y'^2 - \frac{1}{36}x'^2 = 1$.

5. $x'^2 - y'^2 = 8$.   **7.** $y''^2 = 3x''$.

9. $x'^2 + 12y' = 0$.   **11.** $4x''^2 + y''^2 = 16$.

13. $10x''^2 - 15y''^2 - 359 = 0$.

Sec. 5.3, page 176

1. $\Delta = 0$; $(x - 2y + 6)(3x + 26 - 2) = 0$; two intersecting lines.

3. $\Delta = -48$.

5. $\Delta = 0$; $(2x - y - 2)(3x + 2y - 1) = 0$; two intersecting lines.

7. $\Delta = 0$; $\left(x + \frac{3 + \sqrt{3}i}{2}\, y - \frac{1}{2} + \frac{\sqrt{3}}{2}\, i\right)\left(x + \frac{3 - \sqrt{3}i}{2}\, y - \frac{1}{2} - \frac{\sqrt{3}}{2}\, i\right)$; the point $(2, -1)$.

Sec. 5.4, page 183

1. $B^2 - 4AC = 5 > 0$, $\Delta \neq 0$; hyperbola.

3. $B^2 - 4AC = 1 > 0$, $\Delta \neq 0$; hyperbola.

5. $B^2 - 4AC < 0$, $\Delta \neq 0$; ellipse.

7. $B^2 - 4AC = 0$, $\Delta \neq 0$; parabola.

9. $B^2 - 4AC = 0$, $\Delta = 0$; two parallel (coincident) lines, L: $3x - 2y - 2 = 0$.

11. $B^2 - 4AC < 0$, $\Delta \neq 0$; ellipse.   **13.** $(x'')^2 - (y'')^2 = 9/(8\sqrt{2})$.

Sec. 6.1, page 188

3. $\frac{1}{15}\pi$.   **5.** $\frac{2}{9}\pi$.   **7.** $108°$.   **9.** $-270°$.

15. The curve appears to be a circle.

Sec. 6.3, page 201

1. Cardioid.   **3.** Cardioid.

5. 4-leaved rose.   **7.** Lemniscate.

9. Circle with center at the origin and radius 4.

11. Line through the origin.

Sec. 6.4, pages 208–209

1. $(0, -3)$; $(-3, 3)$; $(3, 0)$; $(-2, 2\sqrt{3})$.

3. $[-12, \frac{1}{6}\pi]$ and $[12, \frac{7}{6}\pi]$; $[3, \pi]$ and $[-3, 0]$; $[4\sqrt{2}, -\frac{1}{4}\pi]$ and $[4\sqrt{2}, \frac{7}{4}\pi]$; $[3\sqrt{2}, \frac{1}{4}\pi]$ and $[-3\sqrt{2}, \frac{5}{4}\pi]$.

5. $r\cos\theta = 4$.   **7.** $r = 4$.

9. $r^2(\cos^2\theta + 4\sin^2\theta) = 4$.   **11.** $x^2 + y^2 = 9$.

13. $x^3 = 9y^2$.   **15.** $2x + 3y = 5$.

17. $x^2 = 16 - 8y$.

Sec. 6.5, pages 212–213

1. $r\cos\theta = 6$.   **3.** $r\sin\theta + 2 = 0$.

5. $r + 12\cos\theta = 0$.   **7.** $r - 8\cos\theta = 0$.

9. $[\frac{7}{2}, 0]$, $\frac{7}{2}$.   **11.** $[3, \frac{1}{2}\pi]$, 3.

Sec. 6.6, page 219

1. $e = \frac{1}{2}$; ellipse.
3. $e = \frac{1}{3}$; ellipse.
5. $e = 1$; parabola.
7. $e = \frac{1}{2}$; ellipse.
9. $r = 6/(1 - \cos \theta)$.

Sec. 6.7, pages 222–223

3.

θ	$\frac{19}{6}\pi$	$\frac{10}{3}\pi$	$\frac{7}{2}\pi$	$\frac{11}{3}\pi$	$\frac{23}{6}\pi$	4π
0.10θ	0.995	1.047	1.100	1.152	12.04	12.57
r	9.9	11.1	12.6	14.2	16.0	18.1

Sec. 6.8, pages 229–230

5. O, $P_1[\frac{3}{2}, \frac{1}{3}\pi]$, $P_2[\frac{3}{2}, -\frac{1}{3}\pi]$; C_1 is a circle and C_2 is a cardioid.
7. O, $P_1[1, \frac{1}{2}\pi]$; C_1 is a circle and C_2 is a cardioid.
9. O, $P_1[1, \frac{1}{2}\pi]$, $P_2[1, -\frac{1}{2}\pi]$; C_1 and C_2 are cardioids.
11. O, $P_1[5\sqrt{2}, \frac{1}{4}\pi]$; C_1 and C_2 are circles.
13. O, $P_1[2, \frac{1}{3}\pi]$, $P_2[2, \frac{2}{3}\pi]$; C_1 is a limaçon and C_2 is a circle.
15. O, $P_1[\sqrt[4]{2}\,\sqrt{2}, \frac{1}{8}\pi]$, $P_2[\sqrt[4]{2}\,\sqrt{2}, \frac{9}{8}\pi]$; C_1 and C_2 are lemniscates.
17. O, $P_1[\frac{3}{2}\sqrt{2}, \frac{1}{6}\pi]$, $P_2[\frac{3}{2}\sqrt{2}, \frac{5}{6}\pi]$; C_1 is a lemniscate and C_2 is a circle.
19. O, $P_1[\frac{1}{4}\pi, \frac{1}{4}\pi]$, $P_2[\frac{5}{4}\pi, \frac{5}{4}\pi]$, $P_3[\frac{9}{4}\pi, \frac{9}{4}\pi]$, $P_4[-\frac{3}{4}\pi, -\frac{3}{4}\pi]$, $P_5[-\frac{7}{4}\pi, -\frac{7}{4}\pi]$.
21. O, $P_1[-\frac{1}{2}, \frac{1}{6}\pi]$, $P_2[-\frac{1}{2}, \frac{5}{6}\pi]$.

Sec. 7.2, pages 248–249

7. $\mathbf{v} = \langle -3, \ 4 \rangle$; $\cos \alpha - -\frac{3}{5}$, $\cos \beta = -\frac{4}{5}$.
9. $\mathbf{v} = \langle 1, 2 \rangle$; $\cos \alpha = 1/\sqrt{5}$, $\cos \beta = 2/\sqrt{5}$.
11. $-7/\sqrt{65}$.
13. $\mathbf{u} + \mathbf{v} = \langle 5, 6 \rangle$; $\|\mathbf{u}\| = 2\sqrt{2}$; $\|\mathbf{v}\| = 5$; $\|\mathbf{u} + \mathbf{v}\| = \sqrt{61}$.
15. $\mathbf{u} + \mathbf{v} = \langle 8, -4 \rangle$; $\|\mathbf{u}\| = \sqrt{29}$; $\|\mathbf{v}\| = \sqrt{13}$; $\|\mathbf{u} + \mathbf{v}\| = 4\sqrt{5}$.
17. $\langle 5, 6 \rangle \cdot (\langle x, y \rangle - \langle 3, 4 \rangle) = \mathbf{0}$.   21. $\|\langle x, y \rangle - \langle 2, 3 \rangle\| = 4$.
23. $\|\langle x, y \rangle\| = 5$.

Sec. 7.3, page 253

1. $P_1(3, 0)$, $P_2(5, 0)$, $P_3(0, 12)$, $P_4(0, 4)$; maximum value is 12, minimum value is 3.
3. $P_1(-10, 0)$, $P_2(0, 7)$, $P_3(\frac{25}{6}, \frac{17}{6})$; maximum value is $\frac{4}{3}$, minimum value is -10.
5. $P_1(0, 8)$, $P_2(5, 8)$, $P_3(5, 4)$, $P_4(2, 4)$, $P_5(0, 6)$; maximum value is 21, minimum value is 10.
7. 1,000 units to each customer yields \$3,960 maximum proceeds.

Sec. 7.4, page 256

1. $D_{F_1} = [0; +\infty)$, $D_{F_2} = Re$, $D_{F_1+F_2} = [0; +\infty)$.
3. $D_{F_1} = Re$, $D_{F_2} = Re$, $D_{F_1+F_2} = Re$.
5. $D_{F_1} = Re$, $D_{F_2} = (-\infty; 0) \cup (0; +\infty) = D_{F_1+F_2}$.

7. $D_{F_1} = Re$, $D_{F_2} = [0; 2\pi] = D_{F_1+F_2}$.

9. $D_{F_1} = [-\pi; 2\pi]$, $D_{F_2} = [0; 3\pi]$, $D_{F_1+F_2} = [0; 2\pi]$.

Sec. 8.3, pages 265–266

1. (a) $\sqrt{5}$; (b) 2; (c) $\sqrt{3}$; (d) 6.   **3.** (a) $3\sqrt{5}$; (b) $2\sqrt{10}$; (c) $\sqrt{13}$; (d) 7.

5. (a) 6; (b) 8; (c) 10; (d) 10.

7. $M(3, 4, 0)$, $N(3, 0, 5)$, $Q(0, 4, 5)$; $U(3, 0, 0)$, $V(0, 4, 0)$, $W(0, 0, 5)$.

9. $M(-4, -5, 0)$, $N(-4, 0, -2)$, $Q(0, -5, -2)$; $U(-4, 0, 0)$, $V(0, -5, 0)$, $W(0, 0, -2)$.

11. $P_2(2, 3, 4)$.   **13.** $P_2(-4, -6, -7)$.

15. $P_1(3, 2, 0)$; $P_2(7, 4, 0)$.

17. $\sqrt{22}$.   **19.** $\sqrt{227}$.

21. $\{(x, y, z) \mid y = 0 \text{ and } z = 0\}$; $\{(x, y, z) \mid x = 0 \text{ and } z = 0\}$.

23. Line parallel to the z axis through $(5, 6, 0)$.

25. $(7, 4, \frac{10}{7})$.   **27.** $(-\frac{9}{2}, -\frac{7}{2}, -\frac{5}{2})$.

31. $C(1, -2, 3)$; $r = 3\sqrt{2}$.   **33.** Equation of the null set.

Sec. 8.4, page 273

1. $(-8, -3, 5)$; $\left(\dfrac{-4\sqrt{2}}{7}, \dfrac{-3\sqrt{2}}{14}, \dfrac{5\sqrt{2}}{14}\right)$.   **3.** $(-2, 3, 6)$; $(-\frac{2}{7}, \frac{3}{7}, \frac{6}{7})$.

5. $\frac{1}{2}, \frac{1}{2}\sqrt{2}, -\frac{1}{2}$; $60°, 45°, 120°$.   **7.** $60°$ or $120°$.

Sec. 8.5, pages 275–276

1. $x = 2 + 3t$, $y = 3 + 4t$, $z = 4 + 5t$; $Q(0, \frac{1}{3}, \frac{2}{3})$, $R(-\frac{1}{4}, 0, \frac{1}{4})$, $S(-\frac{2}{5}, -\frac{1}{5}, 0)$.

3. $x = 3 - 3t$, $y = 4t$, $z = 4 + t$; $Q(0, 4, 5)$, $R(3, 0, 4)$, $S(15, -16, 0)$.

5. Direction numbers $(2, 1, 5)$; $P_1(-5, 3, 0)$, $P_2(-3, 4, 5)$.

7. Direction numbers $(3, -3, -5)$; $P_1(7, 4, -2)$, $P_2(10, 1, -7)$.

9. One possible answer is $2x = 3y + 1$, $2x = (z - 5)/6$.

11. $P_1(3, 5, -2)$; L_3: $x = 3 + 3p$, $y = 5 - 5p$, $z = -2 - 25p$.

13. $P_1(0, 0, -\frac{1}{2})$; L_3: $x = 3p$, $y = p$, $z = -\frac{1}{2} - 4p$.

15. $d = 3/\sqrt{2}$.   **17.** $d = \frac{17}{5}\sqrt{3}$.

Sec. 8.6, pages 280–282

1. $6, 3, 2$.   **3.** $-6, -12, -4$.

5. $3x - 2y - 6z = 6$.   **7.** $x - 3y + z - 12 = 0$.

9. $11x + 5y - 7z - 14 = 0$.   **11.** $(1, 2, 2)$.

13. Perpendicular.   **15.** $\cos \theta = \frac{33}{65}$.

17. $3(x - 2) - (y - 1) + 4(z - 5) = 0$; $-2(x - 2) + 5(y - 1) + (z - 5) = 0$.

Sec. 8.7, page 289

3. A circle in the xy plane and with center at the origin and radius 4.

5. Circular cylinder with elements parallel to the z axis and having the circle of Exercise 3 for directrix.

7. Equilateral hyperbola in the plane having $z = -3$ for equation.

9. Circular cylinder with elements parallel to the z axis.

11. Parabolic cylinder with elements parallel to the z axis.
13. Sphere.   **15.** Hyperboloid of one sheet.
17. Cone.   **19.** Elliptic paraboloid.
21. Two intersecting planes.   **23.** Elliptic paraboloid.

Sec. 8.8, page 298
    9. (*a*) $\|\langle x,\, y,\, z\rangle - \langle 1,\, 2;\, 3\rangle\| = k$; (*b*) $(x-1)^2 + (y-2)^2 + (z-3)^2 = k^2$.

Sec. 8.9, pages 301–302
    3. $\langle 1,\, 0,\, -1,\, 2\rangle$.

| INDEX